CONTENTS

WELCOME TO YOUR 2019 GUIDEBOOK!

Printed by Belmont Press. Cover image Whitburgh House Walled Garden, Midlothian

Maps produced by Alan Palfreyman Graphics @APalfreyman Contains OS data © Crown copyright MiniScale 2015

Scotland's Gardens Scheme, 2nd Floor, 23 Castle Street, Edinburgh EH2 3DN
T: 0131 226 3714   E: info@scotlandsgardens.org   W: www.scotlandsgardens.org

CHAIRMAN'S MESSAGE

Charities, like gardens, change and evolve over time and 2018 was indeed a year of change as we said thank you to Catherine Erskine, Trish Kennedy, Minette Struthers and Richard Burns, who stepped down from the Board of Trustees after ably supporting our work for many years. They are replaced by Jonathan Cobb, David Buchanan-Cook, Stephen McCallum and Emily Stair. Thank you to all for volunteering your time and skills to support our mission and to raise money for charity through encouraging, promoting and supporting garden openings.

Looking at the yellow book, our charitable giving, talking with our beneficiaries and members of our wider community, I never cease to be amazed by the power of volunteering. It really can and does change lives for the better, improving health and wellbeing and the quality of life for many within villages, towns and cities across Scotland, from Shetland to Galloway.

Opening a garden may sound an easy task but it only happens as a result of skill, hard work, commitment and a great deal of patience with our ever-changing climate. Rain, hail, snow, sunshine - we saw it all this past Easter. Thank you to all who support our mission in a myriad of ways.

The year 2018 brought considerable change behind the scenes in Head Office, with the introduction of a new database and website. We also addressed GDPR and produced a range of promotional items to support our volunteers. Combined, these activities will make the charity more efficient, welcoming and transparent, ultimately improving outreach, understanding and our ability to generate funds.

Much of this work was only possible at this time thanks to the substantial legacy received from the family of Kirsty Maxwell Stuart to whom we are deeply grateful. The significance and impact of this have been so great that the Board are now considering how we might further develop a legacy programme to better enable our activities in the future.

Remember gardens are a wonderful gift to share; please bring a friend along when you visit, thereby helping us to further change lives for the better across Scotland. Enjoy!

The exceptionally fine weather this summer has brought a huge number of visitors to gardens across Scotland. And I suspect it was a pleasant change to be remembering the sunblock, rather than the umbrellas…

Scotland's Gardens Scheme celebrated the Year of Young People in 2018, so the combination of sunny days and free admission for children meant that many families spent their days out at the 500 garden openings. About a fifth of them offered special activities for children, and there were six storytelling days, which we ran with the Scottish Storytelling Centre.

Another first last year was the partnership with the National Garden Scheme to celebrate 'Gardens and Health' week, giving free admission to people who don't usually have the chance to enjoy a garden. It heralded the theme for 2019 of 'Health': to emphasise the enormous benefits of gardens and gardening – whether physical, mental or social.

And the rewards of growing our own fruit and vegetables will not be forgotten either. Apart from the immense pleasure of shelling peas, pulling up potatoes or relishing the wonderful scent of a freshly-picked tomato, 'growing your own' promotes heathy eating in the best possible way.

And last but by no means least, as the proud President of Scotland's Gardens Scheme, I would like to thank every volunteer, organiser and garden owner for all the hard work that goes on behind the scenes throughout the year to make it possible for these beautiful gardens to be opened to so many visitors.

TIPS FOR USING YOUR GUIDEBOOK

Your guidebook is packed with information about garden open days for you to visit. It's organised alphabetically by geographical district (often the county). At the back of the book is a fold-out map which will help you to locate these districts across the map of Scotland. You'll see that we also use colour coding to highlight our SGS regions.

Most of our Garden Openers elect to raise money for their own nominated charity(s) for up to 60% of their net takings. These nominated charities are listed within each opening description. Some Openers donate all their takings to support our beneficiaries. And a few open commercially and provide us with a donation. After the nominated charity donation, the net remainder is designated for our beneficiaries, highlighted on pages 31-37.

'The daffodil-coloured tome of horticultural promise'

Joanna, Edinburgh Garden Diary, on the Scotland's Gardens Scheme Guidebook

24 Fettes Row, Edinburgh, photo by Phil G

INTRODUCTION TO THE GUIDEBOOK

We gardeners share a secret - our gardens are like a very special friend. A friend who helps us with our health and wellbeing. When we're stressed, our garden calms us. Whether it's the grounding minerals absorbed through our hands as we work the soil, or the physical release of the fight and flight response through our physical labour, it works. A complicated problem suddenly untangles in our mind as we work our garden. And our garden helps us with our physical health, leading a bespoke exercise class that any personal trainer would covet.

Our garden provides a life-line of continuity, as we watch the bulbs, blossom and pale spring leaves emerge each year even after a harsh winter. Our garden gets us out of the house when the winter darkness is tugging at us. And our garden can nourish us, literally. In a relatively small space, we can grow our own fruit and vegetables, avoiding chemicals and artificial additives, providing us with maximum nutrients when we pick to our plate.

Fortunately, even if you're not a gardener, you can enjoy some of the benefits of gardens by visiting. What a wonderful way to spend an afternoon, out in the fresh air and in the serenity of a garden.

Isla helping to harvest courgettes from my garden

This is what we're celebrating with this year's guidebook - gardens and health. Whether you garden yourself, have a desire to learn more or just want to reap the benefits of being in a garden, we've more than 500 gardens to visit so you'll be spoiled for choice. There's a fantastic variety on offer: from allotments to therapeutic gardens; villages and groups; and cottage-styled gardens to castles.

We've hundreds of volunteers across Scotland to whom we're incredibly grateful. They organise our openings, help on open days, manage our social media, photograph gardens, manage local accounts, and serve as our trustees. We rely hugely on volunteers, perhaps you'd like to help. If you have skills to share, please get in touch. It's truly a lovely charity to be a part of.

We hope our 2019 garden openings will inspire you. Thank you for your support.

Terrill Dobson
National Organiser

"Gardens are
not made by singing
'**Oh, how beautiful,**'
and sitting in the shade."

Rudyard Kipling

Out of the Ordinary | **Investec**
Wealth & Investment

At Investec Wealth & Investment we understand the potential of growth, that's why we've been sponsoring Scotland's Gardens Scheme, a source of beauty and inspiration, since 2009.

Our 15 offices across the UK, including Edinburgh and Glasgow, give us national reach with regional insight. That's the reason local opportunities have always been important to us. Whether we're helping individuals and businesses grow their portfolio or ensuring charities meet their goals, our investment managers are committed to securing prosperous futures for everyone.

With Investment Your Capital is at Risk.

To find out more, contact one of our Scottish Offices:
Edinburgh ☎ 0131 226 5000
Glasgow ☎ 0141 333 9323

investecwin.co.uk

SGS PLANT SALES 2019

Too many plants? No such thing. 2018 was a fabulous year for plant sales, with people travelling far and wide to pick up some well-tended bargains. The gardeners of West Linton were chuffed and surprised to have a visitor from Ayrshire armed with bags of potted plants and homemade baking! Good news spreads far and for good reasons.

'Buying plants from local plant sales gives you the opportunity to seek advice from the sellers and ask for their top tips.'

Blair House, Ayrshire. Photo by David Blatchford

RENFREWSHIRE

SGS Kilmacolm Plant Sale outside Kilmacolm Library, Kilmacolm   Saturday 27 April 10am - 12pm

DUNBARTONSHIRE

Glenarn Plant Sale Glenarn Road, Rhu   Saturday 28 April 2pm - 5pm

GLASGOW & DISTRICT

Merrylee Spring Plant Sale   Saturday 4 May 11:30am - 3:30pm
Merrylee Plots, Quadrant Road, Newlands, Glasgow

PERTH & KINROSS

SGS Plant Sale at Bradystone House, Murthly   Sunday 19 May 11am - 6pm

ABERDEENSHIRE

Leith Hall Plant Sale Huntly   Saturday 8 June 10am - 3pm
Glenkindie House Plant Sale Glenkindie, Alford   Wednesday 10 July 12pm - 3pm

ANGUS & DUNDEE

Angus Plant Sale Logie Walled Garden, Kirriemuir   Saturday 7 Sept 2pm - 5pm

DUNBARTONSHIRE

James Street Community Garden Plant Sale Helensburgh   Sunday 8 Sept 12pm - 4pm

FIFE

Hill of Tarvit Plant Sale and Autumn Fair Hill of Tarvit, Cupar   Sunday 29 Sept 10.30am - 2.30pm

NEW GARDENS FOR 2019

Scotland's Gardens Scheme is delighted to have 45 openings with new gardens in 2019 across Scotland. It's a wonderful afternoon out, visiting a new garden. The treat of exploring somewhere new, stumbling across new ideas and, of course, meeting the Garden Openers themselves. We are so grateful to every Garden Opener and especially those braving a new opening this year.
Please visit and help make their first open days successful.

Are you interested in opening your garden for charity?

By opening your garden, you would be joining a long tradition of helping your community through both charitable funding and the pleasure of enabling the public to visit beautiful gardens. You will also benefit from our 88 years of experience in opening gardens, including our promotional support and even insurance coverage. We are looking for all types, shapes and sizes of loved gardens.

THINKING OF OPENING YOUR GARDEN IN 2020? WE'RE HERE TO HELP.

42 Pentland Gardens, Edinburgh. Photography by N Pearson

ABERDEENSHIRE

Glenkindie House Plant Sale

ANGUS & DUNDEE

Brechin Gardens in Spring

Brechin Gardens in Summer

ARGYLL & LOCHABER

Ardno and Strachur House

AYRSHIRE & ARRAN

Auldbyres Farm Garden

Barrmill Community Garden

Gardens of Kilmaurs

The Carriage House

Waterslap Gardens

DUMFRIESSHIRE

Dumfries Station Garden

Ellisland Farm, The Poet's Wild Garden

Stanemuir

Townhead of Glencairn

EAST LOTHIAN

Fairnielaw

Gullane House

EDINBURGH, MIDLOTHIAN & WEST LOTHIAN

19 Gardiner Road

5 Greenbank Crescent

89 Ravenscroft Street

Preston Hall Walled Garden

FIFE

Crail: Small Gardens in the Burgh (new gardens)

Dalgety Bay Gardens

Fife Spring Trail

Fife Summer Trail

Quercus Garden Plants, Peeblesshire & Tweeddale

Auldbyres Farm Garden, Ayrshire & Arran

NEW New garden entries are highlighted in green within the listing pages and with the NEW icon.

GLASGOW & DISTRICT

Berridale Allotments and Gardens

Gartnaval Secret Garden

Kilmardinny Gardens

Merrylee Spring Plant Sale

Milton Community Gardens

Woodbourne House

KIRKCUDBRIGHTSHIRE

Kings Grange House

PEEBLESSHIRE & TWEEDDALE

Abbotsford

Quercus Garden Plants

The Schoolhouse

PERTH & KINROSS

Allotment Association of Crieff

Bridge of Earn Gardens

Cloan

Gleneagles House

SGS Plant Sale at Bradystone House

The Steading at Muchart

RENFREWSHIRE

Wraes

ROXBURGHSHIRE

Whiterigg

STIRLINGSHIRE

43 Thornton Avenue

60 Greenhead

Hutcheson Farm

WIGTOWNSHIRE

Seabank

Allotment Association of Crieff, Perth & Kinross

'We're looking for gardens of all types, big or small'

If you want to raise money for charity and have a garden that you'd like to share, we would love to hear from you! mail: info@scotlandsgardens.org/tel: 0131 226 3714

SNOWDROPS & WINTER WALKS

Scotland's Gardens Scheme is delighted to be celebrating snowdrops and winter walks in 2019.

Across Scotland some 26 gardens and woodlands are opening at this very special time of year, to allow visitors access to some wonderful winter walks. There is something very magical about wrapping up warm for a winter walk, the still, nippy air tastes alive upon inhalation and frost crunching underneath your step.

Many of these gardens welcome dogs on leads, and others have warming cups of tea and coffee, and a healthy slice of cake, for your post-constitutional treat.

Whether you're a galanthophile (snowdrop-lover), or just in need of a brisk walk, there are plenty of places for you to explore.

Craufordland Estate, Ayrshire ©Rob Davies

Many, many welcomes,
February fair-maid,
Ever as of old time,
Solitary firstling,
Coming in the cold time,
Prophet of the gay time,
Prophet of the May time,
Prophet of the roses,
Many, many welcomes,
February fair-maid!

The Snowdrop **by Lord, Alfred Tennyson**

For all winter's beauty, snowdrops are a much-needed reminder that seasons change, and that spring is just around the corner. These delicate petals turn any woodland floor into a wonderful white carpet.

8 Halmyre Mains, Peebleshire & Tweeddale

Craufordland Estate, Ayrshire ©Rob Davies

FIND A WINTER WONDERLAND NEAR YOU

ABERDEENSHIRE

Bruckhills Croft

ANGUS & DUNDEE

Dunninald Castle
Langley Park Gardens
Lawton House

ARGYLL & LOCHABER

Ardmaddy Castle

AYRSHIRE & ARRAN

Blair House, Blair Estate

DUMFRIESSHIRE

Craig

EAST LOTHIAN

Shepherd House

INVERNESS, ROSS, CROMARTY & SKYE

Arbriachan Garden Nursery

KINCARDINE & DEESIDE

Ecclesgreig Castle

KIRKCUDBRIGHTSHIRE

Barholm Castle
Danevale Park

LANARKSHIRE

Cleghorn

MORAY & NAIRN

10 Pilmuir Road West

PEEBLESSHIRE & TWEEDDALE

Kailzie Gardens

PERTH & KINROSS

Braco Castle
Cloan
Fingask Castle
Kilgraston School
Rossie Gardens

ROXBURGHSHIRE

Floors Castle

STIRLINGSHIRE

Duntreath Castle
Gargunnock House Garden
Kilbryde Castle

WIGTOWNSHIRE

Craichlaw

FIFE SPRING TRAIL

With gardens open on weekdays from 16 April to 3 May, this is a treat for any garden lover. It's a unique opportunity to visit some of Fife's most spectacular privately-owned gardens.

The Fife Spring Trail kicks off with the Spring Cambo Plant Fair, a family-friendly day out with a wide range of plants on sale from a selection of local nurseries. There is a wide variety of gardens open, from 17th-century historic terraced gardens with stunning views (Balcaskie), to a thriving community garden complete with woodland, orchard, allotment plots and a Primary School garden (Strathkinness). From rhododendrons to spring bulbs, trilliums to orchards, these gardens showcase an inspirational mix of the best that spring has to offer.

THE GARDENS

Balcaskie
Pittenweem KY10 2RE

Cambo Spring Plant Fair
Kingsbarns KY16 8QD

Cedar Cottage
Mill Road, Craigrothie KY15 5PZ

Kirklands
Saline KY12 9TS

Rosemount Cottage
21 Main Street, Ceres KY15 5NA

Strathkinness Community Garden and Orchard
Bonfield Road, Strathkinness KY16 9RR

Teasses
near Ceres KY8 5PG

OPENING TIMES

SUNDAY PLANT SALE 2019		
Cambo Plant Fair	12pm-3pm	14 April

MONDAY		
Rosemount Cottage	2pm-5pm	29 April

TUESDAY		
Strathkinness Community Garden	2pm-4pm	16, 23, 30 April

WEDNESDAY		
Kirklands	2pm-5pm	17, 24 April and 1 May
Rosemount Cottage	2pm-5pm	1 May

THURSDAY		
Cedar Cottage	1pm-4pm	18, 25 April and 2 May
Rosemount Cottage	2pm-5pm	2 May

FRIDAY		
Balcaskie	1pm-4pm	19, 26 April and 3 May
Teasses	10am-4pm	19, 26 April and 3 May

Strathkinness Community Garden and Orchard, Fife

Teasses, Fife

CHARITIES

40% net of the proceeds goes to Scotland's Gardens Scheme's beneficiary charities. The remainder will be split equally between The Rotary Club of St Andrews' Arclight Eye Project and East Neuk First Responders.

ADMISSION

£25 for entrance to all gardens. Accompanied children free. Pre-sales tickets available only online at Eventbrite (browse 'SGS Fife Spring Trail'). Tickets otherwise available on the day at the gardens. Gardens can also be visited individually for £5.00 each.

Balcaskie, Fife

FIFE SUMMER TRAIL

The gardens open in the Fife Summer Trail, on weekdays from 3 June to 13 June, highlighting the wonderful creativity and dedication of gardeners.

From the formality of a symmetrical layout and fantastic use of colour at Greenhead Farmhouse, to imaginatively clipped yew hedges that form garden 'rooms' in the walled garden at Wormistoune.
The garden at Glenbeg has been designed for wheelchair access, to allow owner Lilian to tend to her raised beds, pond and cut flowers. Visitors can take inspiration from the north-facing garden at Millfield House, with its intricate trees walks of hazel, cherry and mountain ash grove in bulb meadows.

Wormistoune House, Fife

Millfield House, Fife

THE GARDENS

Glenbeg
South Road, Cupar KY15 5JG

Gordonshall Farm
Carnbee, Anstruther KY10 2RU

Greenhead
Greenhead of Arnot, Leslie KY6 3JQ

Kenly Green Farm
Boarhills KY16 8PP

Millfield House
Falkland KY15 7BN

Straiton Farmhouse
Straiton Farm, Balmullo KY16 0BN

The Tower
1 Northview Terrace, Wormit DD6 8PP

Wormistoune House
Crail, KY10 3XH

CHARITIES

40% net of the proceeds goes to Scotland's
Gardens Scheme's beneficiary charities. The
remainder will be split equally between The Rotary
Club of St Andrews' Arclight Eye Project and East
Neuk First Responders.

ADMISSION

£25 for entrance to all gardens. Accompanied
children free. Pre-sales tickets available only
online at Eventbrite (browse 'SGS Fife Spring
Trail'). Tickets otherwise available on the day
at the gardens. Gardens can also be visited
individually for £5.00 each.

OPENING TIMES

MONDAYS		
Glenbeg	1pm-4pm	3, 10 June
Straiton Farmhouse	10am-1pm	3, 10 June
The Tower	4pm-8pm	3, 10 June

TUESDAYS		
Greenhead	4pm-8pm	4, 11 June
Millfield House	4pm-8pm	4, 11 June

WEDNESDAYS		
Gordonshall Farm	10am-4pm	5, 12 June

THURSDAYS		
Kenly Green Farm	1pm-4pm	6, 13 June
Wormistoune	10am-4pm	6, 13 June

The Tower, Fife

CHAMPION TREES

WHAT IS A CHAMPION TREE?
A Champion Tree is a one of a kind for its location and environment: the tallest or the fattest.

WHO RECORDS THESE TREES?
The Tree Register of the British Isles manages the database of large, old, rare and remarkable trees. The information is supplied by volunteer recorders.

CHAMPION TREES IN SCOTLAND'S GARDENS SCHEME
Gardens often have far more unusual trees than they realise. You can spot these trees in the Scotland's Gardens Scheme guidebook by the tree icon on the listing so you can pop along and give a hug to a Champion Tree.

ABERDEENSHIRE

Cruickshank Botanic Gardens
Quercus ilex, *Acer griseum* and
a tri-stemmed *Nothofagus obliqua*

ARGYLL & LOCHABER

Ardkinglas Woodland Garden
The mightiest conifer in Europe and others

EAST LOTHIAN

Gullane House
Elm, Oak

Tyninghame House and the Walled Garden
Two British and seven Scottish

INVERNESS, ROSS, CROMARTY & SKYE

Dundonnell House
Yew and Holly

House of Aigas and Field Centre
Douglas fir, Atlas cedar and *Sequoiadendron giganteum*

Old Allangrange
Yew

KIRKCUDBRIGHTSHIRE

Threave Garden
Acer platanoides 'Princeton Gold'

Polylepis australis, Filo pastry tree, Logan Botanical Gardens

PEEBLESHIRE & TWEEDDALE

Dawyck Botanic Garden
Numerous

Kailzie Gardens
Larch planted 1725

PERTH & KINROSS

Megginch Castle
Acer palmatum (Japanese maple)

Fingask Castle
Pinus wallichiana (Bhutan pine)

WIGTOWNSHIRE

Castle Kennedy and Gardens
6 British, 11 Scottish and 25 for Dumfries and
Galloway

Logan Botanic Garden
Polylepis and *Eucalyptus*

Metrosideros umbrellata, New Zealand Christmas tree, Logan Botanical Gardens, Wigtownshire

NATIONAL PLANT COLLECTIONS

National Plant Collections® aim to create and curate comprehensive living plant libraries representing the diversity of our cultivated plants.

These gardens do a wonderful job of safeguarding these plants, some of which might otherwise be lost to future generations.

For more information about the National Plant Collections, see the Plant Heritage website, www.plantheritage.org.uk.

Gunnera, Leptospermum, Logan Botanic Garden, Wigtownshire

Lilies, Parkhead house, Perth & Kinross

Meconopsis 'Lingholm' at Explorers' Garden, Perthshire

VISIT A NATIONAL PLANT COLLECTION

ANGUS & DUNDEE

3 Balfour Cottages
Primula auricula (alpine)

ARGYLL & LOCHABER

Benmore Botanic Garden
Abies, South American temperate conifers,
Picea

PEEBLESSHIRE & TWEEDDALE

Dawyck Botanic Garden
Larix and *Tsuga*

PERTH & KINROSS

Explorers Garden
Meconopsis

Glendoick
Rhododendron sect. *Pogonanthum*, subsect.
Uniflora, subsect. *Campylogyna* & subsect.
Glauca and Cox hybrids

Megginch Castle
Scottish cider apples, Scottish Heritage
apples and pears

Parkhead House
Lilium (Mylnefield lilies)

WIGTOWNSHIRE

Logan Botanic Garden
Gunnera, Leptospermum, Griselinia, Cianthus
and *Sutherlandia*

Primula auricula, **3 Balfour Cottages, Angus**

'Visit Explorer's Garden,
a Scottish plant hunter's
garden known for its
Meconopsis collection.'

'See national collections
in a world-famous
arboretum at Dawyck
Botanic Garden.'

'Do you have a budding
love for a particular
plant? Why not start
your own collection and
save it for posterity?'

THE MAGIC OF MAOLACHY

Maolachy's Garden, Argyll, Photo by Nick Edgington

by Yvonne Anderson, Area Organiser for Argyll

As you wind your way along the enchanting paths in Maolachy's Garden, you would be forgiven for believing in faeries. There is magic at work around every corner.

As you approach the traditional stone farmhouse and courtyard, near Lochavich, the garden is obscured from view. You have no idea what awaits you.

'Gardens should be welcoming, warm & peaceful.'

In the early 70's, Georgina and Tony Dalton began digging paths and planting the wild garden through six-foot-high bracken and couch grass. Now the ground is carpeted with bugle, campion and many other wildflowers. They dug steps and paths by hand following the contours of the land and tumbling burn that flows through it.

The '25 Steps' was built by willing friends. No lunch till the task was completed. Family skills have

constructed bridges and pathways, which lead you to surprising places. Past mature rhodies and fragrant azaleas, pathways carry you over a peat bog on a raft crafted from the branches and shreddings of a fallen beech tree. Intriguingly, none has an end

Photo by Nick Edgington

Freshly dug new potatoes. Photo by Phil Gillespie

Photo by Nick Edgington

- except one ... Maolachy's garden is created in a wee glen, over four miles from the nearest village. It feels quite remote. 'Not everyone would choose to live here. They might not even survive!' But it's clear Georgina is more than surviving. 'I walk in my back door and I feel loved and safe.' The wildlife feels at home too, with log-pile houses for insects, warm stone heaps for slow worms, damp clumps for toads and grey-headed wagtails chattering in a nearby nest.

'My gardening life began in order to feed the family,' says Georgina. 'There is nothing more satisfying than growing edibles. The taste is so special.' I mumble agreement as my teeth sink into her home-made bread and blackcurrant jam. She laughs, 'I once fed eleven people on 50 pence. And the 50 pence was for cheese!'

'There is nothing more satisfying than growing edibles. The taste is so special.'

Photo by Yvonne Anderson

'My garden provides me with space for fresh air to flow in and a variety of exercise. It's not just the bending and stretching kind - it's fresh air for the brain. Difficulties are ironed out while tilling the soil. Jumbled thoughts get untangled by a bit of weeding and pruning and creative ways around problems are found'.

'I once fed eleven people on 50 pence. And the 50 pence was for cheese!'

Photo by Nick Edgington

A polytunnel now provides warmth for tender vegetables such as sweetcorn and runner beans, while outside there is good ground for tatties, courgettes and fruit bushes.

Georgina's creative energy and resourcefulness touches everything in this garden. Into its fifth decade, with valuable gardening help from Christophe, she still has big plans. 'Gardens should be welcoming, warm and peaceful and contain some things you're not expecting'. Asked which is her favourite plant, she pauses for some time. Yes, that's it. A white *Ranunculus* gifted in a bag of plants by a holidaymaker. Now planted by the pond, it is bearing hundreds of flowers, each one a ball of tightly packed, luminous petals. Together they seem to glow like lanterns.

From its beginnings as a provider of food for the family, Maolachy's Garden has diversified in size and nature with plants that have been purchased, gathered, divided, propagated, healed, donated and

Courgette flower. Photo by Phil Gillespie

found. Georgina knows a thing or two about growing in Argyll, although she would never say that. 'I'm always learning,' she says. How do you get a monkey puzzle in a Skoda? You can ask her yourself!

Maolachy's Garden is open 2pm - 5pm several days from April - September, see page 84 for details.

Photo by Nick Edgington

OUR MENTAL HEALTH

The Potting Shed, Peebleshire & Tweedale. Photo by Kathy Henry

by Joan Johnson, District Organiser for East Lothian

It's been a beautiful day, so many appreciative visitors. Another garden opening is over – great! Then you see him lying in the grass, face-up, eyes closed, immobile. Is he dead?

Your panic is instantaneous. Suddenly he stands up, shakes himself, smiles, thanks you and is off. He wasn't dead - what a foolish thought! But your disquiet lingers, was he unwell, maybe mentally unwell?

What would you think after such an incident? How would you recover? And how might he feel realising that you might have taken him for dead? Isn't gardening meant to de-stress - not do the opposite!

> ## 'Why don't we recognise that we all have a state of mental as well as physical health?'

We talk about promoting positive mental health and wellbeing, reducing stress, addressing self-harm and suicide, loneliness, changing our sedentary lifestyles ... Yet do you feel comfortable talking about your own mental health and wellbeing?

Who could you tell about your depression; your recent bi-polar diagnosis; or your partner's suspicion that you may be on the autistic spectrum? Despite increased discussion of mental health, and disclosures by prominent people, the societal stigma and the enduring fear of what we may not understand persists.

Physical illness elicits compassion and concern - so long as the illness is not one we might 'catch'. We empathise with a broken leg, or an Ebola victim; but why can't we identify with a broken spirit, a deep sense of desolation, obvious hopelessness? Perhaps because, unlike the broken leg, the cause isn't obvious? Why don't we recognise that everyone has

Dahlia at 42 Astle, Caithness & Sutherland. Photo by Colin Gregory

a state of mental as well as physical health? Maybe that man lying on the grass, perhaps meditating, was looking after his mental health?

Gardening and garden visiting is good for your mental health too. Eating your own produce; opening your garden to enthusiastic and grateful visitors gives a boost, a buzz, a positive feeling, a sense of calm, perhaps a connection to something greater than you and your immediate concerns. The stress before

> ## A garden visit lets us hit pause & focus on the moment, unwind & release.

opening your garden dissipates with the realisation that visitors are delighted that you are sharing something you love and care deeply about; are pleased that your garden's not perfect - and never even notice the odd weed.

Holmes Farm, Ayrshire. Photo by Rob Davies

The Sheiling, West Linton, Peebleshire & Tweedale. Photo by Kathy Henry

Lennelbank, Berwickshire. Photo by K Patterson

Scotland's Garden Scheme is becoming more inclusive, engaging those hitherto not so well served by our events, younger folk, people with disabilities; partnering in 2018 with the National Garden Scheme for 'Gardens & Health' Week to give free garden access to those otherwise unable to visit due to social or health reasons. Communities are reaching out too, reclaiming derelict gardens, creating allotments and encouraging volunteering from those with disabilities and with lived experience of poor mental health.

We are slowly waking up to the damage to our planet, to the plastic in our seas and the toxins in our watercourses. We must also wake up to the loneliness , social isolation and disconnection from the natural world that contributes to poor mental health. We gardeners have a truly wonderful way of doing this, by bringing us and those who visit our gardens back to our roots, to our connection with the earth. Gardening is therapeutic in our lives. Let's, over the coming years, work consciously to share this with others.

Joan, a social work professional, spent 35 years in both frontline and management roles, promoting the mental health and wellbeing of individuals and families. She supported people to help them develop a sense of belonging - something she passionately believes minimises the risk of social isolation and poor mental health.

'Gardens & Health Week gives free garden access to those otherwise unable to visit due to social or health reasons.'

Waterslap, Ayrshire. Photo by Rob Davies

SOCIAL GARDENING

Musselburgh Allotments, East Lothian, Photo by Malcolm

Scotland's Gardens Scheme is delighted to have 19 community gardens and a further 34 villages and groups opening in 2019.

Gardening is a community across time and its network ignores barriers of culture, age and gender, uniting its members in a common understanding. Gardening is sharing: of produce from an over-prolific plum tree and hardy seedlings, to knowledge, and advice.

The resurgence of community gardens brings individuals together with a common goal. With this in mind, Scotland's Gardens Scheme reached out to discover what our visitors and Garden Openers make of gardening's role in the community.

'Brings communities together'

'Healthy competition - who doesn't want to grow prize-winning dahlias or mammouth courgettes?'

Volunteer at Netherthird Community Garden, Ayrshire, Photo by Rob Davis

'Sharing knowledge and expertise'

Ernest Street Allotments, Photo by Steven Whittaker

Yew Tree Allotments, Roxburghshire, Photo by Kenny Patterson

'Sharing food, which is the most important part of society in so many cultures'

'Do your research. Join a Facebook page for other local gardeners and experiment!'

S. Grant

Bravehound–Erskine Hospital, Renfrewshire

WHAT HAPPENS TO THE MONEY RAISED?

Our garden openings support hundreds of charities, big and small, local and national. Our Garden Openers can elect for up to 60% raised at the opening to be donated to a charity of their choice.

WHO ARE SCOTLAND'S GARDENS SCHEME'S BENEFICIARIES?

The net remaining of the money raised by our openings helps our three core beneficiaries: The Queen's Nursing Institute Scotland, Maggie's Centres and Perennial. Read more about them in the following pages.

Search and Rescue Dog Association Scotland (SCIO) Lamancha And District Community Association Scottish Association For Mental Health Abernethy in Bloom Fauna & Flora International Croick Church Dogs Trust Dogs for Good Friends of the Rose Garden, Arbroath Ardgowan Hospice Ltd Fiddlefolk The British Red Cross Society Laggan Church of Scotland The Gurkha Wel… thcarron Project The Royal British Legion Coylton Parish Church (Church of Scotland) Beatson Cancer Charity Suzy Lamp… onal Stalking Helpline East Fife and Scooniehill Riding for the Disabled SCIO Inch Church Of Scotland Home-Start Wigto… itectural Heritage Society of Scotland Children's Liver Disease Foundation Tarbolton Parish Church of Scotland Argyll Animal… District Community Association Pastoral Foundation Berridale Allotments Friends Of Anchor Ayrshire Hospice Eluanfoot Tru… rs SCIO Freedom from Fistula Foundation The Woodland Trust Glen Art Brechin Day Care Limited Unicorn Preservation Socie… m Scottish Men's Sheds Association St Saviours Episcopal Church: Bridge Of Allan Keep Scotland Beautiful Leuchie Befriend A… e Welfare Earl Haig Fund (Scotland) Scottish Society For The Prevention Of Cruelty To Animals Camphill Scotland Royal Zoolo… otland St Modocs Episcopal Church Coldstream Gateway Association Corsock & Kirkpatrick Durham Church Of Scotland Ma… ks Cancer Caring Centres Trust Unity Enterprise Kirkandrews Kirk Trust Accord Hospice The Dark Sky Observatory Craigenti… ments Crail Preservation Society Friends of Craufurdland SCIO Feedback Trust Friends Of The Cruickshank Botanic G… ntary Service Coulter Public Library Trust Upper Nithsdale Youth Pipeband Kilmore & Kilbride Village Hall Committee St Mai… rch: Kirriemuir Kirkmahoe Parish Church of Scotland Independence from Drugs & Alcohol Scotland St Columbas Hospice ABF… ity The Little Haven (Forth) Pirnmill Village Association Gardeners' Royal Benevolent Society Dr. Neils Garden Trust Shelter… paign For Homeless People Limited Appin Parish Church (Church of Scotland) John Buchan Heritage Museum Trust Stobo an… rch of Scotland British Limbless Ex-Service Men's Association Loch Arthur Camphill Community Limited Insch Parish Chu… es Compassion in World Farming MND Scotland Leuchars: St Athernase Church of Scotland Royal Scots Dragoon Guards Regi… entre (Therapy Centre) Aberdeen Royal Infirmary Roof Garden Borders Childrens Charity Girl Guiding Montrose Friends Of Ell… Others Trellis Scotland Host Friends of Autism Highland East Neuk First Responders The Rotary Club of St Andrews Aberdeen… ted All Saints Church, Glencarse Fingask Follies Forget Me Not Care & Counselling Craigo Community Association The British … iple Sclerosis Society Gargunnock Community Trust Ltd Scotland's Charity Air Ambulance The Conservation Volunteers Ga… ng For The Disabled Association SCIO St Kessog's Episcopal Church - Auchterarder Stillbirth and Neonatal Death So… idation Fortingall Parish Church WWF-UK Gordon Lennox Trust Scottish Veterans Residences Newburgh Community Trus… life Rescue Trust Orkidstudio Buccleuch And Queensberry Caledonia Pipe Band Coronation Hall, Muckhart The National Trust… ick Allan-Fraser Of Hospitalfield Trust Mamie Martin Fund Lothian Cat Rescue Society Of Friends Of Dunblane Cathedra… idation James Street Community Garden Erskine Hospital St Columba's - Poltalloch Chest Heart & Stroke Scotland Kew on G… d Garden Fund Friends of St. Modan's, Rosneath Leighton Library Trust Elsie Normington Foundation Marie Curie Newlife - Th… bled Children Barnardo's Hot Chocolate Trust Strathcarron Hospice Highland Hospice Christ Church, Kincardine O'neil Child… s Partnership Feis na h'apainne Trustees Of Appin Village Hall Elizabeth Finn Care Forth Driving Group RDA SCIO Saline Er… ap Christ Church Scottish Episcopal Church CLIC Sargent Cancer Care for Children The Brae Riding for Disabled Royal Nati… itution The Julia Thomson Memorial Trust British Heart Foundation Board Of Trustees Of The Royal Botanic Garden Edinb… k Garden Club The Hope Project Scotland (SCIO) Merrylee Plotholders Association Milton Community Garden and Food Hub Euo… tre for Motor Neurone Disease Research The Katie McKerracher Trust St Ebba Episcopal Church: Eyemouth Netherthir… elopment Group Edzell Lethnot Glenesk Church of Scotland Survival International Charitable Trust British Diabetic Associat… Gardens The Guide Dogs For The Blind Association Médecins Sans Frontières The National Council for the Conservation of Plai… n and District Men's Shed St Mary On The Rock Episcopal Church: Ellon Fighting For Sight Aberdeen Juvenile Diabetes Researc… ted Pittenweem Community Library and Information Centre RNIB Charity My Name'5 Doddie Foundation Breast Cance… donian Horticultural Society St Peter's Scottish Episcopal Church: Linlithgow Friends Of Loch Lomond & The Trossachs Child… ociation Scotland Lyme Disease Action Hillfoot Harmony Barbershop Singers Blairgowrie Riding For The Disabled (SCIO)… clefields Trust Mary's Meals Book Aid International Brooke Action for Working Horses & Donkeys Lanark Community Devel… epsy Society Trustees Of Stobo Village Hall Family Service Unit Scotland Great Ormond Street Hospital Children's Charity A… al Voluntary Organisations (Rural South Lanarkshire) Bield Christian Company Limited Dalry Trinity Church of Scotland Frie…

OUR GUEST CHARITY

HORATIO'S GARDEN

Beginning in 2018, Scotland's Gardens Scheme offered a bursary of up to £5,000 for projects that are concerned with the physical, mental and emotional wellbeing of adults and/or children across Scotland. These projects should be associated with gardens and gardening and the sustaining help that these can bring. Those interested can apply by December year-end for decision the following spring. For more information see the SGS website.

Garden therapy with patients and volunteers. Photo by Horatio's Garden

This year we are pleased to announce that our first bursary was provided to Horatio's Garden, an award-winning charity that creates and cares for beautiful, accessible gardens in NHS regional spinal injury centres. They will use this money to help build a garden room in the woodland garden at the Spinal Unit at the Queen Elizabeth University in Glasgow. They aim to have this project completed by the time of their SGS Open Day on 1 September 2019.

The charity is named after Horatio Chapple. Horatio volunteered at the spinal centre in Salisbury and had the vision of a garden for all those connected to the centre. Horatio's life was cut short in 2011 at the age of 17. The first Horatio's Garden opened in Salisbury in 2012, following an outpouring of support and love - there was a strong desire to ensure a legacy for Horatio's life. Designer Cleve West joined the team and the garden developed into an incredible sanctuary for all those touched by spinal injury. The charity was formed with the aim of bringing these oases to all 11 spinal injury centres across the UK.

A volunteer team worked tirelessly to bring about the opportunity to create another space in Horatio's name, this time for those patients in Scotland. With James Alexander Sinclair on board, fundraising started in earnest and in 2016 Scotland opened its own Horatio's Garden at the Queen Elizabeth National Spinal Injuries Unit. The unit at South Glasgow University Hospital, looks after all Scottish-based patients with spinal paralysis from Shetland to Dumfries. There are 48 beds on the spinal injuries ward and 170 new patients every year. There are also 2,600 outpatients a year and multiple visitors for the 170 in-patients. Around 5,000 people visit Scotland's Horatio Garden every year.

For Horatios's family, friends and those touched by his life, these evolving gardens, which offer sanctuary, improve wellbeing and become so significant to those affected by spinal cord injury, take over his legacy.

Woodland Garden. Photo by Horatio's Garden

www.horatiosgarden.org.uk

Qnis 130

CELEBRATING
EST. 1889
YEARS

Promoting excellence in community nursing

www.qnis.org.uk   @QNI_Scotland

BENEFICIARY MESSAGES

THE QUEEN'S
NURSING
INSTITUTE
SCOTLAND

2019 marks 130 years of Queen's Nursing in Scotland. Since 1931 we have enjoyed a successful partnership with Scotland's Gardens Scheme and we have been supported by generations of generous garden owners and visitors.

An important part of our work has been funding projects for nurse-led community projects aimed at reducing health inequalities through our Catalysts for Change programme. There have been 19 projects so far, each led by a community-based nurse connecting with other local charities to make a real difference.

Thanks to the generous funding from Scotland's Garden's Scheme, we have been able to strengthen this area of our work and in 2019 we will be able to support a range of new projects all tackling health inequalities.

Our projects to date have had powerful results.

• Providing care for people in police custody to link them with welfare and recovery support. This proved so successful that funding has been found to continue the work.

• A Men's Shed was opened in Govan, with a dedicated and enthusiastic community nurse supporting the group to take better care of their own health and wellbeing.

• The medical practice which used our funding to develop an accessible walking group received an award from the British Heart Foundation for their contribution to reducing higher-than-average levels of heart disease.

• A project seeking to normalise and promote breastfeeding through schools has seen success in changing attitudes in an area with particularly low breastfeeding rates.

In addition, the new Queen's Nurse title continues

to grow, with 41 Queen's Nurses currently working in communities across Scotland, and a further 20 beginning the programme in March.

Our established Queen's Nurses continue making an impact in their fields and the communities where they work. For example, Parish Nurse Rachel who has launched a recovery road map – a pocket guide detailing support available across Dundee for those recovering from addictions.

Throughout 2019 we will be holding events to mark our 130th anniversary. As part of the celebrations, we have partnered with Orkney-based jewellers Ortak to develop a range of celebratory jewellery designed around our new badge with a thistle at its heart. The range of thistle jewellery is available on the Ortak website and proceeds support QNIS.

We are proud to be a Beneficiary Charity of Scotland's Garden's Scheme, and we look forward to continuing the relationship for another 88 years.

Clare Cable
Chief Executive and Nurse Director, QNIS

Find your way through cancer

Come to Maggie's

Maggie's provides free practical, emotional and social support for people with cancer and their family and friends.

Built in the grounds of NHS hospitals, our network of Centres across the UK are warm and welcoming places, with professional staff on hand to offer the support you need to find your way through cancer.

Maggie's Centres are open Monday to Friday, 9am–5pm, and no referral is required.

Maggie's Centres across Scotland receive vital funds from every garden opening. Our heartfelt thanks go to everyone who supports Scotland's Gardens Scheme by opening their garden, volunteering or visiting a garden.

www.maggiescentres.org

Scotland's
GARDENS
Scheme
OPEN FOR CHARITY

Everyone's home of cancer care

All too often the first time someone comes to Maggie's, that person is feeling both frightened and vulnerable. It takes courage to come in.

For many of our visitors, through, the sight of a beautiful flower, or someone tending a shrub, can make it easier to walk over and start chatting - someone who might never consider signing up for a therapy session or be too nervous to walk through the door. The garden makes it possible for people to come in to Maggie's.

2019 will bring a stunning new garden to Maggie's Edinburgh. Moving into previously unused land adjacent to the Centre, this long, winding garden will help guide people to the Centre.

Its unique design, with plants carefully chosen for their all-year-round interest, will offer a peaceful space, with uplifting views – a welcoming extension of the inside of the Centre; a place to sit in almost all weathers, for refuge and perhaps to share feelings and experiences with other people. As well as a visual and sensory experience, the garden will host core parts of our programme such as tai chi, relaxation, meditation and creative writing - drawing on the flora and fauna present.

The garden will be open to anyone and we do hope you will visit.

I would like to take this opportunity to thank you all for your most welcome support of Maggie's in Scotland again this year. All of our Centres benefit from Scotland's Gardens Scheme donations and from every garden opening, for which we are enormously grateful.

We look forward to a wonderful year of gardening ahead, and enjoying the many green spaces and delightful gardens that Scotland's Gardens Scheme has made accessible to everyone.

MAGGIE'S
Everyone's home of cancer care

Maggie's Glasgow Gartnavel
Architect: OMA
Garden design: Lily Jencks
Photography © Nick Turner

Best wishes

Laura Lee
Chief Executive
Maggie's

PERENNIAL

GARDENERS' ROYAL BENEVOLENT SOCIETY

Helping Horticulturists In Need Since 1839

Help us reach more people – tell a friend about Perennial

Perennial has been providing life-changing support to people working in horticulture and its related industries for 180 years. This type of employment is generally low paid, often seasonal and in today's challenging economic times, even those in steady work can struggle to cope with the financial pressures that family life can bring.

We know the biggest barrier to people approaching Perennial for help is simply not knowing about us. Those living and working remotely are even more difficult to reach. We rely on the extended Perennial family, including all those who visit gardens as part of Scotland's Gardens Scheme, to help us spread the word by telling a friend about Perennial.

Thank you for your ongoing support and remember, by telling just one person about Perennial's services you're helping us widen the net.

We want everyone who works in horticulture to know about us so that if they ever need help or support, they'll know where to turn.

Dougal Philip
Chairman, Perennial
Owner, New Hopetoun Gardens, Edinburgh

"On behalf of everyone at Perennial, thank you for your continued support and generosity. Thanks also to the hundreds of volunteers who open their wonderful gardens for the enjoyment of thousands of people in Scotland every year.

With your help we are raising important funds for Perennial in Scotland and we are spreading the word about our services to horticulturists who may be in need of our help. Perennial is here for people for as long as it takes and thanks to our partnership with Scotland's Gardens Scheme we are helping more individuals and families every year."

Carole Baxter
Trustee and presenter BBC Scotland Beechgrove TV programme

John's Story

John had worked as a gardener for over 20 years, mostly in Argyll & Bute. He had moved from working on a private estate with tied accommodation to work for the Local Authority Parks Department, meaning he and his family lost their furnished home and had to rent privately. With the cost of moving and having to purchase furniture and white goods, John and his family started to struggle financially. They were living on a very tight budget and had to consolidate debts with a loan just to get by.

Photo is posed by a model.

The cost of the private accommodation became too much to manage, so they moved into a static caravan to lower costs. However, when the site closed for the winter they had to leave.

A colleague at work suggested that John contact Perennial. We were able to help the family move into a flat, assisting with essential items as well as providing financial advice.

Perennial also awarded a regular child education payment to help John's son who is at secondary school with a laptop for homework, printer, school uniform and lunches, helping the family provide for his education while keeping to their budget.

> ## "I don't know where we would be without Perennial. How they have been able to help us is so much more than we expected."
> John

Read more about how Perennial has changed lives at perennial.org.uk/personal-stories

Donate now

Help us to build better futures for horticulturists and their families.

To make a donation please visit perennial.org.uk/donate or call 0800 093 8792

Perennial 115-117 Kingston Road, Leatherhead, Surrey KT22 7SU.

Registered charity nos: 1155156 I Scotland SC040180. Perennials debt advice service is authorised and regulated by the Financial Conduct Authority (www.fca.org,uk).

We need you

Scotland's Gardens Scheme helps keep Perennial's dedicated caseworker in Scotland in action, improving the lives of hundreds of horticulturists and their families. During 2017, Perennial helped 128 families in Scotland, of whom 70% were under retirement age and made direct grants totalling £36,000. **With your help we can support more people this year.**

DIANA MACNAB AWARD
FOR OUTSTANDING SERVICE

Rose-Anne Cuninghame. Photo by David Blatchford

The Diana MacNab Award goes to a volunteer who has shown outstanding service to Scotland's Gardens Scheme. It comes with little surprise that this year's winner, one of the longest-serving current volunteers, is the lovely Rose-Ann Cunninghame.

Rose-Ann Cuninghame's (née Greig) introduction to Scotland's Gardens Scheme came after she retrained, throwing her enthusiasm into a Diploma in Horticulture at Scottish Agricultural College. However, her passion for plants and gardens started at a young age.

Indeed, it was at school that Rose-Ann's interest in gardens was sparked, as she enjoyed the peace and tranquillity of the Gertrude Jekyll garden in the school grounds. She and many of her school have since taken up the role of Scotland's Gardens Scheme volunteer. Rose-Ann took her interest across the world, seizing the chance to go plant hunting in Pakistan, Spain and the Azores, Portugal, and she spent two summers gardening in Maryland, USA.

In 1992 Rose-Ann was delighted to be asked to be a Scotland's Gardens Scheme Area Organiser following an invite to the AGM by Diana MacNab herself. Since this initial encouragement she, in turn, has tried to encourage others to further their interest in gardening. However, to Rose-Ann, this means healthy exercise, the chance to engage in the seasonality of nature and produce and bring it into the home (preferably home-grown apples or spinach), shelves of gardening books, planning (for her goal to plant more evergreens) and friendship with like-minded people from all backgrounds.

Rose-Ann 'helped' at her first charity open day in her uncle's garden in 1949. The traditional charity open days of the private gardens of country houses are now equalled in number by group or village opening, with lots of interest from smaller gardens, allotments and community gardens. The visitors and donations have changed too, with welcome garden lovers coming from further afield.

As a long-serving volunteer, including her current title of District Organiser, and Garden Opener Rose-Ann has seen her fair share of openings, come rain or shine. Her top tips for any opening, regardless of the weather, include stout footwear and getting posters and signs out early. She always encourages Garden Openers to get involved speaking to visitors and when possible to provide a simple guide to the garden, and smashing teas never go amiss!

Rose-Ann has brought new ideas to Scotland's Gardens Scheme, including the 'Pop-up' garden opening, running a successful raffle and so much more. It's more than just gardens and events, it's also about community and charity, and Rose-Ann has relished her time being part of the unique team called 'SGS' and working with so many delightful owner and volunteers.

LONG SERVICE AWARDS

In 2019, Scotland's Gardens Scheme is delighted to be celebrating two milestones of long service. Leith Hall, Aberdeenshire, has opened with us off and on since 1931. At the other end of the country, one of Scotland's finest botanical garden, Benmore, celebrates its 25th year of opening for charity.

These gardens showcase the time and commitment involved in tending a garden. Time has definitely been a key factor in these two gardens. Benmore Botanic Garden was established in 1863; over 150 years later their majestic giant redwoods have had plenty of time to develop and they are a wonderful sight to behold.

The gardens at Leith Hall were initially laid out by Charles and Henrietta Leith-Hay around the beginning of the 20th century. The garden never ceases to develop, however, with the dedicated gardening team of The National Trust of Scotland introducing a rose catenary and rock garden with seasonal planting.

Why not see these wonderful gardens yourself?

Dolphin pond at Benmore Botanical Gardens, Argyll

 Leith Hall Garden, pg 51 (Aberdeenshire)

 Benmore Botanic Garden, pg 78 (Argyll & Lochaber)

Summertime borders at Leith Hall, Aberdeenshire

WHO'S WHO IN OUR CHARITY

Scotland's Gardens Scheme is supported by Trustees and Staff in the Head Office, each of whom brings their own expertise to the table.

At the heart of the charity are our Volunteers, without whom there would be no gardens to visit. The Trustees and Staff are devoted to the charity.

Scotland's Gardens Scheme is delighted to have HRH The Duchess of Rothesay as our President.

In keeping with our theme of Gardens and Health, we've asked our Trustees and Staff, and President, to share their favourite fruit and vegtables.

OUR PRESIDENT

HRH The Duchess of Rothesay
© Press Association

My favourite fruit and vegetables are broad beans and peaches.

HEAD OFFICE

Terrill Dobson
National Organiser

My favourite would have to be kale. I grew a kale yard this year with all sorts of varieties. The cabbage whites were very grateful! And then for fruit, home-grown Scottish raspberries.

Hazel Reid
Office Manager

Carrots because of their sweet taste. My favourite fruit depends on the season, but raspberries have to win!

Imogen McCaw
Marketing Officer

Home grown corn on the cob, drizzled in butter. I can't say no to ripe conference pears either.

Lisa Pettersson
Graphic Design

Raspberries, especially the wild ones. My favourite vegetables are raw sugar snap peas or mangetout, easy to grow and very addictive.

ABERDEENSHIRE

Scotland's Gardens Scheme 2019 Guidebook is sponsored by INVESTEC WEALTH & INVESTMENT

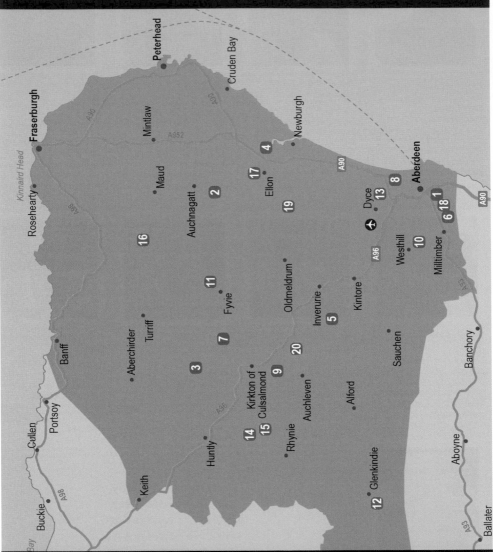

1. 105 Inchgarth Road
2. Airdlin Croft
3. An Teallach
4. Auchmacoy
5. Birken Cottage
6. Blairwood House
7. Bruckhills Croft
8. Cruickshank Botanic Gardens
9. Drumrossie Mansion House
10. Easter Ord Farm
11. Fyvie Castle
12. Glenkindie House Plant Sale
13. Grandhome
14. Laundry Cottage
15. Leith Hall Plant Sale
16. Middle Cairncake
17. Parkvilla
18. Pinetrees Cottage
19. Pitmedden Garden
20. Westhall Castle

ABERDEENSHIRE

OUR VOLUNTEER ORGANISERS

District Organiser:	Verity Walters	Tillychetly, Alford AB33 8HQ
		E: aberdeenshire@scotlandsgardens.org
Area Organisers:	Linda Colquhoun	Hillview, Rothienorman, Inverurie AB51 8YL
	Gill Cook	Old Semeil, Strathdon AB36 8XJ
	Jennie Gibson	6 The Chanonry, Old Aberdeen AB24 1RP
	Anne Lawson	Asloun, Alford AB33 8NR
	Penny Orpwood	Middle Cairncake, Cuminestown, Turriff AB53 5YS
	Helen Rushton	Bruckhills Croft, Rothienorman AB51 8YB
Treasurer:	Tony Coleman	Templeton House, Arbroath DD11 4QP

GARDENS OPEN ON A SPECIFIC DATE

Auchmacoy, Ellon	Sunday, 14 April
Westhall Castle, Oyne, Inverurie	Sunday, 28 April
Airdlin Croft, Ythanbank, Ellon	Friday/Saturday/Sunday, 7/8/9 June
Leith Hall Plant Sale, Huntly	Saturday, 8 June
Birken Cottage, Burnhervie, Inverurie	Sunday, 16 June
Bruckhills Croft, Rothienorman, Inverurie	Sunday, 30 June
Glenkindie House Plant Sale, Glenkindie, Alford	Wednesday, 10 July
Cruickshank Botanic Gardens, 23 St Machar Drive, Aberdeen	Wednesday, 10 July
Drumrossie Mansion House, Insch	Sunday, 14 July
Middle Cairncake, Cuminestown, Turriff	Sunday, 14 July
Parkvilla, 47 Schoolhill, Ellon	Saturday/Sunday, 27/28 July
Middle Cairncake, Cuminestown, Turriff	Sunday, 28 July
Pitmedden Garden, Ellon	Sunday, 11 August

GARDENS OPEN REGULARLY

Fyvie Castle, Fyvie, Turriff	5 January - 22 December

GARDENS OPEN BY ARRANGEMENT

Laundry Cottage, Culdrain, Gartly, Huntly	1 January - 31 December
Bruckhills Croft, Rothienorman, Inverurie	16 February - 17 March
Grandhome, Danestone, Aberdeen	1 April - 31 October
105 Inchgarth Road, Pitfodels, Cults, Aberdeen	1 May - 30 June
Blairwood House, South Deeside Road, Blairs	9 - 23 May, 1 - 30 June & 25 August - 8 Sept
Pinetrees Cottage, Banchory-Devenick	20 May - 20 July
Birken Cottage, Burnhervie, Inverurie	20 May - 14 July
Airdlin Croft, Ythanbank, Ellon	1 June - 31 July
An Teallach, Largue, Huntly	1 June - 31 August
Easter Ord Farm, Easter Ord, Skene, Westhill	15 June - 25 August
Middle Cairncake, Cuminestown, Turriff	1 July - 31 July

Aberdeenshire

1 **105 INCHGARTH ROAD**
Pitfodels, Cults, Aberdeen AB15 9NX
Mr and Mrs W McGregor
T: 01224 861090 **E:** wahmcgregor@me.com

Informal cottage-style garden situated in one third of an acre featuring azaleas, rhododendrons, orchids, peonies and a selection of alpines.

Open: Open by arrangement 1 May - 30 June, admission £4.00, children free. Teas by arrangement.

Directions: From North Deeside Road, turn off along Station Road, Pitfodels. Access and parking along back lane.

· *The Archie Foundation*

2 **AIRDLIN CROFT**
Ythanbank, Ellon AB41 7TS
Richard and Ellen Firmin
T: 01358 761491 **E:** rsf@airdlin.com
W: www.airdlin.com

A large woodland garden, eventually destined to fill our five-acre croft, features species of rhododendrons, hydrangeas, viburnums, ferns, hostas and other shade-tolerant plants. A sheltered, sunny terrace hosts some tender exotics. One of two polytunnels houses the 'library collection' of container-grown hosta cultivars. We go out of our way to attract wildlife with 100 bird species recorded here since 1983.

Open: Friday/Saturday/Sunday, 7/8/9 June, 10am - 4pm. Also open by arrangement 1 June - 31 July. Admission £4.00, children free.

Directions: From the A948, three miles north of Ellon, take the left turn towards Drumwhindle. After another couple of miles take the second left towards Cairnorrie. Proceed for nearly a mile, ignoring the first Airdlin Croft at Coalmoss, and turn left at the first bend, go down our 300 yard track, parking is in the field at the bottom.

· *Fauna & Flora International*

3 **AN TEALLACH**
Largue, Huntly AB54 6HS
Gary and Victoria Morrison
T: 01464 871471 **E:** gary.k.morrison@gmail.com

This young cottage garden of approximately one acre (and growing) was created in 2013 and has become established in a remarkably short time. Surrounded by uninterrupted views of rolling hills and farmland, the garden includes a charming variety of colourful herbaceous, mixed borders, a terraced woodland bank, rose garden, fruit and vegetable beds, and an (as yet) untamed quarry area. The growing collection of plants and flowers provides interest from May to October.

Open: Open by arrangement 1 June - 31 August, admission £4.00, children free.

Directions: Leaving Largue on the B9001, head towards Rothienorman. An Teallach is the first track on the left, after the national speed limit sign.

· *Dogs Trust*

Aberdeenshire

4

AUCHMACOY
Ellon AB41 8RB
Mr and Mrs Charles Buchan

Auchmacoy House's attractive policies feature spectacular displays of thousands of daffodils.

Open: Sunday 14 April, 1pm - 4pm, admission £3.00, children free. Concessions £2.50. Buchan Pipe Band will play. Please, NO dogs. Homemade teas and soup.

Directions: A90 from Aberdeen. Turn right to Auchmacoy/Collieston.

· *The Royal British Legion: Ellon Branch*

Hundreds of Daffodils at Auchmacoy

5

BIRKEN COTTAGE
Burnhervie, Inverurie AB51 5JR
Clare and Ian Alexander
T: 01467 623013 **E:** i.alexander@abdn.ac.uk

This steeply sloping garden of just under one acre is packed with plants. It rises from a wet stream-side gully and woodland, past sunny terraces and a small Parterre, to dry flowery banks. Visitors in 2018 described the garden as 'magnificent', 'inspirational' and 'the highlight of our tour'.

Open: Sunday 16 June, 2pm - 5pm. Also open by arrangement 20 May - 14 July. Admission £4.00, children free.

Directions: Burnhervie is about three miles west of Inverurie. Leave Inverurie by the B9170 (Blackhall Road) or B993 (St James' Place).

· *Friends Of Anchor*

Aberdeenshire

6 **BLAIRWOOD HOUSE**
South Deeside Road, Blairs AB12 5YQ
Ilse Elders
T: 01224 868301 **M:**07732 532276 **E:** ilse.elders@yahoo.co.uk

A mature, densely planted, one-acre garden full of flowering shrubs, herbaceous perennials and bulbs. The garden is laid out in naturally curving lines to harmonise with the surrounding fields. It includes a pond, a small but beautifully designed vegetable garden, a herb garden and a sunken patio. A lovely short walk leads to the river and back.

Open: Open by arrangement 9 May - 23 May, 1 June - 30 June & 25 August - 8 September, admission £4.00, children free.

Directions: Please do not use SatNav to find this garden. From Bridge of Dee roundabout take the South Deeside road for about four minutes until you see the road sign *Riverside of Blairs*. Almost immediately you will see a large electricity pylon on your right and an electronic speed sign on your left. Entrance is opposite the speed sign. Coming from Milltimber Bridge, turn left towards Aberdeen. Follow the South Deeside road for a few minutes until you see Greenbank 4x4 Centre on your left. Entrance is about 100 yards beyond.

· Elvanfoot Trust

Plantings on the stream gully at Birken Cottage, photo by Fay Smith

Aberdeenshire

BRUCKHILLS CROFT
Rothienorman, Inverurie AB51 8YB
Paul and Helen Rushton
T: 01651 821596 **E:** helenrushton1@aol.com

An informal country-cottage garden extending to three-quarters-of-an-acre with a further acre as wildflower meadow and pond. The pond has been extensively replanted with primulas and irises. Themed borders include a White Border, a Butterfly Alley and a Blue and Yellow Border. We specialise in rabbit-proof planting. Relax on one of the many seats in the garden, enjoy a cuppa and homebake in the pavilion, and children can follow the treasure trail. Our snowdrops featured on *The Beechgrove Garden* in 2017: the collection consists of 400 named varieties.

Open: Open by arrangement 16 February - 17 March for Snowdrops and Winter Walks. Also open Sunday 30 June, 12pm - 5pm. Admission £4.00, children free.

Directions: At Rothienorman take the B9001 north, just after Badenscoth Nursing Home turn left; in one mile you will be directed where to park depending if it is the winter or summer opening.

· *Befriend A Child Ltd*

Galanthus sandersii at Bruckhills Croft

CRUICKSHANK BOTANIC GARDENS
23 St Machar Drive, Aberdeen AB24 3UU
Cruickshank Botanic Garden Trust, Aberdeen University
W: www.abdn.ac.uk/botanic-garden/

An evening tour is offered by the Curator, Mark Paterson, and Head Gardener, Richard Walker. The garden comprises a sunken garden with alpine-lawn, a rock garden built in the 1960s complete with cascading water and pond system, a long double-sided herbaceous border, a formal rose garden with drystone walling, and an arboretum. It has a large collection of flowering bulbs and rhododendrons, and many unusual shrubs and trees. It is sometimes known as 'The Secret Garden of Old Aberdeen'.
Champion Trees: *Quercus ilex, Acer griseum* and a tri-stemmed *Nothofagus obliqua*.

Open: Wednesday 10 July, 6:30pm - 8:30pm, admission £5.00, children free.

Directions: Come down St Machar Drive over the mini roundabout, just before the first set of traffic lights turn left into the Cruickshank Garden car park. The pedestrian garden entrance is off The Chanonry.

· *Friends Of The Cruickshank Botanic Garden*

Aberdeenshire

 9

DRUMROSSIE MANSION HOUSE
Insch AB52 6LJ
Mr and Mrs Hugh Robertson

The property, which can be traced back to the Crusades, is surrounded by three acres of landscaped lawns, formal walled garden, veg and greenhouse area and a newly planted orchard. There are 27 acres of wooded walks, paddocks and a large wildlife pond. Vegetables are grown in raised beds. The walled garden is laid out in lawns of a very high standard, with herbaceous borders and fruit trees on the south-facing wall. There is a large collection of hostas and alstroemerias, as well as herbaceous plants, heathers and azaleas, a productive vegetable garden, plant-raising area and polytunnel for early veg and flowers, a large glasshouse for tomatoes and a sunken greenhouse, which provides over-wintering heat for tender plants. A main feature is the well, which in days gone by provided the water supply to the house.

Open: Sunday 14 July, 1pm - 5pm, admission £4.00, children free.

Directions: Do not follow SatNav. Enter drive from Drumrossie Street off the crossroads in centre of village. The drive is through trees at the back of McColl's supermarket.

· *Insch Parish Church*

 10

EASTER ORD FARM
Easter Ord, Skene, Westhill AB32 6SQ
Catherine Fowler
T: 01224 742278 **E:** catherine.a.fowler@gmail.com

A one-acre mature cottage garden with year-round interest. The garden has an open aspect with views towards Lochnagar. It is made up of 'rooms'. There is a fruit garden, large herbaceous borders, lawn areas, small wildlife pond, vegetable garden and mini orchard with wild flowers.

Open: Open by arrangement 15 June - 25 August, admission £4.00, children free. Teas and home baking available at reasonable cost.

Directions: Can be reached using full postcode on SatNav. We are two miles from Westhill. From Aberdeen take A944 towards Westhill. At the traffic lights before Westhill take the slip road on to the B9119 then immediately left towards Brotherfield. After one mile turn right at the T junction. After 350 yards turn left into the lane. Garden is first entrance on right.

· *Aberdeen Royal Infirmary Roof Garden*

Aberdeenshire

FYVIE CASTLE
Fyvie, Turriff AB53 8JS
The National Trust for Scotland
T: 01651 891363 / 891266 **E:** gthomson@nts.org.uk
W: www.nts.org.uk/visit/places/Fyvie-Castle/

An 18th-century walled garden developed as a garden of Scottish fruits and vegetables. There is also the American Garden, Rhymer's Haugh Woodland Garden, a loch and parkland to visit. Expert staff are always on hand to answer any questions. Learn about the collection of Scottish fruits and their cultivation, and exciting projects for the future. Check the Fyvie Castle Facebook page for up-to-date information on fruit and vegetable availability.

Open: 5 January - 22 December, 9am - dusk, admission details can be found on the Fyvie Castle's website.

Directions: Off the A947 eight miles south east of Turriff and 25 miles north west of Aberdeen.

· *The National Trust for Scotland: Fyvie Garden*

GLENKINDIE HOUSE PLANT SALE
Glenkindie, Alford AB33 8SU
Mr and Mrs J P White

Glenkindie House gardens are laid out around the house in an Arts and Crafts style. The lawns are resplendent with unusual topiary figures: look out for teddy bears, soldiers and *Alice in Wonderland* characters. There are ancient rubble walls, rose beds planted with *Rosa* 'Brave Heart', herbaceous borders and a large pond.

Open: Wednesday 10 July, 12pm - 3pm, admission £8.00, children free. Admission to include soup lunch, which will be served in the house. There is limited disabled access in the house due to stairs. Bring-and-buy plant stall with a wonderful selection of plants, all locally grown. We welcome donations of plants, labelled if possible.

Directions: On the A97 Alford/Strathdon road, 12 miles west of Alford.

· *Save the Children UK: (Grampian Branch) & Willow*

'Creating an inspiring,
rewarding and enjoyable
experience for volunteers
and visitors alike'

Aberdeenshire

GRANDHOME
Danestone, Aberdeen AB22 8AR
Mr and Mrs D R Paton
T: 01224 722202 **E:** davidpaton@btconnect.com

Eighteenth-century walled garden incorporating a rose garden (replanted 2010) and policies with daffodils, tulips, rhododendrons, azaleas, mature trees and shrubs.

Open: Open by arrangement 1 April - 31 October, admission £4.00, children free.

Directions: From the north end of North Anderson Drive, continue on the A90 over Persley Bridge, turning left at the Tesco roundabout. After one and three quarter miles, turn left through the pillars on a left-hand bend.

· *Children 1st*

Summertime herbaceous borders at Grandhome

LAUNDRY COTTAGE
Culdrain, Gartly, Huntly AB54 4PY
Judith McPhun
T: 01466 720768 **E:** judith.mcphun@btinternet.com

An informal cottage-style garden of about one-and-a-half acres by the river Bogie. Two contrasting steep slopes make up the wilder parts. The more intensively gardened area round the cottage includes a wide variety of herbaceous plants, shrubs and trees, an orchard area and fruit and vegetable plots, making a garden of year-round interest.

Open: Open by arrangement, admission £4.00, children free.

Directions: Four miles south of Huntly on the A97.

· *Amnesty International (UK Section) Charitable Trust*

Aberdeenshire

 ## LEITH HALL PLANT SALE

Huntly AB54 4NQ
The National Trust for Scotland
W: www.nts.org.uk/visit/places/leith-hall

The west garden was made by Charles and Henrietta Leith-Hay around the beginning of the 20th century. In summer the magnificent zigzag herbaceous and serpentine catmint borders provide a dazzling display. A lot of project work has been ongoing in the garden, including a rose catenary along with large borders, which have been redeveloped in a Gertrude Jekyll-style, and a laburnum archway with spring interest borders. The carefully reconstructed rock garden is a work in progress with new planting being added throughout the season.

Open: Saturday 8 June, 10am - 3pm, admission £3.50, children free. The plant sale will be held in the walled garden and will be a fantastic opportunity to buy a wide selection of potted perennials from the garden's herbaceous borders.

Directions: On the B9002 one mile west of Kennethmont.

· *The National Trust for Scotland: Leith Hall Garden*

 ## MIDDLE CAIRNCAKE

Cuminestown, Turriff AB53 5YS
Nick and Penny Orpwood
T: 01888 544432 **E:** orpwood@hotmail.com

The shape of our property has determined our garden plan of a series of 'rooms' with different plantings. Our prime aim has been to make a garden which appeals to the senses: roses selected for their scent, planting generally to please the eye. The kitchen garden with its polytunnel creates self-sufficiency, and the pond adds interest. Sustainability, wildlife and recycling are priorities. The garden has views over the surrounding countryside.

Open: Sunday 14 July and Sunday 28 July, 2pm - 5pm. Also open by arrangement 1 July - 31 July. Admission £4.00, children free. Groups welcome by arrangement. Tea will be served in our winter garden.

Directions: Middle Cairncake is on the A9170 between New Deer and Cuminestown. It is clearly signposted.

· *Parkinsons UK*

Aberdeenshire

 17 **PARKVILLA**
47 Schoolhill, Ellon AB41 9AJ
Andy and Kim Leonard

A south-facing Victorian walled garden, lovingly developed from a design started in 1990, for colour and interest all year. Enjoy densely planted herbaceous borders, pause under the pergola clothed in clematis, honeysuckle and rambling roses, continue on to the bottom of the garden where three ponds and a wild flower bed reflect a strong focus on wildlife. A hidden gem of a garden that has won awards including *Ellon Best Garden* and with plants rarely seen in north east Scotland.

Open: Saturday/Sunday, 27/28 July, 2pm - 5pm, admission £4.00, children free.

Directions: From centre of Ellon head north towards Auchnagatt. Schoolhill is third left. From Auchnagatt head into Ellon along Golf Road, Schoolhill is first right after the golf course. Limited on-street parking, car parks in Ellon (five minutes walk) and Caroline Well Wood.

· St Mary On The Rock Episcopal Church Ellon, Alzheimer Scotland & Ellon Men's Shed

 18 **PINETREES COTTAGE**
Banchory-Devenick AB12 5XR
Angela and Derek Townsley
T: 01224 869141 **E:** angela.townsley@me.com

A mature garden, set in three quarters of an acre, filled with a wide range of hardy plants, including rhododendrons, azaleas, acers, topiary and roses, with two ponds. An alpine house is fronted by stone troughs filled with rock plants. Set in a backdrop of mature pine trees to the north and open fields to the south.

Open: Open by arrangement 20 May - 20 July, admission £4.00, children free. Teas by arrangement.

Directions: Banchory-Devenick is four miles from Bridge of Dee. Turn off B9077 at Banchory-Devenick church. Follow to T junction, turn right. Next right is Butterywells Steading. Turn into opening and follow track, go around the back of farmhouse (Lochend) and continue on track to Pinetrees.

· Fighting For Sight Aberdeen

Aberdeenshire

19

PITMEDDEN GARDEN
Ellon AB41 7PD
The National Trust for Scotland
E: pitmeddengarden@nts.org.uk
W: www.nts.org.uk/visit/places/Pitmedden-Garden/

Pitmedden is a 17th-century walled garden on two levels. Original garden pavilions with ogival roofs look down on an elaborate spectacle of four rectangular boxwood parterres flanked by fine herbaceous borders and espalier-trained apple trees on south and west-facing granite walls. An avenue of yew obelisks runs from east to west and up to 30,000 bedding plants add to the wow factor of this immaculately kept formal garden.

Open: Sunday 11 August, 6:30pm - 8:30pm, admission £12.50, children free. Head Gardener's evening guided walk, with refreshments included.

Directions: On the A920, one mile west of Pitmedden village and 14 miles north of Aberdeen.

· The National Trust for Scotland: Pitmedden Garden

Parterres at Pitmedden Garden © NTS

20

WESTHALL CASTLE
Oyne, Inverurie AB52 6RW
Mr Gavin Farquhar and Mrs Pam Burney
T: 01224 214301 **E:** enquiries@ecclesgreig.com

Set in an ancient landscape in the foothills of the impressive foreboding hill of Bennachie is a circular walk through glorious daffodils with outstanding views. This interesting garden in early stages of restoration, with large groupings of rhododendrons and specimen trees. Westhall Castle is a 16th-century tower house, incorporating a 13th century building of the bishops of Aberdeen. There were additions in the 17th, 18th and 19th centuries. The castle is semi-derelict, but stabilised from total dereliction. A fascinating house encompassing 600 years of alteration and additions.

Open: Sunday 28 April, 1am - 4pm, admission £4.00, children free.

Directions: Marked from the A96 at Old Rayne and from Oyne Village.

· Bennachie Guides

ANGUS & DUNDEE

Scotland's Gardens Scheme 2019 Guidebook is sponsored by INVESTEC WEALTH & INVESTMENT

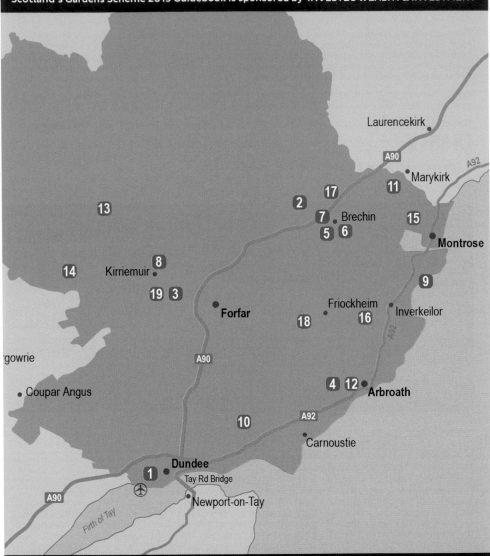

1. 12 Glamis Drive
2. 3 Balfour Cottages
3. Angus Plant Sale
4. Arbroath Collection of Gardens
5. Brechin Castle
6. Brechin Gardens in Spring
7. Brechin Gardens in Summer
8. Dalfruin
9. Dunninald Castle
10. Dunvorist Cottage
11. Gallery Garden
12. Hospitalfield Gardens
13. Inchmill Cottage
14. Kilry Village Gardens
15. Langley Park Gardens
16. Lawton House
17. Newtonmill House
18. Pitmuies Gardens
19. The Herbalist's Garden
    at Logie

ANGUS & DUNDEE

OUR VOLUNTEER ORGANISERS

District Organisers:	Terrill Dobson	Logie House, Kirriemuir, DD8 5PN
		E: angusdundee@scotlandsgardens.org
Area Organisers:	Pippa Clegg	Easter Derry, Kilry, Blairgowrie, PH11 8JA
	Moira Coleman	Templeton House, Arbroath, DD11 4QP
	Frances & John Dent	12 Glamis Drive, Dundee, DD2 1QL
	Mary Gifford	Kinnordy House, Kinnordy, Kirriemuir, DD8 5ER
	Jan Oag	Lower Duncraig, 2 Castle Street, Brechin, DD9 6JN
	Jeanette Ogilvie	House of Pitmuies, Guthrie, DD8 2SN
	Sue Smith	Balintore House, Balintore, by Kirriemuir, DD8 5JS
	Mary Stansfeld	Dunninald Castle, By Montrose, DD10 9TD
	Claire Tinsley	Ethie Mains, Ethie, DD11 5SN
Treasurer:	James Welsh	Dalfruin, Kirtonhill Road, Kirriemuir, DD8 4HU

GARDENS OPEN ON A SPECIFIC DATE

Langley Park Gardens, Montrose	Saturday/Sunday, 23/24 February
Langley Park Gardens, Montrose	Saturday/Sunday, 2/3 March
Lawton House, Inverkeilor, by Arbroath	Sunday, 17 March
Brechin Castle, Brechin	Sunday, 5 May
Inchmill Cottage, Glenprosen, nr Kirriemuir	Thursday, 9 May
Dalfruin, Kirktonhill Road, Kirriemuir	Sunday, 12 May
Inchmill Cottage, Glenprosen, nr Kirriemuir	Thursday, 23 May
Gallery Garden, Gallery, by Montrose	Saturday/Sunday, 25/26 May
3 Balfour Cottages, Menmuir	Saturday, 1 June
Brechin Gardens in Spring, Locations across Brechin	Sunday, 2 June
Inchmill Cottage, Glenprosen, nr Kirriemuir	Thursday, 6 June
Kilry Village Gardens, Kilry, Glen Isla	Saturday/Sunday, 15/16 June
Inchmill Cottage, Glenprosen, nr Kirriemuir	Thursday, 20 June
Newtonmill House, by Brechin	Sunday, 30 June
Inchmill Cottage, Glenprosen, nr Kirriemuir	Thursday, 4 July
Arbroath Collection of Gardens, Locations across Arbroath	Saturday, 13 July
Gallery Garden, Gallery, by Montrose	Saturday/Sunday, 13/14 July
Inchmill Cottage, Glenprosen, nr Kirriemuir	Thursday, 18 July
Brechin Gardens in Summer, Locations across Brechin	Sunday, 21 July
Inchmill Cottage, Glenprosen, nr Kirriemuir	Thursday, 8 August
Inchmill Cottage, Glenprosen, nr Kirriemuir	Thursday, 22 August
Inchmill Cottage, Glenprosen, nr Kirriemuir	Thursday, 5 September
Angus Plant Sale, Logie Walled Garden	Saturday, 7 September
Inchmill Cottage, Glenprosen, nr Kirriemuir	Thursday, 19 September
12 Glamis Drive, Dundee	Saturday/Sunday, 12/13 October
Hospitalfield Gardens, Hospitalfield House, Westway, Arbroath	Saturday, 26 October

ANGUS & DUNDEE

GARDENS OPEN REGULARLY

Dunninald Castle, Montrose	1 February - 28 February
Pitmuies Gardens, House of Pitmuies, Guthrie, By Forfar	1 April - 30 September
Langley Park Gardens, Montrose	3 May - 29 September (Fridays, Saturdays & Sundays)
Dunninald Castle, Montrose	15 May - 31 August
Gallery Garden, Gallery, by Montrose	1 June - 31 August (Tuesdays only)
Dunvorist Cottage, Drumsturdy Road, Kingennie, Dundee	15 July - 16 July & 18 July - 19 July

GARDENS OPEN BY ARRANGEMENT

The Herbalist's Garden at Logie, Logie House, Kirriemuir	1 June - 31 August
Dunvorist Cottage, Drumsturdy Road, Kingennie, Dundee	1 June - 30 September
Gallery Garden, Gallery, by Montrose	1 June - 31 August

Angus & Dundee

12 GLAMIS DRIVE
Dundee DD2 1QL
John and Frances Dent

....

This established garden with mature trees occupies a half-acre south-facing site overlooking the River Tay and Fife hills. Come in the afternoon for tea and cake and enjoy seasonal herbaceous planting set off by vibrant autumn colours of the trees and shrubs. Stay later to see the water features and hidden corners come to life with coloured floodlights and snippets of recorded music.

Open: Saturday/Sunday, 12/13 October, 3pm - 7pm, admission £4.00, children free.

Directions: Buses 22, 73 or 5 from Dundee city centre. Please note there is no roadside parking on Glamis Drive. Limited disabled parking available at the house.

· The Church Of Scotland: Guild project to tackle loneliness & UK Committee Dr Graham's Homes, Kalimpong, India

3 BALFOUR COTTAGES
Menmuir DD9 7RN
Dr Alison Goldie and Mark A Hutson
T: 01356 660280 **E:** alisongoldie@btinternet.com
W: www.angusplants.co.uk

....

Small cottage garden packed with rare and unusual plants. It comprises various 'rooms' containing myriad plants from potted herbs, spring bulbs and alpines in a raised bed, to a 'jungle' with a range of bamboos. Many other interesting plants include primula, hosta, meconopsis, fritillaria, trillium, allium, a large display of bonsai and auriculas.
National Plant Collection: *Primula auricula* (alpine).

Open: Saturday 1 June, 12pm - 4pm, admission £3.00, children free.

Directions: Leave the A90 two miles south of Brechin and take the road to Menmuir (three-and-a-half miles). At the T junction turn right and No 3 is in the first group of cottages on your left (175 yards).

· Scotland's Charity Air Ambulance

Angus & Dundee

Plant for sale at the Angus Plant Sale

ANGUS PLANT SALE
Logie Walled Garden DD8 5PN
SGS Angus & Dundee Organisers
E: pippaclegg@hotmail.com

Now in our third year, we will hold our next plant sale again in September. We will offer a good, interesting selection, sourced from private gardens and with some donations from our local nurseries. It's advisable to come promptly and bring boxes and trays. Donations of plants either before or during sales will always be welcome.

Open: Saturday 7 September, 2pm - 5pm, admission £3.00, children free. Light refreshments will be available. The garden will also be open.

Directions: From the A90, take A926 towards Kirriemuir. Just after the *Welcome to Kirriemuir* sign take a sharp left on to a single track road, or from Kirriemuir take A926 towards Forfar and fork right at Beechwood Place onto the single track road. Take the first left and follow signs to *The Walled Garden*.

· SGS Beneficiaries

Angus & Dundee

ARBROATH COLLECTION OF GARDENS
Locations across Arbroath DD11 3RB
Gardeners of Arbroath
W: www.ashbrook.co.uk

....

Two small gardens, two allotments and a Nursery Garden Centre, including:
10 George Street Arbroath DD11 3BU (Wilma Simpson): A small delightful walled garden in the Lochlands area well worth a visit with a collection of 70 varieties of clematis and interesting perennials, a gem of a garden.
24 Hospitalfield Gardens Arbroath DD11 2LW (Mr and Mrs N Milne): Another small garden in the Hospitalfield area which features wonderful hanging baskets, window boxes and bedding plants. NEW!
Arbroath Allotments Association Arbroath, DD11 4AH: The Brechin Road site is open this year and as always has loads of interest including plants, vegetables, fruit and creative sheds and shelters. A team of helpers will be there to answer any questions.
Ashbrook Nursery and Garden Centre Forfar Road, Arbroath DD11 3RB (Anne Webster): This family-run garden centre will also join the collection and run tours of the nursery at 2pm, 3pm and 4pm.
HOPE Organic Garden The Westway, Arbroath DD11 2NH: An organic fruit and vegetable garden, which provides training and work experience for adults with learning and/or physical disabilities.

Open: Saturday 13 July, 1pm - 5pm, admission £5.00, children free. Teas will be served at Ashbrook Nursery.

Directions: Tickets and maps will be available from the various gardens and Ashbrook Nursery on the day. Look for the SGS yellow arrows around town to help you locate the gardens.

· *Friends of the Rose Garden, Arbroath*

10 George Street, Abroath Collection of Gardens, photo by Steven Whittaker

Angus & Dundee

5 **BRECHIN CASTLE**
Brechin DD9 6SG
The Earl and Countess of Dalhousie
T: 01356 624566 **E:** mandyferries@dalhousieestates.co.uk
W: www.dalhousieestates.co.uk

The uniquely curving walls of the garden at Brechin Castle are just the first of many delightful surprises in store. The luxurious blend of ancient and modern plantings is the second. Find charm and splendour in the wide gravelled walks, secluded small paths and corners. May sees the rhododendrons and azaleas hit the peak of their flowering to wonderful effect, with complementary underplanting and a framework of great and beautiful trees set the collection in the landscape. This is a lovely garden at any time of year and a knockout in the spring.

Open: Sunday 5 May, 2pm - 5pm, admission £5.00, children free.

Directions: A90 southernmost exit to Brechin, one mile past Brechin Castle Centre, castle gates are on the right.

· *Unicorn Preservation Society & The Dalhousie Centre Day Care For The Elderly*

6 **BRECHIN GARDENS IN SPRING**
Locations across Brechin DD9 6EU
The Gardeners of Brechin

Come and see this lovely collection of gardens, some new this year.
9, Pearse Street DD9 6JR (Irene and James Mackie): A recently redesigned garden with ten newly planted trees, a wide interestingly planted colourful herbaceous border and a lovely lawn. There's a secluded and rural feel to this town garden. A huge collection of ferns is a unique feature of this garden, unusually planted to mingle with other herbaceous plants.
Bishops Walk 11A Argyll St, DD9 6JL (Steff and Mike Eyres): Winding paths lead through an eclectic mix of perennials, shrubs, conifers (including a young wollemi pine in a pot) and roses within this walled garden, accessed through the potting shed. NEW!
Brechin Cathedral Allotments Chanory Wynd, DD9 6EU (Brechin Cathedral Allotments Gardeners): Eleven varied plots reflect the interests and personalities of each plot-holder and include fruit, vegetables and herbs. A unique feature is the historical 'College Well' used by medieval monks. NEW!
East Kintrockat DD9 6RP (Colin and Moira Sandeman): A large open country garden with island beds, natural pond, kitchen garden and riverside walk and featuring primulas, rhododendrons and a newly planted shady garden.
Pearse Croft 8-10 Pearse Street, DD9 6JR (Dr Hamish and Gail Greig): A classic town garden with mature box hedges, rhododendrons, tree and herbaceous peonies, magnolias and late apple blossom.
Westbank Cottage 23 North Latch Road, DD9 6LE (Allison and Alan Ross): A thoughtfully planned compact garden providing its artist-owner with an enclosed retreat packed with cottage-garden planting. A small pond is planned for 2019. NEW!
Westerlea 45, Airlie Street DD9 6JX (Gregor and Elizabeth Mitchell): A two acre secluded natural garden offering a tranquil landscape in an urban setting including mature trees, rhododendrons and a fine wisteria. NEW!

Open: Sunday 2 June, 1pm - 5pm, admission £5.00, children free. Teas and tickets at Brechin Cathedral Hall, Church Lane, DD9 6EU. Also a sale of used gardening books.

Directions: Free parking and car parks are available around the city of Brechin.

· *Brechin in Bloom*

Angus & Dundee

7 BRECHIN GARDENS IN SUMMER
Locations across Brechin DD9 6EU
The Gardeners of Brechin

....

Come and also visit Brechin's gardens in summer with several new gardens this year.
24 North Latch Road DD9 6LE (Alistair and Mary Gray): Learn how the owners grow and show vegetables and how these can be a spectacular display of colourful bedding-full greenhouses.
Bishops Walk 11A Argyll St, DD9 6JL (Steff and Mike Eyres): Winding paths lead through an eclectic mix of perennials, shrubs, conifers (including a young wollemi pine in a pot) and roses within this walled garden, accessed through the potting shed! NEW!
Brechin Cathedral Allotments Chanory Wynd, DD9 6EU (Brechin Cathedral Allotments Gardeners): Eleven varied plots reflect the interests and personalities of each plot-holder and include fruit, vegetables and herbs. A unique feature is the historical 'College Well' used by medieval monks. NEW!
Brechin in Bloom Community Garden Montrose Street DD9 7EF (Brechin Community Garden Volunteers): Started in 2015 on an abandoned allotment site, this community scheme shares experience and learning skills involved in gardening for their own use and for local people. Additions since last year include a log cabin and mud kitchen.
Liscara Castle Street, DD9 6JW (June and Mike Hudson): A 'secret' south-facing small garden with raised beds, circular lawn and fountain, espaliered pear tree and pretty summerhouse. NEW!
Lower Duncraig 2, Castle Street, DD9 6JN (Jan Oag): A small town garden recently redesigned to include less grass and more plants. Plants are selected mainly for their value to wildlife and a small pond supports this. Space has been found for a few trees and 20 different roses.
Westbank Cottage 23 North Latch Road, DD9 6LE (Allison and Alan Ross): A thoughtfully planned compact garden providing its artist owner with an enclosed retreat packed with cottage-garden planting. A small pond is planned for 2019. NEW!

Open: Sunday 21 July, 1pm - 5pm, admission £5.00, children free. Teas and tickets at Brechin Cathedral Hall, Church Lane, DD9 6EU. Also a sale of used gardening books.

Directions: Free parking and car parks are available around the city of Brechin.

· *SMSA: Brechin Men's Shed*

8 DALFRUIN
Kirktonhill Road, Kirriemuir DD8 4HU
Mr and Mrs James A Welsh

....

A well stocked connoisseur's garden of about a third-of-an-acre situated at the end of a short cul-de-sac. There are many less common plants like varieties of trilliums, meconopsis (blue poppies), tree peonies (descendants of ones collected by George Sherriff and grown at Ascreavie), dactylorhiza and codonopsis. There is a scree garden and collection of ferns. The vigorous climbing rose, Paul's Himalayan Musk, grows over a pergola. Interconnected ponds encourage wildlife.

Open: Sunday 12 May, 2pm - 5pm, admission £4.00, children free.

Directions: From the centre of Kirriemuir turn left up Roods. Kirktonhill Road is on the left near top of the hill. Park on Roods or at St Mary's Episcopal Church. Disabled parking only in Kirktonhill Road. Bus 20 (from Dundee) getting off at either stop on the Roods.

· *St Marys Episcopal Church*

Angus & Dundee

DUNNINALD CASTLE
Montrose DD10 9TD
The Stansfeld family
T: 01674 672031 **E:** estateoffice@dunninald.com
W: www.dunninald.com

We welcome our visitors to explore our 100 acres of woods, wild garden, policies and a walled garden. From January to May the main interest is the wild garden and policies where snowdrops in January are followed by daffodils and finally bluebells in May. In June the emphasis turns to the walled garden- rich in interest and colour throughout the summer. Situated at the bottom of the beech avenue, the walled garden is planted with rose borders, traditional mixed borders, vegetables, herbs, soft fruits and fruit trees and there is a greenhouse.

Open: 1 February - 28 February, 10am - 4pm for Snowdrops and Winter Walks. Also open 15 May - 31 August, 1pm - 5pm. Admission £5.00, children free. Castle tours: 29 June - 28 July (closed Mondays) (last entry 4:30pm).

Directions: Three miles south of Montrose, ten miles north of Arbroath, signposted from the A92.

· **Donation to SGS Beneficiaries**

DUNVORIST COTTAGE
Drumsturdy Road, Kingennie, Dundee DD5 3RE
Karen Fraser
T: 07854 167717 **E:** specialkfraser@hotmail.co.uk

Dunvorist Cottage is a small rural garden with all-year colour and interest. The garden has an open sunny aspect and includes a white rear garden with rural views, raised herbaceous borders, a small wildlife pond, golden border, a rose gardens patio, herb garden, heuchera shady garden, quirky garden pod, vegetable garden and a wildflower corner.

Open: 15 July - 16 July and 18 July - 19 July, 10am - 4pm. Also open by arrangement 1 June - 30 September. Admission £4.00, children free. Refreshments available for £2.50.

Directions: On the B961 (Drumsturdy Road), a quarter mile west of Newbigging and half-mile east of Kingennie. Opposite the Laws. Look for greenhouse behind the hedge and gated entrance.

· **Parkinsons UK: Dundee group**

Raised herbaceous borders at Dunvorist Cottage

Angus & Dundee

GALLERY GARDEN

Gallery, by Montrose DD10 9LA
Mr John Simson
T: 07903 977395 **E:** galleryhf@googlemail.com

The redesign and replanting of this historic garden have preserved and extended its traditional framework of holly, privet and box. A grassed central alley, embellished with circles, links themed gardens, including the recently replanted Gold Garden and Hot Border, with the fine collection of old roses and the fountain and pond of the formal White Garden. A walk through the woodland garden, home to rare breed sheep, with its extensive border of mixed heathers, leads to the River North Esk. From there rough paths lead both ways along the bank. This very special garden has been featured in *Homes & Gardens* in 2015, *English Garden* in 2017, *Country Life* in 2018 and *Scottish Field* in January 2019.

Open: Saturday/Sunday, 25/26 May, 2pm - 5pm. Also open Saturday/Sunday, 13/14 July, 2pm - 5pm. And open 1 June - 31 August (Tuesdays only), 1pm - 5pm. And open by arrangement 1 June - 31 August. Admission £5.00, children free.

Directions: Please DO NOT use SatNav - see map for location. From the A90 south of Northwater Bridge take the exit to Hillside and next left to Gallery and Marykirk, OR from the A937 west of rail underpass follow signs to Gallery and Northwater Bridge.

· *Craigo Community Association*

HOSPITALFIELD GARDENS

Hospitalfield House, Westway, Arbroath DD11 2NH
Hospitalfield Trust
E: info@hospitalfield.org.uk
W: www.hospitalfield.org.uk

Be among the first to experience the new design by Nigel Dunnett for the walled gardens at Hospitalfield. Part of the garden too will be the restored 19th-century fernery and new glass-house café designed by architects Caruso St John. The walled gardens have been cultivated from the early medieval period, from the medicinal garden and the orchard to the Victorian passion for collecting ferns. The wonderful neo-Gothic Victorian house now standing on this medieval site was designed and built by the artist Patrick Allan Fraser (1812- 1890). By autumn 2019 the Hospitalfield Trust will have completed the first phase of development and restoration of what is perhaps one of Scotland's most important Arts and Crafts buildings. A really very important part of the Trust's Future Plan is to bring great artists, architects and designers to contribute to the future of the site, and the gardens are the first element that will be made open to the public.

Open: Saturday 26 October, 11am - 3pm, admission £4.00, children free. Enjoy lunch in the new Hospitalfield café.

Directions: See website for directions and more details about Hospitalfield.

· *The Hospitalfield Trust*

'I've had my hands in the soil all my life and I
swear it's kept my immune system tip top'
Fife Gardener

Angus & Dundee

INCHMILL COTTAGE
Glenprosen, nr Kirriemuir DD8 4SA
Iain Nelson
T: 01575 540452

This is a long, sloping and terraced garden at over 800 feet in the Braes of Angus, developed to be a garden for all seasons. Half is dominated by bulbs, rhododendrons, azaleas, primulas, meconopsis and clematis. The other half mainly later summer bulbs, herbaceous plants and roses. There is also a rockery/scree and fernery.

Open: Thursdays 9, 23 May, 6, 20 June, 4, 18 July, 8, 22 August, 5, 19 September, 2pm - 5pm, admission £3.00, children free. Car parking beside the church (50 yards away) and by the village hall opposite.

Directions: Please DO NOT use SatNav. From Kirriemuir take the B955 (sign-posted to *The Glens*) to Dykehead (about five miles). From there follow the *Prosen* sign for about five miles. Inchmill is the white-fronted cottage beside the phone box.

· *The Archie Foundation*

KILRY VILLAGE GARDENS
Kilry, Glen Isla PH11 8HS
Kilry Garden Club

A varied selection of gardens in the magnificent setting of Glen Isla.
Cotton of Craig Kilry, Blairgowrie PH11 8HW (Rachel and Nick Joy): Old walled garden with espaliered fruit trees, herbaceous borders, vegetable garden, greenhouse, specimen trees and robot lawn mower.
Easter Cammock Glen Isla, Blairgowrie PH11 8PF (June and John Browning): Panoramic views of Glen Isla. Large pond surrounded by water plants, perennial and annual wild flowers and many relatively young plants. Established woodland area, rockery, herbaceous borders. Access by farm track.
Easter Derry Kilry PH11 8JA (Pippa and Roger Clegg): With heather-clad hills as backdrop lies thus two-acre garden with lily pond, herbaceous borders, scree bed, vegetable garden, greenhouse and polytunnel.
Estir Bogside Alyth PH11 8HU (Morag and Andrew Buist): Garden started in 1995. Herbaceous borders, cottage garden and potager. In 2010 the garden was extended to adjacent land to allow planting of native trees, wild flowers, mown paths and a pond.
The Mill Glen Isla, Blairgowrie PH11 8QL (Valerie and Charles Summers): Wonderful location in Glen Isla includes small wood, stream and natural pond. Haven for wildlife. Island beds, formal herbaceous borders and rockery around the house, blending with wilder areas.
Whinloans Kilry, Blairgowrie PH11 8HY (Linda and Malcolm Connor): One third of an acre laid out attractively with lawn, herbaceous border, two ponds, large vegetable plot and polytunnel. Planters and hanging baskets.

Open: Saturday/Sunday, 15/16 June, 12pm - 5pm, admission £5.00, children free. Soup, teas and plants with tickets, toilet and maps from the central point of Kilry Village Hall (PH11 8HS).

Directions: From Perth take the A94 to Coupar Angus and just before Meigle take the B954 and follow signs to *Glenisla* and then to *Kilry* signed to the left. From Dundee take the A923 to Muirhead and then B954 to Meigle and Kilry.

· *Hot Chocolate Trust & Barnardo's Scotland: Dundee Group*

Angus & Dundee

15

LANGLEY PARK GARDENS
Montrose DD10 9LG
Marianne and Philip Santer
T: 01674 810735 **E:** philipsanter1@gmail.com
W: www.langleyparkgardens.co.uk

Set overlooking Montrose Basin, Langley Park Gardens include four walled gardens, three filled with herbaceous borders, fruit trees and vegetable plots, the fourth is a small arboretum. The 27 acres of policies contain woodland walks among both ancient and recently planted trees. Walk down through the 20-acre wildflower meadow along the banks of the wildlife pond, enjoy the views over Montrose, The Basin and the hills beyond. In winter enjoy long woodland walks among our stunning snowdrops.

Open: Saturday/Sunday, 23/24 February and Saturday/Sunday, 2/3 March, 12pm - 4pm for Snowdrops and Winter Walks. Also open 3 May - 29 September (Fridays, Saturdays and Sundays), 10am - 4pm. Admission £5.00, children free.

Directions: Just off the A935 Montrose to Brechin Road, one and a half miles from Montrose.

• The Brae RDA Partnership (Saturday/Sunday, 23/24 February & Saturday/Sunday, 2/3 March) & Donation to SGS Beneficiaries (3 May - 29 September)

The Mill, Kilry Village Gardens

Angus & Dundee

Statue at Pitmuies Gardens

16 LAWTON HOUSE
Inverkeilor, by Arbroath DD11 4RU
Katie and Simon Dessain

Woodland garden of beech trees, carpeted with snowdrops, aconites and crocuses in spring, set around a 1755 house. There is also a walled garden planted with fruit trees and vegetables. The property was owned for many years by Elizabeth and Patrick Allan Fraser who built Hospitalfield House in Arbroath.

Open: Sunday 17 March, 2pm - 5pm for Snowdrops and Winter Walks, admission £3.00, children free. St Patrick's Day teas – soda bread and more.

Directions: Take B965 between Inverkeilor and Friockheim, turn right at sign for *Angus Chain Saws*. Drive approximately 200 yards, then take first right.

· *The Julia Thomson Memorial Trust*

17 NEWTONMILL HOUSE
by Brechin DD9 7PZ
Stephen and Rose Rickman
E: rrickman@srickman.co.uk
W: www.newtonmillhouse.co.uk

Newtonmill House looks over and into the semi-formal walled garden. The entrance to the garden is through a wrought iron gate that reflects the mill wheel from which Newtonmill derives its name. The central pathway is flagged by herbaceous borders, sheltered by a fine *Prunus cerasifera* 'Pissardii' hedge. The garden is divided into four squares of kitchen garden, spring garden, croquet lawn with summer-house, and the recently completed autumn garden. Through the rose arch at the south end of the garden are peony and shrub rose beds, a small pond area and doocot. Adjacent to the house is a rose-garlanded terrace and raised beds.

Open: Sunday 30 June, 2pm - 5pm, admission £5.00, children free.

Directions: From the A90, exit B966 Brechin/Edzell towards Edzell.

· *Edzell Lethnot Glenesk Church of Scotland: Development fund*

Angus & Dundee

PITMUIES GARDENS
House of Pitmuies, Guthrie, By Forfar DD8 2SN
Jeanette and Ruaraidh Ogilvie
T: 01241 828245 **E:** ogilvie@pitmuies.com
W: www.pitmuies.com

Two renowned semi-formal walled gardens adjoin an 18th-century house and steading and shelter long borders of herbaceous perennials, superb old-fashioned delphiniums and roses, together with pavings rich with violas and dianthus. An extensive and diverse collection of plants, interesting kitchen garden, spacious lawns, river and lochside walks beneath fine trees. A wide variety of shrubs with good autumn colour and a picturesque turreted doo'cot and a 'Gothick' wash house. Myriad spring bulbs include carpets of crocus following massed snowdrops and daffodils.

Open: 1 April - 30 September daily, 10am - 5pm, admission £5.00, children free. Dogs on lead please.

Directions: From Forfar take A932 east for seven miles and gardens are signposted on the right. From Brechin take A933 south to Friockheim and turn right onto A932; then gardens are signposted on the left after one-and-a-half miles.

· *Donation to SGS Beneficiaries*

THE HERBALIST'S GARDEN AT LOGIE
Logie House, Kirriemuir DD8 5PN
Terrill and Gavin Dobson
E: herbalistsgarden@gmail.com

This garden, featured on *The Beechgrove Garden* in 2014, is set amid an 18th century walled garden and large Victorian-style greenhouse within Logie's organic farm. Featuring more than 150 herbs, the physic garden is divided into eight rectangles including medicinal herbs for different body systems. All the herbs are labelled with a brief description of actions to help novices learn more about this ancient art. The garden also features a herbaceous border and productive fruit and vegetable garden.

Open: Open by arrangement 1 June - 31 August, admission £5.00, children free. Open for groups of six or more. Teas available by prior arrangement.

Directions: From the A90, take A926 towards Kirriemuir. Just after the *Welcome to Kirriemuir* sign take a sharp left on to a single track road, or from Kirriemuir take A926 towards Forfar and fork right at Beechwood Place onto the single track road. Take the first left and follow signs to *The Walled Garden*.

· *The Glens and Kirriemuir Old Parish Church of Scotland: Thrum's Tots & Messy Church*

ARGYLL & LOCHABER

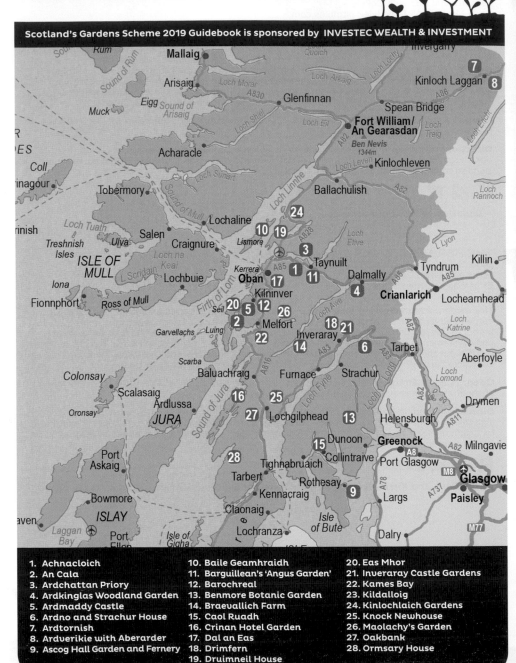

Scotland's Gardens Scheme 2019 Guidebook is sponsored by INVESTEC WEALTH & INVESTMENT

1. Achnacloich
2. An Cala
3. Ardchattan Priory
4. Ardkinglas Woodland Garden
5. Ardmaddy Castle
6. Ardno and Strachur House
7. Ardtornish
8. Arduerikie with Aberarder
9. Ascog Hall Garden and Fernery
10. Baile Geamhraidh
11. Barguillean's 'Angus Garden'
12. Barochreal
13. Benmore Botanic Garden
14. Braevallich Farm
15. Caol Ruadh
16. Crinan Hotel Garden
17. Dal an Eas
18. Drimfern
19. Druimneil House
20. Eas Mhor
21. Inveraray Castle Gardens
22. Kames Bay
23. Kildalloig
24. Kinlochlaich Gardens
25. Knock Newhouse
26. Maolachy's Garden
27. Oakbank
28. Ormsary House

ARGYLL & LOCHABER

OUR VOLUNTEER ORGANISERS

District Organiser:	Minette Struthers	Camasmaddy, Ardmaddy Castle, by Oban PA34 4QY E: argyll@scotlandsgardens.org
Area Organisers:	Yvonne Anderson	Melfort House, Kilmelford, by Oban PA34 4XD
	Grace Bergius	Craignish House, Ardfern, by Lochgilphead PA31 8QN
	Mary Lindsay	Dal an Eas, Kilmore, Oban PA34 4XU
	Patricia McArthur	Bute Cottage, Newton, Strachlachan PA27 8DB
Treasurer:	Minette Struthers	Camasmaddy, Ardmaddy Castle, by Oban PA34 4QY

GARDENS OPEN ON A SPECIFIC DATE

Maolachy's Garden, Lochavich, by Taynuilt	Saturday, 20 April
Knock Newhouse, Lochgair	Saturday/Sunday, 27/28 April
Benmore Botanic Garden, Benmore, Dunoon	Sunday, 28 April
Kames Bay, Kilmelford	Saturday/Sunday, 4/5 May
Knock Newhouse, Lochgair	Sunday, 12 May
Braevallich Farm, by Dalmally	Sunday, 19 May
Ardno and Strachur House, Cairndow	Saturday/Sunday, 25/26 May
Maolachy's Garden, Lochavich, by Taynuilt	Saturday/Sunday, 25/26 May
Ardverikie with Aberarder, Kinlochlaggan	Sunday, 26 May
Braevallich Farm, by Dalmally	Sunday, 9 June
Knock Newhouse, Lochgair	Sunday, 9 June
Drimfern, Inveraray, Argyll	Sunday, 23 June
Dal an Eas, Kilmore, Oban	Saturday/Sunday, 29/30 June
Maolachy's Garden, Lochavich, by Taynuilt	Saturday/Sunday, 29/30 June
Caol Ruadh, Colintraive	Saturday/Sunday, 20/21 July
Maolachy's Garden, Lochavich, by Taynuilt	Saturday/Sunday, 27/28 July
Maolachy's Garden, Lochavich, by Taynuilt	Saturday/Sunday, 24/25 August
Maolachy's Garden, Lochavich, by Taynuilt	Saturday/Sunday, 28/29 September

GARDENS OPEN REGULARLY

Ardkinglas Woodland Garden, Cairndow	1 January - 31 December
Ardmaddy Castle, by Oban	1 January - 31 December
Barguillean's 'Angus Garden', Taynuilt	1 January - 31 December
Achnacloich, Connel, Oban	1 January - 31 December (Saturdays only)
Ardtornish, by Lochaline, Morvern	1 January - 31 December
Kinlochlaich Gardens, Appin	3 March - 15 October
Druimneil House, Port Appin	30 March - 31 October
Ardchattan Priory, North Connel	1 April - 31 October
An Cala, Ellenabeich, Isle of Seil	1 April - 31 October
Ascog Hall Garden and Fernery, Ascog, Isle of Bute	1 April - 31 October
Inveraray Castle Gardens, Inveraray	1 April - 31 October

Argyll & Lochaber

Crinan Hotel Garden, Crinan	1 May - 31 August
Oakbank, Ardrishaig	1 May - 31 July
Baile Geamhraidh, Isle of Lismore, Oban, Argyll	1 June - 1 September (Wednesdays only)

GARDENS OPEN BY ARRANGEMENT

Braevallich Farm, by Dalmally	1 January - 31 December
Kinlochlaich Gardens, Appin	1 January - 31 December
Ormsary House, Ormsary, Lochgilphead, Argyll	1 January - 31 December
Knock Newhouse, Lochgair	14 April - 14 September
Barochreal, Kilninver, Oban, Argyll	1 May - 30 September
Dal an Eas, Kilmore, Oban	1 May - 31 July
Eas Mhor, Cnoc-a-Challtuinn, Clachan Seil, Oban	1 May - 30 September
Kildalloig, Campbeltown	1 May - 31 October
Baile Geamhraidh, Isle of Lismore, Oban, Argyll	1 June - 1 September

Nibbling nectar, photo by Nick Edgington

Argyll & Lochaber

ACHNACLOICH
Connel, Oban PA37 1PR
Mr T E Nelson
T: 01631 710796 **E:** charlie_milne@msn.com

Scottish baronial house by John Starforth of Glasgow. Succession of wonderful bulbs, flowering shrubs, rhododendrons, azaleas, magnolias and primulas. Woodland garden with ponds above Loch Etive. Good autumn colours.

Open: Year-round on Saturdays only, 10am - 4pm, admission £4.00, children free.

Directions: On the A85 three miles east of Connel. Parking is on the right at the bottom of the drive.

· *Macmillan Cancer Support*

AN CALA
Ellenabeich, Isle of Seil PA34 4QY
Mrs Shelia Downie
W: www.gardens-of-argyll.co.uk/view-details.php?id=447

A wonderful example of a 1930s designed garden, An Cala sits snugly in its horseshoe shelter of surrounding cliffs. A spectacular and very pretty garden with streams, waterfall, ponds, many herbaceous plants as well as azaleas, rhododendrons and cherry trees in spring. Archive material of Mawson's design was found recently.

Open: 1 April - 31 October, 10am - 6pm, admission £4.00, children free.

Directions: Proceed south from Oban on Campbeltown Road for eight miles, turn right at *Easdale* sign, a further eight miles on B844; garden is between the school and village. Bus Oban - Easdale.

· *Donation to SGS Beneficiaries*

Rain drop covered apaganthus at An Cala

Argyll & Lochaber

ARDCHATTAN PRIORY
North Connel PA37 1RQ
Mrs Sarah Troughton
T: 01796 481355 **E:** admin@ardchattan.co.uk
W: www.ardchattan.co.uk

Overlooking Loch Etive, Ardchattan Priory Garden has a mature rockery, extensive herbaceous and rose borders to the front of the house. On either side of the drive lie shrub borders, numerous roses and ornamental trees, together with bulbs these give colour throughout the season. The Priory, founded in 1230, is now a private house. The ruins of the chapel and graveyard are in the care of *Historic Environment Scotland* and open with the garden.

Open: 1 April - 31 October, 9:30am - 5:30pm, admission £5.00, children free. 28 October is a fête.

Directions: From north, turn left off A828 at Barcaldine onto B845 for six miles. From east or from Oban on A85, cross Connel Bridge and turn first right, proceed east on Bonawe Road.

· *Donation to SGS Beneficiaries*

Ardchattan Priory, photography Nick Edgington

Argyll & Lochaber

4

ARDKINGLAS WOODLAND GARDEN
Cairndow PA26 8BG
Ardkinglas Estate
T: 01499 600261
W: www.ardkinglas.com

In a peaceful setting overlooking Loch Fyne, the garden contains one of the finest collections of rhododendrons and conifers in Britain. This includes the mightiest conifer in Europe, a silver fir, as well as many other Champion Trees. There is a gazebo with an unique Scriptorium based around a collection of literary quotes. The garden now has the only Gruffalo trail in Scotland; come and find him! It is a *VisitScotland* 3-star garden.
Champion Trees: The mightiest conifer in Europe and others.

Open: Daily, dawn - dusk, admission details can be found on the garden's website.

Directions: Entrance through Cairndow village off the A83 Loch Lomond/Inveraray road.

· *Donation to SGS Beneficiaries*

5

ARDMADDY CASTLE
by Oban PA34 4QY
Mr and Mrs Archie Struthers
T: 01852 300353 **E:** minette@ardmaddy.com
W: ardmaddy.com/places-visit/

The gardens, in a most spectacular setting, are shielded by mature woodlands, carpeted with bluebells and daffodils and protected from the winds by the elevated castle. The walled garden is full of magnificent rhododendrons, a collection of rare and unusual shrubs and plants, the Clock Garden with its cutting flowers, the new Crevice Garden, fruit and vegetables grown with labour saving formality, all within dwarf box hedging. Beyond, a woodland walk, with its 60-foot hydrangea, leads to the water gardens - in early summer a riot of candelabra primulas, irises, rodgersias and other damp-loving plants and grasses. Lovely autumn colour. A plantsman's garden for all seasons.

Open: Daily, 9am - dusk including for Snowdrops and Winter Walks, admission £5.00, children free. Seasonal vegetables, summer fruit and plant stall. Toilet suitable for the disabled. See garden website for other details.

Directions: Take the A816 south of Oban for eight miles. Turn right B844 to Seil Island/Easdale. Four miles on, turn left on to Ardmaddy Road (signed) for a further two miles.

· *Donation to SGS Beneficiaries*

'Gardening is cheaper
than therapy and you get
tomatoes'

Argyll & Lochaber

Ardornish

 6 ## ARDNO AND STRACHUR HOUSE
Cairndow PA26 8BE
Kate How and Sir Charles & Lady Maclean

Ardno Cairndow PA26 8BE (Kate How): From the rich varied landscape, a romantic garden has been created from scratch over the past 25 years. Visitors can stroll in the walled garden, through the old oak wood, and past the gorge and waterfall. There is a beautiful meadow with irises and the collection of unusual trees down to Loch Fyne.

Strachur House Flower & Woodland Gardens Strachur PA27 8BX (Sir Charles and Lady Maclean): The flower garden is sheltered by magnificent beeches, limes, ancient yews and Japanese maples. There are herbaceous borders, a burnside rhododendron and azalea walk, rockery, tulips and spring bulbs. Enjoy the old woodland of Strachur Park, laid out 1782, and the wildlife-rich lochan.

Open: Saturday/Sunday, 25/26 May, Ardno is open 10am - 5pm, Strachur House is open 1pm - 5pm, admission £7.50, children free. Or £4 for individual garden.

Directions: Ardno: situated at the top end of Loch Fyne between Cairndow and St Catherines, off the A815. **Strachur House**: turn off A815 at Strachur House Farm entrance. Park in farm square. Bus Dunoon - Inveraray. From Edinburgh/Glasgow take ferry from Gourock to Dunoon.

· *British Red Cross & Fiddlefolk*

 7 ## ARDTORNISH
by Lochaline, Morvern PA80 5UZ
Mrs John Raven

Wonderful gardens of interesting mature conifers, rhododendrons, deciduous trees, shrubs and herbaceous, set amid magnificent scenery.

Open: Daily, 10am - 6pm, admission £4.00, children free.

Directions: A884 Lochaline three miles.

· *Donation to SGS Beneficiaries*

Argyll & Lochaber

ARDVERIKIE WITH ABERARDER
Kinlochlaggan PH20 1BX
The Feilden family, Mrs P Laing and Mrs E T Smyth-Osbourne
T: 01528 544300

Aberarder Lodge Kinlochlaggan PH20 1BX (The Feilden family): The garden has been laid out over the last 20 years to create a mixture of spring and autumn plants and trees, including rhododendrons, azaleas and acers. The elevated view down Loch Laggan from the garden is exceptional.

Ardverikie House Kinlochlaggan PH20 1BX (Mrs P Laing and Mrs E T Smyth-Osbourne): Lovely setting on Loch Laggan with magnificent trees. Walled garden with large collection of acers, shrubs and herbaceous plants. Architecturally interesting house (not open) featured in *Monarch of the Glen* and *The Crown*.

Open: Sunday 26 May, 2pm - 5:30pm, admission £5.50, children free.

Directions: On the A86 between Newtonmore and Spean Bridge. The entrance to Aberarder Lodge is 200 yards west of the Ardverikie entrance next to the small cottage. The entrance to Ardverikie House is at the east end of Loch Laggan by the gate lodge over the bridge.

· *Laggan Parish Church & Highland Hospice*

Ardverikie

Argyll & Lochaber

ASCOG HALL GARDEN AND FERNERY
Ascog, Isle of Bute PA20 9EU
Karin Burke
T: 01700 503461 **E:** info@ascogfernery.com
W: www.ascogfernery.com

The outstanding feature of this three-acre garden is the Victorian Fernery, a magnificent gilded structure fed by natural spring waters and housing many fern species, including Britain's oldest exotic fern, a 1,000 year old *Todea babara* or king fern. Rare and unusual species await the visitor wandering through the original garden 'rooms' while the stables and coach house ruins feed the imagination with memories of long-lost times. The garden is generally well labelled and contains a plant hunters' trail. New for 2018 is a climate change biotape.

Open: 1 April - 31 October, 10am - 5pm, admission £5.00, children free. Restricted mobility parking at the top of the drive (close to the house). Personal assistance available for disabled access to the Fernery.

Directions: Three miles south of Rothesay on A844. Close to the picturesque Ascog Bay. Bus every half hour Rothesay - Kilchattan.

· *Donation to SGS Beneficiaries*

BAILE GEAMHRAIDH
Isle of Lismore, Oban, Argyll PA34 5UL
Eva Tombs
T: 01631 760128 **E:** eva.tombs@gmail.com

This unique garden forms part of a biodynamic farm on the Island of Lismore in the Inner Hebrides. Created quite recently from a field, the garden has a strong geometric layout that reflects the ecclesiastical history of the island. It has a vegetable garden, a tree nursery, a physic garden and an orchard. Wildflowers, birds, bees and butterflies abound. Standing stones, meadows, new woodlands, mountains and the sea encompass the whole. Some weeds and long grass benefit the Lismore herd of rare breed Shetland horned cattle that roam the fields round about.

Open: 1 June - 1 September (Wednesdays only), 10am - 5pm. Also open by arrangement. Admission £4.00, children free. Plants, seeds, vegetables, flowers and meat for sale.

Directions: From the Oban to Lismore ferry (4/5 per day) travel west then north for seven miles till you see the *SGS* yellow sign. Travel up the track over two cattle grids and follow the arrows. From Port Appin to Lismore ferry (foot and cycles) travel one-and-a-half miles till you see the *SGS* yellow sign and as above.

· *SGS Beneficiaries*

BARGUILLEAN'S 'ANGUS GARDEN'
Taynuilt PA35 1HY
The Josephine Marshall Trust
T: 01866 822333 **E:** info@barguillean.co.uk
W: www.barguillean.co.uk

Nine-acre woodland garden around an 11-acre loch set in the Glen Lonan Hills. Spring-flowering shrubs and bulbs, extensive collection of rhododendron hybrids, deciduous azaleas, conifers and unusual trees. The garden contains a large collection of North American rhododendron hybrids from famous contemporary plant breeders. Some paths can be steep. Three marked walks from 30 minutes to one-and-a-half hours.

Argyll & Lochaber

Open: Daily, 9am - dusk, admission £3.50, children free. Coach tours by appointment.

Directions: Three miles south off A85 Glasgow/Oban road at Taynuilt, road marked *Glen Lonan*, three miles up single track road, turn right at the sign.

· *Donation to SGS Beneficiaries*

BAROCHREAL
Kilninver, Oban, Argyll PA34 4UT
Nigel and Antoinette Mitchell
T: 01852 316151 **E:** toni@themitchells.co.uk
W: www.barochreal.co.uk

A young garden evolving since 2006. After much fencing, stone clearing and rewalling, digging and ditching, each year another area has been completed to provide a bank of rhododendrons and azaleas, a rose garden, water feature with rockery, a pond with island, raised vegetable beds, and waterfalls and burns. This is a bee-friendly garden with active beehives. Maintained walking tracks in the fields and to viewpoints. The two hard winters of 2010/11 and 2011/12 destroyed many plants in their infancy; these are being replaced and added to constantly.

Open: Open by arrangement 1 May - 30 September, admission £3.00, children free.

Directions: Please disregard SatNav. On the main A816 Oban to Lochgilphead road just to the south of the village of Kilninver on the left hand side of the road. Bus Oban - Lochgilpead stops at Kilninver School, short walk after.

· *Argyll Animal Aid*

Barochreal

Argyll & Lochaber

13

BENMORE BOTANIC GARDEN
Benmore, Dunoon PA23 8QU
A Regional Garden of the Royal Botanic Garden Edinburgh
T: 01369 706261 **E:** benmore@rbge.org.uk
W: www.rbge.org.uk/visit/benmore-botanic-garden

Benmore's magnificent mountainside setting is a joy to behold. Its 120 acres boast a world-famous collection of plants from the Orient and Himalayas to North and South America, as well as an impressive avenue of giant redwoods, one of the finest entrances to any botanic garden. Established in 1863, these majestic giants stand over 150 foot high. Seven miles of trails throughout lead to a restored Victorian Fernery and dramatic viewpoint at 420 feet looking out to surrounding mountains and Holy Loch. There is also traditional Bhutanese and Chilean pavilions and the magnificent Golden Gates. Keep an eye out for red squirrels and other wildlife as you explore the garden.
National Plant Collection: *Abies*, South American Temperate Conifers, *Picea*.

Open: Sunday 28 April, 10am - 6pm, admission details can be found on the garden's website. See website for details of regular opening times.

Directions: Seven miles north of Dunoon or 22 miles south from Glen Kinglass below Rest and Be Thankful pass. On A815. Bus service is limited.

· *Donation to SGS Beneficiaries*

Redwood at Benmore Botanic Garden

Argyll & Lochaber

BRAEVALLICH FARM
by Dalmally PA33 1BU
Mr Philip Bowden-Smith
T: 01866 844246 **E:** philip@brae.co.uk

Discover two gardens, one at the farm and another 1,200 feet above. The former is approximately one-and-a-half acres and developed over the last 40 years; its principal features include dwarf rhododendron, azaleas (evergreen and deciduous), large drifts of various primula and meconopsis and bluebells, and mixed herbaceous perennials/shrubs; there is also quite a serious kitchen garden. The latter garden has been developed over the last 30 years out of a birch and sessile oak wood and is a traditional West Coast glen garden intersected by two pretty burns with waterfalls. The garden has been extended over the last two years and now covers nearly ten acres with extensive new paths, and a suspension bridge over the ravine. Whilst the plants are important, many say that it is the topography with its differing vistas which make this garden such a peaceful and special place. Bud-set in 2018 was exceptional so 2019 should be spectacular.

Open: Sunday 19 May & Sunday 9 June, 1pm - 5:30pm. Also open by arrangement. Admission £5.00, children free.

Directions: South east of Loch Awe on B840, 15 miles from Cladich, seven miles from Ford.

· *Mary's Meals*

CAOL RUADH
Colintraive PA22 3AR
Mr and Mrs C Scotland

Delightful seaside garden on the old B866 shore road looking out over Loch Riddon and the Kyles of Bute in this very beautiful corner of Argyll. There are water features with interesting new plantings and the added attraction of a unique outdoor sculpture park featuring works from a variety of Scottish artists.

Open: Saturday/Sunday, 20/21 July, 2pm - 5pm, admission £5.00, children free.

Directions: Drive south on A886 (Strachur - Colintraive road) until signposted *Colintraive 'Argyll's Secret Coast'*. Turn right onto B866 coastal road following road round to the right for 800 yards. Red brick entrance on left. From Dunoon take the A815 north for about three-and-a-half miles, then left on to B836. After ten miles at T junction turn left onto the A886.

· *SGS Beneficiaries*

CRINAN HOTEL GARDEN
Crinan PA31 8SR
Mrs N Ryan
T: 01546 830261 **E:** nryan@crinanhotel.com
W: www.crinanhotel.com

Small rock garden with azaleas and rhododendrons created in a steep hillside over a century ago with steps leading to a sheltered, secluded garden with sloping lawns, herbaceous beds and spectacular views of the canal and Crinan Loch.

Open: 1 May - 31 August, dawn - dusk, admission by donation. Raffle of signed limited-edition fine art print by Frances Macdonald. Tickets available at coffee shop, art gallery and hotel.

Directions: Lochgilphead A83, then A816 to Oban, then A841 Cairnbaan to Crinan. Daily bus.

· *Feedback Madagascar*

Argyll & Lochaber

DAL AN EAS
Kilmore, Oban PA34 4XU
Mary Lindsay
T: 01631 770246 **E:** dalaneas@live.com

Recently created informal country garden with the aim of increasing the biodiversity of native plants and insects while adding interest and colour with introduced trees, shrubs and naturalised perennials. The structured garden has a pond, a burn with pool, wildflower meadow with five different species of native orchid and a vegetable plot. Grass paths lead to waterfalls, views and ancient archaeological sites.

Open: Saturday/Sunday, 29/30 June, 1pm - 6pm. Also open by arrangement 1 May - 31 July. Admission £4.00, children free.

Directions: Take A816 to Kilmore three-and-a-half miles south of Oban. Turn left on road to Barran and Musdale. Keep left at junction for Connel. Dal an Eas is approximately one mile on the left before the big hedges.

· *Kilmore & Kilbride Village Hall Committee & Mary's Meals*

DRIMFERN
Inveraray, Argyll PA32 8XJ
Judith Witts

This small, semi-wild garden has been developed on the hillside amongst farm fields. It is protected by native trees and hedging, with mown paths leading through wild flower strewn grasses, and across interlinked ponds. There is a vegetable and fruit garden, varied trees, shrubs and flowers, including a rock garden. The garden is about 400 feet above sea level.

Open: Sunday 23 June, 11:30am - 4:30pm, admission £4.00, children free.

Directions: Off the A819, five miles north of Inveraray on the left. Go over a cattle grid, steeply, then a winding dirt track (rough). Drimfern is the first house on the left. Coming from Dalmally the entrance is ten miles down to the right.

· *Shelter Scotland*

DRUIMNEIL HOUSE
Port Appin PA38 4DQ
Mrs J Glaisher (Gardener: Mr Andrew Ritchie)
T: 01631 730228 **E:** druimneilhouse@btinternet.com

Large garden overlooking Loch Linnhe with many fine varieties of mature trees and rhododendrons and other woodland shrubs. Nearer the house, an impressive bank of deciduous azaleas is underplanted with a block of camassia and a range of other bulbs. A small Victorian walled garden is currently being restored.

Open: 30 March - 31 October, dawn - dusk, admission by donation. Teas normally available. Lunch by prior arrangement.

Directions: Turn in for Appin off A828 (Connel/Fort William Road). After two miles, sharp left at Airds Hotel, second house on right.

· *Appin Parish Church (Church of Scotland)*

Argyll & Lochaber

EAS MHOR
Cnoc-a-Challtuinn, Clachan Seil, Oban PA34 4TR
Mrs Kimbra Lesley Barrett
T: 01852 300 469 **E:** kimbra1745@gmail.com

All the usual joys of a west coast garden plus some delightful surprises! A small contemporary garden on a sloping site - the emphasis being on scent and exotic plant material. Unusual and rare blue Borinda bamboos (only recently discovered in China) and bananas. The garden is at its best in mid to late summer when shrub roses and sweet peas fill the air with scent. The delightful sunny deck overlooks stylish white walled ponds with cascading water blades. Recent additions include a 20-foot citrus house, Chinese pergola walk and peony border.

Open: Open by arrangement 1 May - 30 September, admission £4.00, children free.

Directions: Turn off A816 from Oban onto B844 signed *Easdale*. Over the bridge onto Seil Island, pass Tigh an Truish pub and turn right after a quarter mile up Cnoc-a-Challtuin road. Public car park is on the left at the bottom; please park there and walk up the road. Eas Mhor on right after second speed bump. Please do not block driveway. Bus Oban - Clachan Seil, two/three per day.

· **MS Centre (Therapy Centre): Oban**

Wildflower meadow at Dal an Eas, photo by Nick Edgington

Argyll & Lochaber

21 **INVERARAY CASTLE GARDENS**
Inveraray PA32 8XF
The Duke and Duchess of Argyll
T: 01499 302203 **E:** enquiries@inveraray-castle.com
W: www.inveraray-castle.com

....

Rhododendrons and azaleas abound and flower from April to June. Very fine specimens of *Cedrus deodars*, *Sequoiadendron giganteum* (wellingtonia), *Cryptomeria japonica*, *Taxus baccata* and others thrive in the damp climate. The Flag-Borders on each side of the main drive with paths in the shape of Scotland's national flag, the St Andrew's Cross, are outstanding in spring with *Prunus* 'Ukon' and *P. subhirtella* and are underplanted with rhododendrons, eucryphias, shrubs and herbaceous plants giving interest all year. Bluebell Festival during flowering period in May.

Open: 1 April - 31 October, 10am - 5:45pm, admission £5.00, children free (under five years). Wheelchair users please note that there are gravel paths. Guidedogs are welcome. Last admission to garden is 5pm.

Directions: Inveraray is 60 miles north of Glasgow on the banks of Loch Fyne on the A83 and 15 miles from Dalmally on the A819. Regular bus service from Glasgow - Lochgilphead.

· *Donation to SGS Beneficiaries*

22 **KAMES BAY**
Kilmelford PA34 4XA
Stuart Cannon
T: 01852 200205 **E:** stuartcannon@kames.co.uk

....

Kames Bay garden has evolved from two acres of scrub and bracken on an exposed lochside hill into a natural, almost wild, garden spread over 13 acres, which blends into the contours of the coastal landscape. A garden where visitors can wander at peace on the woodland walk, or the hillside walk edged with wild primroses and violets, or around the pond edged with hydrangeas. Relax on hidden benches to enjoy the magnificent views over Loch Melfort and the islands to the west. An enchanting garden full of vibrant colours, especially in the spring, with more than 100 varieties of azaleas and rhododendrons.

Open: Saturday/Sunday, 4/5 May, 2pm - 6pm, admission £4.00, children free.

Directions: On the A816 Oban to Lochgilphead road opposite. Kames Bay and the fish farm. Two and a half miles south of Kilmelford and two-and-a-half miles north of Arduaine.

· *St Columba's - Poltalloch*

23 **KILDALLOIG**
Campbeltown PA28 6RE
Mr and Mrs Joe Turner
E: kildalloig@gmail.com

....

Coastal garden with some interesting and unusual shrubs and herbaceous perennials. Woodland walk. Pond area under construction.

Open: Open by arrangement 1 May - 31 October, admission £3.00, children free.

Directions: A83 to Campbeltown, then three miles south east of town past Davaar Island.

· *Marie Curie & Macmillan Cancer Support*

Argyll & Lochaber

Ornamental grasses at Kildalloig

24

KINLOCHLAICH GARDENS
Appin PA38 4BD
Miss F M M Hutchison
T: 07881 525754 **E:** fiona@kinlochlaich.plus.com
W: www.kinlochlaichgardencentre.co.uk

Walled garden incorporating a large Nursery Garden variety of plants growing and for sale. Extensive grounds with woodland walk and spring garden. Many rhododendrons, azaleas, trees, shrubs and herbaceous plants, including many unusual such as embothrium, davidia, stewartia, magnolia, eucryphia and tropaeolum. A quarter of the interior of the walled garden is borders packed with many unusual and interesting plants, espaliered fruit trees, and with an ancient yew in the centre.

Open: 3 March - 15 October, 11am - 4pm. Also open by arrangement. Admission £3.00, children free.

Directions: On the A828 in Appin between Oban, 18 miles to the south, and Fort William, 27 miles to the north. The entrance is next to the police station. Bus Oban to Fort William.

· *The Appin Village Hall & Feis na h'apainne*

Argyll & Lochaber

25 KNOCK NEWHOUSE

Lochgair PA31 8RZ
Mr and Mrs Hew Service
T: 01546 886628 **E:** corranmorhouse@aol.com

The six-acre woodland garden is centred on a small waterfall, an 250 foot lochan and lily pond. Since the 1960s there has been constant planting including major plantings in 1989 and the 90s. The storms of 2011/12 caused great damage to trees and bushes, but created space for additional azaleas, rhododendrons, camellias, hoheria, eucryphia and other flowering shrubs. There are over 100 species of rhododendron, as well as hybrids. Among the mature and young trees are cut leaf oak and alder, specimen conifers, redwoods, eucalyptus, acers and a wollemi pine, which was thought to be extinct until found in Australia in 1994.

Open: Saturday/Sunday, 27/28 April, Sunday 12 May & Sunday 9 June, 1:30pm - 5pm. Also open by arrangement 14 April - 14 September. Admission £4.00, children free. Waterproof footwear is highly recommended other than in very dry weather.

Directions: On the A83. The house is not visible from the road. From Lochgilphead, half-a-mile south of Lochgair Hotel and on the left-hand side of the road, and from Inveraray on the right side of the road half a mile after the Lochgair Hotel; the drive opening is marked and enters the woods.

· **MND Scotland & Christ Church Scottish Episcopal Church**

26 MAOLACHY'S GARDEN

Lochavich, by Taynuilt PA35 1HJ
Georgina Dalton
T: 01866 844212

Three acres of woodland garden with a tumbling burn - created in a small glen over 40 years. At an altitude of 450 feet and two weeks behind the coastal changes, we have a shorter growing season. By not struggling to grow tender or late species we can enjoy those that are happy to grow well here and give us all much pleasure. Snowdrops, followed by early rhododendrons, masses of daffodils in many varieties, bluebells, wildflowers and azaleas, primulas and irises. A productive vegetable patch and tunnel feed the gardener and family.

Open: Saturday 20 April, Saturday/Sunday, 25/26 May, Saturday/Sunday, 29/30 June, Saturday/ Sunday, 27/28 July, Saturday/Sunday, 24/25 August and Saturday/Sunday, 28/29 September, 2pm - 5pm, admission £4.00, children free.

Directions: Ignore SatNav. A816 to Kilmelford. Turn uphill between shop and church, signposted *Lochavich 6*, steep and twisty road with hairpin bend shortly after leaving village, check for passing places. Maolachy Drive is four miles from village. Cross three county cattle grids; after the third Ignore the foresty tracks to left and right. Continue downhill towards Loch Avich, and Maolachy is up on the left, first house after Kilmelford.

· **The Hope Project Scotland (SCIO): Oban**

> '60% of a garden's gross
> proceeds can be donated
> to garden owner's choice
> of charity.'

Argyll & Lochaber

27 **OAKBANK**
Ardrishaig PA30 8EP
Helga Macfarlane
T: 01546 603405 **E:** helga@macfarlane.one
W: www.gardenatoakbank.blogspot.com

....

This unusual and delightful garden will appeal to adults and children alike with lots for each to explore, including a secret garden. It extends to some three acres of hillside with a series of paths winding among a varied collection of trees, shrubs, bulbs and wild flowers. There are several small ponds, many wonderful wood carvings, an active population of red squirrels and a viewpoint overlooking Loch Fyne to the Isle of Arran.

Open: 1 May - 31 July, 1pm - 6pm, admission £4.00, children free.

Directions: On the Tarbert (south) side of Ardrishaig - entry to the garden is at the junction of Tarbert Road (A83) and Oakfield Road opposite the more southerly *Scottish Water* lay-by.

· *Diabetes UK*

28 **ORMSARY HOUSE**
Ormsary, Lochgilphead, Argyll PA31 8PE
Lady Lithgow
T: 01880 770738 **E:** mclithgow@ormsary.co.uk

....

Ormsary is on the shore of Loch Caolisport looking across to Islay and Jura. The house policies are resplendent in spring with bluebells and daffodils under fine oak trees. There are woodland gardens with azaleas, rhododendrons and a collection of trees and shrubs. The walled garden, which has evolved over a couple of centuries, is on two levels. The top half is a kitchen garden producing plants, fruit and vegetables for the house; a winter garden and 'Muscat of Alexandria' vinery have been heated by hydroelectric power for a 100 years. A magnificent *Polylepis australis* beckons to the lower 'secret garden' with its lawn, roses, magnolias and long mixed border. It opens onto the banks of Ormsary Water. There are also woodland walks accessed through the upper woodland garden.

Open: Open by arrangement, admission £5.00, children free.

Directions: Take the A82 road from Lochgilphead towards Campbeltown for four miles, then take B8024 signed to *Kilberry* and travel ten miles and follow signs to the *Estate office* to collect directions to the garden.

· *SGS Beneficiaries*

AYRSHIRE & ARRAN

Scotland's Gardens Scheme 2019 Guidebook is sponsored by **INVESTEC WEALTH & INVESTMENT**

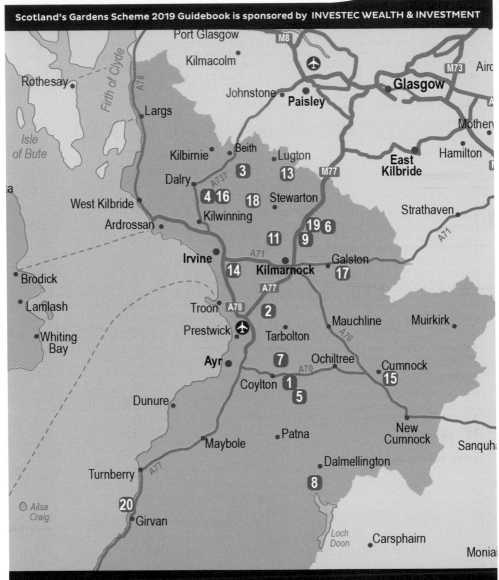

1. **Auldbyres Farm Garden**
2. **Barnweil Garden**
3. **Barrmill Community Garden**
4. **Blair House, Blair Estate**
5. **Burnside**
6. **Clover Park**
7. **Coylbank**
8. **Craigengillan Estate and Scottish Dark Sky Obseruatory**
9. **Craufurdland Estate**
10. **Dougarie**
11. **Gardens of Kilmaurs**
12. **Glenapp Castle**
13. **High Fulwood**
14. **Holmes Farm**
15. **Netherthird Community Garden**
16. **The Carriage House**
17. **The Wildings**
18. **Townend of Kirkwood**
19. **Waterslap Gardens**
20. **Whitewin House**

AYRSHIRE & ARRAN

OUR VOLUNTEER ORGANISERS

District Organisers:	Rose-Ann Cuninghame	45 Towerhill Ave, Kilmaurs, Kilmarnock KA3 2TS
	Lavinia Gibbs	Dougarie, Isle of Arran KA27 8EB
		E: ayrshire@scotlandsgardens.org
Area Organisers:	Anne MacKay	Pierhill, Annbank, Ayr KA6 5AW
	Kim Main	Afton Cottage, 2 Dunlop Road, Stewarton KA3 5BE
	Fiona McLean	100 Main Road, Fenwick KA3 6DY
	Wendy Sandiford	Harrowhill Cottage, Kilmarnock KA3 6HX
	Jane Tait	The Wildings, Bankwood, Galston KA4 8LH
Treasurers:	Lizzie Adam	Bayview, Pirnmill, Isle of Arran KA27 8HP
	Kim Donald	19 Waterslap, Fenwick, Kilmarnock KA3 6AJ

GARDENS OPEN ON A SPECIFIC DATE

Blair House, Blair Estate, Dalry, Ayrshire	Sunday, 24 February
Coylbank, nr Coylton, Ayrshire	Saturday, 18 May
Craigengillan Est Scottish Dark Sky Observatory, Dalmellington	Sunday, 19 May
Craufurdland Estate, nr Fenwick, Kilmarnock	Saturday, 25 May
Barnweil Garden, Craigie, nr Kilmarnock	Sunday, 26 May
Clover Park, Langdyke, Waterside, Kilmarnock	Saturday, 1 June
Holmes Farm, Drybridge, by Irvine	Saturday/Sunday, 8/9 June
The Carriage House, Blair Estate, Dalry	Sunday, 23 June
Dougarie, Isle of Arran	Tuesday, 2 July
Waterslap Gardens, 15 & 19 Waterslap, Fenwick	Sunday, 7 July
Whitewin House, Golf Course Road, Girvan	Saturday/Sunday, 13/14 July
Gardens of Kilmaurs, Kilmaurs	Sunday, 14 July
Whitewin House, Golf Course Road, Girvan	Saturday/Sunday, 20/21 July
Clover Park, Langdyke, Waterside, Kilmarnock	Sunday, 21 July
Whitewin House, Golf Course Road, Girvan	Saturday/Sunday, 27/28 July
Auldbyres Farm Garden, Coylton	Sunday, 28 July
Whitewin House, Golf Course Road, Girvan	Saturday/Sunday, 3/4 August
Netherthird Community Garden, Craigens Road, Cumnock	Saturday, 10 August
Whitewin House, Golf Course Road, Girvan	Saturday/Sunday, 10/11 August
Barrmill Community Garden, Barrmill Park and Gardens	Sunday, 18 August

GARDENS OPEN BY ARRANGEMENT

Blair House, Blair Estate, Dalry, Ayrshire	1 January - 31 December
Glenapp Castle, Ballantrae, Girvan	17 March - 22 December
Clover Park, Langdyke, Waterside, Kilmarnock	1 April - 29 September
Burnside, Littlemill Road, Drongan	1 April - 31 August
Townend of Kirkwood, Stewarton	15 April - 31 October
High Fulwood, Stewarton	1 May - 31 August
The Wildings, Bankwood, Galston	15 May - 31 August

Ayrshire & Arran

1 **AULDBYRES FARM GARDEN**
Coylton KA6 6HG
Marshall and Sue Veitch

This exposed location has been challenging but compensated for by stunning views towards Arran. Shelter is provided by an unobtrusive boundary fence, 'borrowing' the panoramic landscape. Surrounded by a working farm, the garden has mature shrubs, wildlife pond, bog garden and stream. Specimens of interest are gunnera, phormium, cordyline, cardoon, rudbeckia and cloud-pruned conifer. Packed with year-round interest, this garden reaches a July crescendo of massed phlox and hemerocallis, supported by key annuals of cosmos and nicotiana. The rear close protects a large container garden, where moveable pots ensure seasonal displays. Summer stars include tulbaghia, large-flowered fuchsias, pelargoniums, dahlias and begonias. There are small vegetable beds, a five-bay polytunnel (grapevine, tomatoes, basil, cucumber and oleanders), potting/nursery area and compost midden.

Open: Sunday 28 July, 2pm - 5pm, admission £4.00, children free. Dog walking around farm welcome, sorry no dogs in garden.

Directions: In Coylton take road signed B742, past Coylton Arms pub in Low Coylton, Auldbyres signed on left after half a mile.

· *Coylton Parish Church (Church of Scotland) & Beatson Cancer Charity*

Auldbyres Farm Garden

Ayrshire & Arran

BARNWEIL GARDEN
Craigie, nr Kilmarnock KA1 5NE
Mr and Mrs Ronald W Alexander
E: ronaldwalexander@btinternet.com

Opening a month earlier this year brings a different range of plants to the fore in this north-facing two-acre garden. Rhododendrons and azaleas thrive in the woodlands set on heavy clay soil with dense underplanting of candelabra primulas and other woodlanders. Oscar's Ditch, dug two years ago, is fully planted with gunnera, rheum, grasses, iris, ferns and hostas. A path leads from the lawn on the south side of the house, through heavy shade bursting into the Golden Glade with golden-leaved or -flowered trees, shrubs designed to give a blink of sunshine on dreich days - acer, elderflower, *Philadelphus coronarious* 'Aureus' and a young magnolia 'Lemon Chimes' which might flower for the first time. Nearby are wcoronhite candelabra primula self-seeding every year, interplanted with meconopsis and black iris. Rose borders will show early single varieties and two new borders have a wide range of planting.

Open: Sunday 26 May, 2pm - 5pm, admission £5.00, children free.

Directions: Craigie two miles. Right off B730, two miles south of A77 heading to Tarbolton.

· *Tarbolton Parish Church of Scotland & CLDF: Children's Liver Disease Foundation*

Scenic views at Barnweil Garden, photo by Rob Davis

Ayrshire & Arran

BARRMILL COMMUNITY GARDEN
Barrmill Park and Gardens KA15 1HW
The Barrmill Conservation Group
T: 07920 098171

This large woodland garden is carved from a 19th-century whinstone quarry and situated within an 1890's parkland, once known for the quoiting green provided for the village thread mill and ironstone pit workers of that time. Enhancement of the gardens began in 2011 by volunteers with assistance from *The Beechgrove Garden*. Features include enchanted woodland walks, the Vale Burn, views of the Dusk Water, a restored 19th-century cholera pit aka 'the Deid Man's Plantin', wish trees, wishing wells, doors to the Elfhame, guided walks, nature trail and traditional Ayrshire quoits game. The woodland backdrop is complemented by an understore of natural planting throughout.

Open: Sunday 18 August, 2pm - 5pm, admission £3.00, children free.

Directions: From Stewarton take A735 to Dunlop, left down Main Street B706 to Burnhouse, over at crossroads to Barrmill B706. From Lugton south on A736, right at Burnhouse, B706 to Barrmill. From Glasgow on M8 take J28a signed *Irvine*, on Beith by-pass take left B706 to Barrmill.

· *Barrmill and District Community Association*

BLAIR HOUSE, BLAIR ESTATE
Dalry, Ayrshire KA24 4ER
Charles and Sallie Hendry
T: 01294 833100 **E:** enquiries@blairestate.com
W: www.blairestate.com

Blair has beautiful landscaped gardens, with a collection of trees dating back to the 19th-century. Over the past seven years, the gardens have been undergoing restoration, with new beds created including a collection of rhododendrons, magnolias and azaleas. At our opening in February enjoy beautiful displays of snowdrops. Walks on the estate will include access to the private gardens.

Open: Sunday 24 February, 12pm - 4pm for Snowdrops and Winter Walks. Also open by arrangement. Admission £5.00, children free. Light refreshments. Sorry no dogs. Please wear stout footwear.

Directions: From A737 in Dalry, take road signposted to the station and continue for half a mile. Access via North Lodge gates on the right. A one way system will be in place. Public transport to Dalry.

· *Ayrshire Hospice*

BURNSIDE
Littlemill Road, Drongan KA6 7EN
Sue Simpson and George Watt
T: 01292 592445 **E:** suesimpson33@btinternet.com

This maturing and constantly changing six-and-a-half-acre garden began in 2006. There is a wide range of plants from trees to alpines, ensuring colour and variability throughout the year. Adjacent to the roadway flows the Drumbowie Burn parallel to which is a 500-foot woodland border displaying snowdrops, erythroniums, hellebores, trilliums and more, along with rhododendrons and acers. Near to the house is a raised bed and a large collection of troughs displaying a large range of alpines. The garden also boasts herbaceous beds, an ericaceous garden, screes, three alpine glass houses with award-winning plants, a polytunnel, a pond and arboretum, the last being underplanted with daffodils, camassia, fritillaries and crocus.

Open: Open by arrangement 1 April - 31 August, admission £5.00, children free.

Ayrshire & Arran

Directions: From A77 Ayr bypass take A70 Cumnock for five and a quarter miles, at Coalhall, turn onto B730 Drongan (south) for two and a half miles. Burnside entrance immediately adjacent before black/white parapeted bridge. Ordinance survey grid ref: NS455162.

· *Beatson Cancer Charity*

CLOVER PARK
Langdyke, Waterside, Kilmarnock KA3 6JA
Alistair Paterson and Iain MacClure
T: 01560 700555 **E:** clover.park@outlook.com

Clover Park was created almost ten years ago from a blank canvass. Developed by the owners into an eclectic mix of architectural, ornamental and atmospheric features which include a woodland and azalea walk, fernery, gunnera bog and many other points of interest. A paddock is home to a small herd of friendly pygmy goats. Recent additions are a polytunnel, hardy palms and other exotics. Seating areas are positioned for contemplation and relaxation. A garden of great interest created in a relatively short time.

Open: Saturday 1 June and Sunday 21 July, 2pm - 5pm. Also open by arrangement 1 April - 29 September. Admission £5.00, children free. Sorry, no dogs.

Directions: From Glasgow on the M77 take J6 on to A77. After about one and a half miles take left for Galston A719. Drive through hamlet of Waterside, a little further on there is a dip in the road over the Hareshaw Water, look for the sign for *Langdyke & Clover Park* on the left hand side (farm road). From Ayr/Kilmarnock take J7 off the M77 heading north on to A77. At the Fenwick/Stewarton roundabout follow signs to Galston. After one mile turn right onto the A719 Galston as above.

· *Royal Zoological Society Of Scotland & CLIC Sargent*

COYLBANK
nr Coylton, Ayrshire KA6 5LB
Mr and Mrs E K Han
T: 07738 464957 **E:** ekandhelenhan@gmail.com

An afternoon of music in this well-established garden. Coylbank hides behind an old tall beech hedge. At the entrance lies a raised lawn with shrubbery and herbaceous planting. In the back gardens there are lawns framed by rhododendrons, azaleas and mature trees. Beyond this is an area for chickens, turkeys and other creatures of interest. More gardens continue to the north of the house leading back to the front driveway. Of note is a collection of oriental garden artefacts.

Open: Saturday 18 May, 2pm - 5pm, admission £4.00, children free. Music by the Young Musicians at 3pm and 4pm.

Directions: From A77 Sandyford roundabout take the B742 marked *Mossblown* and *Annbank*, go through Mossblown and two miles on to three-way junction, take the middle one B742 to Coylton (left fork Tarbolton right Annbank) continue for about one and a half miles and uphill where Coylbank is on right side just before crossroads (farm opposite gates).

· *Unity: For Ayr Unity*

Ayrshire & Arran

CRAIGENGILLAN ESTATE AND SCOTTISH DARK SKY OBSERVATORY
Dalmellington KA6 7PZ
Mark Gibson & Fi McClelland
T: 01292 551118 **E:** fi@craigengillan.com
W: www.scottishdarkskyobservatory.co.uk

Peacefully set in a rugged 'Highland' landscape recognised by Historic Environment Scotland's Inventory of Gardens and Designed Landscapes. Beautiful gardens, recently uncovered 'rock and water garden' by James Pulham & Sons. Extensive displays of native bluebells with great swathes of vibrant blue under the fresh greens of newly forming leaf canopies. At night there are some of the darkest skies that most people will ever see with stars, planets, comets and constellations all visible.

Open: Sunday 19 May, 2pm - 5pm, admission £4.00, children free. Immersive Planatarium and Stellarium Presentation available at the Dark Sky Observatory during the opening. Times and prices on the website. Advisable to bring walking boots or shoes. Not suitable for prams or wheelchairs.

Directions: A713 from Ayr, at the round red 30mph sign on entering Dalmellington turn right (signed *Craigengillan Stables*) - drive for about two and a quarter miles to Craigengillan House. From Carsphairn, stay on the main road through Dalmellington then take first turning on left after the Jet petrol station.

· *The Scottish Dark Sky Observatory*

CRAUFURDLAND ESTATE
nr Fenwick, Kilmarnock KA3 6BS
Mr and Mrs Simon Craufurd
T: 01560 600760
W: www.craufurdland.co.uk

Coming through the gates, drive through woodland along to the Fishery and the road continues to the Castle. You will see that the woods around the castle have wonderful examples of many different types of trees, rhododendrons, azaleas and bluebells at this time of year. You can stroll through the woodland at leisure, on paths we have created, viewing the best of Craufurdland and the countryside views along the way.

Open: Saturday 25 May, 2pm - 5pm, admission £3.00, children free.

Directions: For SatNav follow Marchbank House KA3 6BX. Once in Fenwick village at the bottom of Main Road, turn into Waterslap, follow the road out of the village for approximately one mile, Marchbank is on the left, a little further on there is a sharp bend, the gates to Craufurdland Estate are straight ahead. Parking at the Fishery/Wee Cafe car park.

· *Friends of Craufurdland SCIO*

Ayrshire & Arran

DOUGARIE
Isle of Arran KA27 8EB
Mrs S C Gibbs
E: office@dougarie.com

Most interesting terraced garden in castellated folly built in 1905 to celebrate the marriage of the 12th Duke of Hamilton's only child to the Duke of Montrose. Good selection of tender and rare shrubs and herbaceous border. Small woodland area with trees including azara, abutilon, eucryphia, hoheria and nothofagus.

Open: Tuesday 2 July, 2pm - 5pm, admission £4.00, children free.

Directions: Five miles from Blackwaterfoot. Regular ferry sailing from Ardrossan and Claonaig (Argyll). Information from Caledonian MacBrayne, Gourock, T: 01475 650100.

· *Pirnmill Village Association*

GARDENS OF KILMAURS
Kilmaurs KA3 2SA
Mrs Rose-Ann Cuninghame (contact for gardens)
E: ayrshire@scotlandsgardens.org

26b Fenwick Road Kilmaurs KA3 2TD (Mr and Mrs B Murphy): The Paddock is a village garden, both front and back but with a difference. Scattered throughout are sculptures created by the owner herself. There are interesting specimen trees including a tulip tree, liquidambar tree and acers.
27 Crosshouse Road Kilmaurs KA3 2SA (Mr and Mrs R Mair): The garden to the rear of the house is in a sheltered position allowing growth of a wide range of plants which offer both spring and summer interest. Each of the two back garden areas contain both a pond and patio. The lower garden has about a third of its area devoted to a productive kitchen garden, soft fruit area and a cold greenhouse. The upper garden is entirely given over to flowering shrubs, perennials, climbers and annuals. We have developed the garden over 40 years.
39 Langmuir Quadrant Kilmaurs KA3 2UA (Mr and Mrs R Vosseler): A small west-facing garden in a new estate was created in spring 2017. The garden is mainly herbaceous perennial plants with roses and evergreen shrubs. A slate path with slate edging meanders through garden. Excellent views of countryside over to Arran. The front garden displays larger perennial plants. The main objective of the garden is to produce cut flowers for the house from April to October. Many of the plants are from cuttings and divided stock from our previous house.
5 Kirkton Road Kilmaurs KA3 2NW (Mr F Murray): A small burn runs through this one-acre garden. Informal planting lies to the south, fairly steeply banked with bulbs, bluebells, specimen trees and a short woodland walk. The north side is laid out in formal lawns, edged by beech hedging and shrub plantations, divided by dry-stone dykes. Visitors will find a 17th-century doocot which once served Tour House as a larder. To the back of the house lies the working garden, with polytunnels for roses, dahlias and chrysanthemums.

Open: Sunday 14 July, 2pm - 5pm, admission £5.00, children free. Garden maps, tickets, homemade teas and plant stall at the Community Association Hall on Irvine Road, KA3 2RJ (former library).

Directions: Kilmaurs village is to the north/west of Kilmarnock and south of Stewarton. From Glasgow or Ayr or M77 take signs to *Kilmaurs* (J7 heading south, or J8 heading north). B751 goes from Fenwick to Kilmaurs.

· *MND Scotland & Multiple Sclerosis Society*

Ayrshire & Arran

12 GLENAPP CASTLE
Ballantrae, Girvan KA26 0NZ
Mr Paul Szkiler
T: 01465 831212 **E:** info@glenappcastle.com
W: www.glenappcastle.com

The 36-acre grounds at Glenapp Castle are secluded and private. Many rare and unusual plants and shrubs can be found, including magnificent specimen rhododendrons. Paths wander round the azalea pond, through established woodland leading to the wonderful walled garden with a 150-foot Victorian glasshouse. Fresh herbs and fruit from the garden are used every day in the castle kitchen. Much of the gardens were designed by Gertrude Jekyll (1843-1932), the world-famous garden architect, applying the principles of the Arts and Crafts Movement, who worked in collaboration with Edwin Lutyens. A new walk has been created opening up the Glen, where Glenapp's Champion Trees will be found.

Open: Open by arrangement 17 March - 22 December, admission £5.00, children free.

Directions: From north take A77 South. Pass through Ballantrae, crossing the River Stinchar as you leave. Take first turning on right, 100 yards beyond the river (not sign posted). From the South take A77 north, turn left 100 yards before bridge over Stinchar at Ballantrae. Castle gates are one mile along this road.

· *Donation to SGS Beneficiaries*

13 HIGH FULWOOD
Stewarton KA3 5JZ
Mr and Mrs Crawford
T: 01560 484705 **E:** judithillsley@aol.com

One acre of mature garden, particularly fine in late spring with rhododendrons, azaleas, trillium, hellebores and other spring-flowering plants and bulbs. There is also an acre of developing garden with herbaceous borders, vegetable garden and orchard at its best during July and August and there are two acres of native broadleaf woodland being created. No neat edges but lots to see at any time.

Open: Open by arrangement 1 May - 31 August, admission £4.00, children free.

Directions: From Stewarton Cross take the B760 Old Glasgow Road for one mile, turn onto the road marked to Dunlop (from Glasgow this turning is half a mile past Kingsford). Continue for two miles and turn right at T junction. High Fulwood is a short distance on the right-hand side.

· *Hessilhead Wildlife Rescue*

Ayrshire & Arran

HOLMES FARM
Drybridge, by Irvine KA11 5BS
Mr Brian A Young
T: 01294 311210 **E:** hfplants@live.co.uk
W: www.holmesfarmplants.com

A plantsman's garden created by a confirmed plantaholic. Meandering paths guide the eye through predominantly herbaceous plantings, with small trees and shrubs. The garden opening will hopefully be timed for the peak bloom of some of the 400 irises in the garden. Some areas of the garden are currently undergoing a partial replant. The plant nursery, Holmes Farm Plants, is located at the garden, where a wide selection of plants from the garden can be purchased.

Open: Saturday/Sunday, 8/9 June, 1pm - 5pm, admission £5.00, children free. Sorry, no dogs.

Directions: Holmes is the only farm between Drybridge and Dreghorn on B730.

· *The National Trust for Scotland: for Threave Gardens*

NETHERTHIRD COMMUNITY GARDEN
Craigens Road, Netherthird, Cumnock KA18 3AR
Netherthird Community Development Group
E: jamielor@aol.com
W: Facebook (Netherthird Community Development Group)

Netherthird Community Garden is an oasis of calm in the centre of the Ayrshire countryside. There is a lovely cottage garden, flower beds filled with perennials and annuals, vegetable beds, polytunnels and wooden gazebos funded by The Prince Charles Foundation. There is also a beach, play area, vintage cafe, a new nature trail and wild garden, fairy door hunt and lots more. 2019 should see the creation of a bog garden. Volunteers run the garden, which is used by a wide range of community groups and all the children and nursery children from the adjacent Netherthird Primary during the week. A wonderful community project.

Open: Saturday 10 August, 12pm - 3pm, admission £3.00, children free.

Directions: Driving south on the A76 Cumnock by-pass look for the roundabout signed B7083, take this exit which heads to Cumnock, after few hundred yards take right turn into Craigens Road, Netherthird Primary School is on the right. Parking available here, Community Garden nearby. Disabled parking at garden.

· *Netherthird Community Development Group*

'Growing my own fruit and
vegetables really helps me
keep a healthy diet'
Edinburgh Gardener

Ayrshire & Arran

16 THE CARRIAGE HOUSE
Blair Estate, Dalry KA24 4ER
Mr and Mrs Luke Borwick
T: 01294 832816 **E:** lina@blairtrust.co.uk

The Stables were built (c1800) on rocky outcrop with little soil depth. In 2001, the Carriage House was created from old stables, cowshed and dairy. The Garden has evolved over the past fifteen years, and has been designed by the owners to provide colour and interest all year round, many plants provided by friends and family. Divided into many different 'rooms', some contain sculptures by artists including Lucy Poett, Lucy Fisher and Mary Stormonth Darling. Ironwork by Kev Paxton. Small copses have been formed in the adjoining ten-acre field, containing many interesting trees and shrubs. Paths are designed to take you round the field to discover items of interest, such as the mermaids rescuing a girl, some unusual trees such as a variegated tulip tree, a golden dawn redwood, and a wellingtonia grown from seed here at Blair.

Open: Sunday 23 June, 2pm - 5pm, admission £4.00, children free.

Directions: From A737 in Dalry take road to station, continue for a half mile, right onto Blair road. Access via South Lodge of Blair Estate. Public transport to Dalry.

· *Dalry Trinity Church of Scotland & Friends of Hilary Storm School Uganda*

17 THE WILDINGS
Bankwood, Galston KA4 8LH
Mr and Mrs Jim Tait
T: 01563 829244 **E:** jane.tait@mypostoffice.co.uk

The Wildings was created in 1999 and is now well established, providing year-round interest. A cottage style front garden leads to a more formal area with a terrace lined with an abundance of climbing plants in pots, stone walls, lawn, imaginatively planted beds, a pond well stocked with water plants, raised vegetable beds and potting shed. A pathway winds up through a mature garden planted with a variety of rhododendrons, azaleas, various shrubs and mature trees. A bluebell wood lies further up the garden planted with mature rhododendrons. This garden is a haven for wildlife.

Open: Open by arrangement 15 May - 31 August, admission £4.00, children free.

Directions: Take Sorn Road from Galston and follow for approximately one and a half miles. Just before reaching Sorn Hill, turn left where signposted *Gibbs Animal Feeds*. Turn left again immediately and The Wildings is the first house on the left.

· *Compassion UK Christian Child Development: Releasing Children from Poverty in Jesus' Name*

Ayrshire & Arran

TOWNEND OF KIRKWOOD
Stewarton KA3 3EN
Mrs Katrina Clow
T: 01560 483926 / 07914 316119 **E:** katrina.clow@btinternet.com

Townend of Kirkwood is a new garden created on three acres of wet field in 2013. On the left towards the house there is extensive planting around a wildlife pond, and on the right some interesting wind breaking planting which is maturing well. There is an excellent range of interesting shrubs and young trees throughout with a well-established set of beds with mixed plantings. To the rear of the house is a delightful sheltered garden with lawn and herbaceous beds full of plants and a path leading to a small young orchard with productive trees. To the front lies a tranquil small landscaped area. Good all-year-round colour.

Open: Open by arrangement 15 April - 31 October, admission £4.00, children free.

Directions: In Stewarton take B778, heading towards the Glasgow / Irvine road. More details when applying.

·The Younger (Benmore) Trust

Wildings, Ayrshire

Ayrshire & Arran

19 **WATERSLAP GARDENS**
15 & 19 Waterslap, Fenwick KA3 6AJ
Graham & Elaine Stott and Kim Donald
E: kd581@aol.com

15 Waterslap Fenwick KA3 6AJ (Mr and Mrs Graham Stott): Already a garden when the Stotts took over Alma Cottage some 14 years ago, it has continued to evolve under their ownership. It is designed in 'rooms' linked by small pathways throughout with interesting tree, shrub and perennial planting, bulbs in spring, water features attracting plenty of bird and butterfly life, a greenhouse for growing many of the plants in the garden and an attractive summerhouse. A raised timber terrace overflowing with plants is a suntrap for sitting and enjoying the garden. Overall an interesting quirky cottage garden showing off the artistic flair of the owners.
19 Waterslap Fenwick KA3 6AJ (Mrs Kim Donald): This new south facing garden began life in 2015 with only four mature chestnut, lime and willow trees. A challenging site, the owner has designed it to give year-round colour. New traditional hedging provides shelter for this contemporary cottage garden planted with a wide variety of well-established trees, shrubs, perennials and bulbs. Herbaceous borders and shrubberies frame a lawn. Paths round the garden link raised vegetable beds, greenhouse, cold frames, fruit trees, shrubberies and small woodland area. The burn inspired the flow of the garden; its banks are now planted with water loving trees, shrubs and gunnera.

Open: Sunday 7 July, 2pm - 5pm, admission £5.00, children free.

Directions: Off M77 from the south take J8 sign *Fenwick*. Into village, past coffee shop turn right into Waterslap. From north take J7 sign *Fenwick*, down Main Road, at bottom turn left into Waterslap.

· *The Brain Tumour Charity*

19 Waterslap, Waterslap Gardens

Ayrshire & Arran

20 **WHITEWIN HOUSE**
Golf Course Road, Girvan KA26 9HW
Linda Finnie and Graeme Finnie
T: 01465 712358 **E:** lafinnie@hotmail.com

Whitewin House has an interesting history. It was the first house to be built on Golf Course Road by the Tate & Lyle sugar-refining family in the late 1800s. It has a prime location with stunning views over the Firth of Clyde and to Ailsa Craig and the Kintyre Peninsula. Set in an acre of ground there are four separate gardens: the Ailsa Craig Garden at the front; the Gable Garden; the Central Rear Garden and the Rear Golf Course Garden. The layout is formal with lawns, borders, shrubs, rockeries and statuary complementing the Victorian architecture of Whitewin.

Open: Saturday/Sunday, 13/14 July, Saturday/Sunday, 20/21 July, Saturday/Sunday, 27/28 July, Saturday/Sunday, 3/4 August and Saturday/Sunday, 10/11 August, 1pm - 5pm, admission £4.00, children free. Dogs on leads only.

Directions: Approaching Girvan from the north on the A77 the turning to Golf Course Road is on the right hand side of the road before the town centre (follow signs for the *Golf Course*). From the south on the A77 come through Girvan, turn left at the lights, then first left and follow signs for the *Golf Course*. Entrance to the property will be signed.

· SGS Beneficiaries

Views of Ailsa Craig from Whitewin House

BERWICKSHIRE

Scotland's Gardens Scheme 2019 Guidebook is sponsored by **INVESTEC WEALTH & INVESTMENT**

Cockburnspath

St Abb's Head

Granthouses

Eyemouth
5

A1

Preston   Chirnside

Duns

Berwick-upon-Tweed

Norham

Greenlaw

1   **4**

Eccles

Etal

2 **3**
Coldstream

Kelso

1. Bughtrig
2. Coldstream Open Gardens

3. Lennel Bank
4. Marlfield and RuthvenGardens
5. Netherbyres

BERWICKSHIRE

OUR VOLUNTEER ORGANISERS

District Organiser: Christine McLennan   Marlfield, Coldstream TD12 4JT
                                                 E: berwickshire@scotlandsgardens.org

Treasurer: Forbes McLennan   Marlfield, Coldstream TD12 4JT

GARDENS OPEN ON A SPECIFIC DATE

Marlfield and Ruthven Gardens, Coldstream, Coldstream   Sunday, 23 June
Netherbyres, Eyemouth   Sunday, 30 June
Lennel Bank, Coldstream   Sunday, 7 July
Coldstream Open Gardens, Coldstream Community Centre   Sunday, 21 July

GARDENS OPEN REGULARLY

Bughtrig, Near Leitholm, Coldstream   1 June - 1 September

GARDENS OPEN BY ARRANGEMENT

Lennel Bank, Coldstream   1 January - 31 December

Berwickshire

BUGHTRIG
Near Leitholm, Coldstream TD12 4JP
Mr and Mrs William Ramsay
T: 01890 840777 **E:** ramsay@bughtrig.co.uk

A traditional hedged Scottish family garden with an interesting combination of sculpture, herbaceous plants, shrubs, annuals and fruit. It is surrounded by fine specimen trees, which provide remarkable shelter.

Open: 1 June - 1 September, 11am - 5pm, admission £5.00, children free.

Directions: Quarter of a mile east of Leitholm on the B6461.

· *Donation to SGS Beneficiaries*

COLDSTREAM OPEN GARDENS
Coldstream Community Centre, High Street, Coldstream TD12 4AP
The Gardeners of Coldstream

Historic Coldstream, Scotland's 'First True Border Town' is home of Coldstream's Guards, the country's second oldest infantry regiment. Cross the bridge over the River Tweed, which forms a natural boundary between England and Scotland, pausing to admire the wonderful views along the river to the Cheviots and beyond. Coldstream, as the *Borders Floral Gateway Awards* best large village winner 2017, will have a great variety of gardens open for the garden enthusiast to explore. Wander around and chat to an exponent of permaculture, a giant vegetable grower and numerous other garden owners who will be delighted to share their gardening triumphs and interests with you.

Open: Sunday 21 July, 1pm - 5pm, admission £5.00, children free. Tickets, teas, plant sales and facilities at the Community Centre.

Directions: Coldstream is on the A697 equidistant between Kelso and Berwick-on-Tweed. The Community Centre (an old church building) is in the west end of town. There is ample parking on the street and in nearby car parks.

· *Coldstream Gateway Association*

Coldstream Open Gardens, photo by Kay Slater

Berwickshire

Overlooking the stream to the scenic views at Lennel Bank, photo by J Bos

3

LENNEL BANK
Coldstream TD12 4EX
Mrs Honor Brown
T: 01890 882297

Lennel Bank is a terraced garden overlooking the River Tweed, consisting of wide borders packed with shrubs and perennial planting, some unusual. The water garden, built in 2008, is surrounded by a rockery and utilises the slope ending in a pond. There is a small kitchen garden with raised beds in unusual shapes. Different growing conditions throughout the garden from dry, wet, shady and sunny lend themselves to a variety of plants, and enhance interest in the garden.

Open: Sunday 7 July, 10:30am - 5pm. Also open by arrangement. Admission £5.00, children free.

Directions: On A6112 Coldstream to Duns road, one mile from Coldstream.

· British Heart Foundation

Berwickshire

MARLFIELD AND RUTHVEN GARDENS
Coldstream TD12 4JT
Christine & Forbes McLennan and Keith & Karen Fountain

Marlfield Coldstream TD12 4JT (Christine & Forbes McLennan): Marlfield is a two-and-a-half-acre garden with extensive lawns, specimen trees, shrubberies, flower beds, a half-acre woodland wind break, half-acre paddock with a large allotment-type raised vegetable garden, fruit cage and small orchard. The present owners have worked extensively over the past five years to create the allotment and fruit beds from a vacant field. The main garden is still a work in progress, restoring or creating order from what was a very neglected garden. The rockery and fish pond are almost complete. Marlfield is a lovely tranquil garden where one can hear little but birds singing and our bees buzzing.

Ruthven House Coldstream TD12 4JU (Keith & Karen Fountain): Ruthven has lovely views toward the Cheviots and is accessed via a sweeping driveway. There are three acres divided into various interconnected areas, including a traditional knot garden, gravel gardens, an orchard set in meadow planting, a newly establish rose garden and informal herbaceous borders which lead to the garden's main feature, two ponds connected by a winding stream. The owners have over the last few years expanded the garden extensively from the original small beds around the house - adding different areas as inspiration struck. The most recent additions are a substantial kitchen garden and (perhaps optimistically) a small lavender field.

Open: Sunday 23 June, 1pm - 5pm, admission £5.00, children free.

Directions: Four miles north of Coldstream on the old Duns Road. Half a mile off the main road.

· *Macmillan Cancer Support: Borders General*

Clear waters at one of the pond at Ruthven, photo by Malcolm Ross

Berwickshire

NETHERBYRES
Eyemouth TD14 5SE
Col S J Furness
T: 01890 750337

A traditional Scottish walled garden, with a mixture of fruit, flowers and vegetables. It is thought to be the only elliptical walled garden in the world, dating from 1740. A pear tree planted at that time still survives, next to the largest rose in Berwickshire (*Rosa filipes* 'Kiftsgate').

Open: Sunday 30 June, 2pm - 5pm, admission £5.00, children free.

Directions: Half a mile south of Eyemouth on the A1107 to Berwick.

· *St Ebba Episcopal Church Eyemouth*

Abundant borders at Netherbyres, photo by K Patterson

CAITHNESS & SUTHERLAND

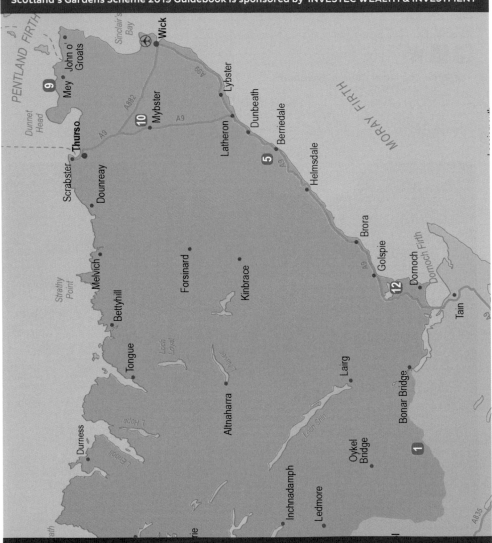

Scotland's Gardens Scheme 2019 Guidebook is sponsored by INVESTEC WEALTH & INVESTMENT

SHETLAND

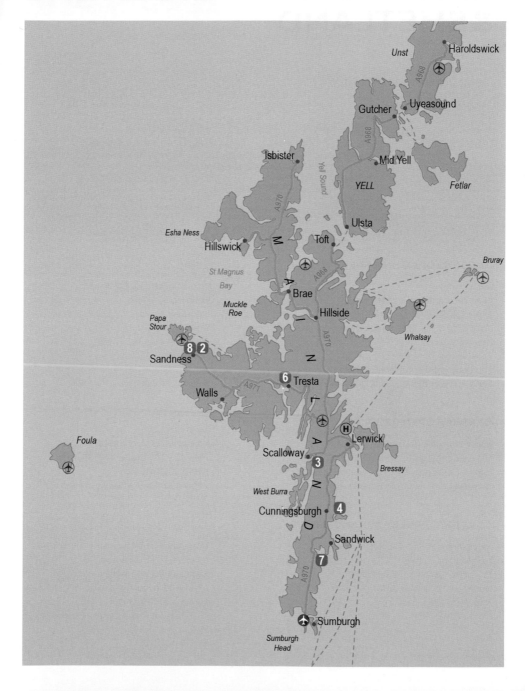

CAITHNESS, SUTHERLAND &SHETLAND

OUR VOLUNTEER ORGANISERS

District Organiser:	Sara Shaw	Amat, Ardgay, Sutherland IV24 3BS E: caithness@scotlandsgardens.org
Area Organisers:	Caroline Critchlow	The Quoy of Houton, Orphir, Orkney KW17 2RD
	Mary Leask	VisitScotland, Market Cross, Lerwick, Shetland, ZE1 0LU
	Steve Mathieson	VisitScotland, Market Cross, Lerwick Shetland, ZE1 0LU
Treasurer:	Nicola Vestey	The Old School House, Bunloit, Drumnadrochit IV63 6XG

GARDENS OPEN ON A SPECIFIC DATE

Amat, Ardgay	Saturday/Sunday, 1/2 June
The Castle & Gardens of Mey, Mey	Wednesday, 3 July
Three Gardens near Dornoch	Saturday, 13 July
The Castle & Gardens of Mey, Mey	Wednesday, 17 July
Langwell, Berriedale	Sunday, 4 August
The Castle & Gardens of Mey, Mey	Saturday, 10 August
The Quoy of Houton, Orphir, ORKNEY	Sunday, 11 August
The Garden at the Auld Post Office B&B, Spittal-by-Mybster	Sunday, 18 August

GARDENS OPEN REGULARLY

Norby, Burnside, Sandness, SHETLAND	1 January - 31 December
Lea Gardens, Tresta, SHETLAND	1 March - 30 October (not Thursdays)
Highlands Garden, East Voe, Scalloway, SHETLAND	1 May - 31 October
Nonavaar, Levenwick, SHETLAND	1 May - 31 August (Sundays only)

GARDENS OPEN BY ARRANGEMENT

Amat, Ardgay	1 January - 31 December
Langwell, Berriedale	1 January - 31 December
Cruisdale, Sandness, SHETLAND	1 January - 31 December
Nonavaar, Levenwick, SHETLAND	1 May - 31 August
Keldaberg, Cunningsburgh, SHETLAND	1 June - 30 September

Caithness, Sutherland, Orkney & Shetland

1

AMAT
Ardgay IV24 3BS
Jonny and Sara Shaw
E: sara.amat@aol.co.uk

Riverside garden surrounded by the old Caledonian Amat Forest. Herbaceous borders and rockery set in a large lawn looking onto a salmon pool. Old and new rhododendrons grow along the woodland and river walk, plus large specimen trees in policies. Red squirrels were reintroduced six years ago and are often seen in and around the garden.

Open: Saturday/Sunday, 1/2 June, 2pm - 5pm. Also open by arrangement. Admission £5.00, children free.

Directions: Take the road from Ardgay to Croick, nine miles. Turn left at the red phone box and the garden is 500 yards on the left.

· *Horatio's Garden & Croick Church*

2

CRUISDALE
Sandness, SHETLAND ZE2 9PL
Alfred Kern
T: 01595 870739

The garden is in a natural state with many willows, several ponds and a variety of colourful hardy plants that grow well in the Shetland climate. It is a work in progress, started about 16 years ago and growing bigger over the years with more work planned.

Open: Open by arrangement, admission £3.00, children free.

Directions: From Lerwick head north on the A970, then at Tingwall take the A971 to Sandness, on the west side of Shetland. Cruisdale is opposite the school, on the right-hand side with a wind generator in the field.
· *Royal Voluntary Service*

3

HIGHLANDS GARDEN
East Voe, Scalloway, SHETLAND ZE1 0UR
Sarah Kay
T: 01595 880526 **E:** info@easterhoull.co.uk
W: www.selfcatering-shetland.co.uk/the-garden/

The garden is in two parts. The upper garden is mostly a rockery, with a large selection of plants, shallow pond, seating area and newly built polycrub and greenhouse with fruit and vegetables. The lower garden is on a steep slope with a spectacular sea view over the village of Scalloway. There is a path to lead visitors around and the garden features a large collection of plants, vegetable patch, deep pond and pergola. It was awarded a *Shetland Environmental Award* in 2014 for its strong theme of recycling.

Open: 1 May - 31 October, 9am - 9pm, admission £3.50, children free.

Directions: Follow the A970 main road towards the village of Scalloway. Near the top of the hill heading towards Scalloway take a sharp turn to the left, signposted *Easterhoull Chalets*. Follow the road to chalets (painted blue with red roofs) and you will see the yellow *SGS* sign for the garden. Bus 4 from Lerwick/Scalloway.

· *Macmillan Cancer Support: Shetland Branch*

Caithness, Sutherland, Orkney & Shetland

KELDABERG
Cunningsburgh, SHETLAND ZE2 9HG
Mrs L Johnston
T: 01950 477331 **E:** linda.keldaberg@btinternet.com

A 'secret garden' divided into four areas. A beach garden of grasses, flowers and driftwood. The main area is a sloping perennial border leading down to a greenhouse, vegetable plot, up to a decked area with containers and exotic plants including agaves, pineapple lilies, cannas and gunneras. The new area has trees, raised vegetable beds, a rockery, retaining walls and an arbour in which to rest. There is a pond with goldfish and aquatic plants and, now a polycrub to grow vegetables, fruit trees and a grapevine.

Open: Open by arrangement 1 June - 30 September, admission £3.50, children free.

Directions: On the A970 south of Lerwick is Cunningsburgh, take the Gord junction on the left after passing the village hall. Continue along the road to the second house past the *Kenwood* sign.

· *Chest Heart & Stroke Scotland*

LANGWELL
Berriedale KW7 6HD
Welbeck Estates
T: 01593 751278 / 751237 **E:** caithness@welbeck.co.uk

A beautiful and spectacular old walled garden with outstanding borders situated in the secluded Langwell Strath. Charming wooded access drive with a chance to see deer.

Open: Sunday 4 August, 12pm - 4pm. Also open by arrangement. Admission £4.00, children free.

Directions: Turn off the A9 at Berriedale Braes, up the private (tarred) drive signposted *Private - Langwell House*. It is about one-and-a-quarter miles from the A9.

· *RNLI*

LEA GARDENS
Tresta, SHETLAND ZE2 9LT
Rosa Steppanova
T: 01595 810454

Lea Gardens, started in the early 1980s, now covers almost two acres. The plant collection, the largest north of Inverewe Gardens, consists of 1,500 different species and cultivars from all over the world, including phyto-geographic elements of collections of plants from New Zealand, South Africa and South America. Planted to provide all-year-round interest, it has been divided into a variety of habitats: woodland and shade, borders, wetland, raised beds, and acid and lime lovers. A winner of the 2011 *Shetland Environmental Award*.

Open: 1 March - 30 October (not Thursdays), 2pm - 5pm, admission £4.00, children free.

Directions: From Lerwick take the A970 north, turn left at Tingwall onto the A971 past Weisdale along Weisdale Voe and up Weisdale hill. Coming down, Lea Gardens is on your right surrounded by trees.

· *Donation to SGS Beneficiaries*

Caithness, Sutherland, Orkney & Shetland

7

NONAVAAR
Levenwick, SHETLAND ZE2 9HX
James B Thomason
T: 01950 422447

This is a delightful country garden, sloping within drystone walls, and overlooking magnificent coastal views. It contains ponds, terraces, trees, bushes, varied perennials, annuals, vegetable garden and greenhouse.

Open: 1 May - 31 August (Sundays only), 12pm - 6pm. Also open by arrangement 1 May - 31 August. Admission £4.00, children free.

Directions: Head south from Lerwick. Turn left at the *Levenwick* sign soon after Bigton turnoff. Follow the road to the third house on the left after the Midway stores. Park where there is a *Garden Open* sign. Bus 6 from Lerwick - Sumburgh.

· *Cancer Research UK*

8

NORBY
Burnside, Sandness, SHETLAND ZE2 9PL
Mrs Gundel Grolimund
T: 01595 870246 **E:** gislinde@tiscali.co.uk

A small but perfectly formed garden and a prime example of what can be achieved in a very exposed situation. Blue painted wooden pallets provide internal wind breaks and form a background for shrubs, climbers and herbaceous plants, while willows provide a perfect wildlife habitat. There are treasured plants such as *Chionochloa rubra*, pieris, Chinese tree peonies, and a selection of old-fashioned shrub roses, lilies, hellebores and grasses from New Zealand.

Open: Daily, dawn - dusk, admission £3.00, children free.

Directions: Head north on the A970 from Lerwick then west on the A971 at Tingwall. At Sandness, follow the road to Norby, turn right at the Methodist Church, Burnside is at the end of the road. Bus 10 Sandness - Walls.

· *Survival International Charitable Trust*

9

THE CASTLE AND GARDENS OF MEY
Mey KW14 8XH
The Queen Elizabeth Castle of Mey Trust
T: 01847 851473 **E:** enquiries@castleofmey.org.uk **W:** www.castleofmey.org.uk

Her Majesty Queen Elizabeth, The Queen Mother bought what was then Barrogill Castle in 1952 before renovating and restoring the z-plan castle and creating the beautiful gardens you see today, renaming it The Castle and Gardens of Mey. This romantic and unique garden is a reminder that, however daunting the weather, it is often possible with a little vision and energy to create and maintain a garden in the most unlikely of locations. The castle now includes an animal centre, gift shop and tearoom serving delicious locally sourced food and drinks, often using produce from the castle's very own gardens.

Open: Wednesday 3 July and Wednesday 17 July, 10am - 5pm. Also open Saturday 10 August, 10am - 5pm. Admission details can be found on the garden's website. The gardens are also open 1 May - 30 September 10am - 5pm. Please check our website for opening details as dates can be subject to change.

Directions: On the A836 between Thurso and John O'Groats.

· *Donation to SGS Beneficiaries*

Caithness, Sutherland, Orkney & Shetland

THE GARDEN AT THE AULD POST OFFICE B&B

Spittal-by-Mybster KW1 5XR
Lynne and Weyland Read
T: 01847 841391 **E:** auldpostoffice@btinternet.com
W: www.auldpostoffice.com

Surrounded by eight acres of Alaskan Lodgepole pine trees, this secluded garden has a variety of beds and borders containing evergreen plants, shrubs, grasses and perennials. The one-third acre garden provides a meandering walk under the pergola to beds set in the lawn. The fish share their pond with grasses and lilies, and the garden walk continues beneath 20-year-old pine trees, under-planted with shade-loving perennials. Heather, junipers and conifers provide an all-year-round centrepiece. There are many seating areas to rest awhile and, for the hardy, a stout footwear walk can be taken through the surrounding woodland. Planting has been chosen to encourage bees, birds and butterflies, and the hens potter in their woodland enclosure.

Open: Sunday 18 August, 2pm - 5pm, admission £4.00, children free.

Directions: On the A9 at Spittal.

· *Cancer Research UK*

THE QUOY OF HOUTON

Orphir, ORKNEY KW17 2RD
Kevin and Caroline Critchlow
T: 01856 811237 **E:** c.kritchlow258@btinternet.com

An historic walled garden a stone's throw away from the sea and completely restored in 2008. The garden is planted to withstand winds in excess of 100 mph and features drystone walling, raised beds and a 60-foot water rill. The planting reflects its coastal location and is planted in the cottage garden style with towering allium, many varieties of geranium and plants collected from around Europe. There are wildflower areas, which encourage bees and butterflies. There is a separate walled vegetable garden and fruit cage which supplies the house and B&B and cottage guests. This year there will be a new garden housing hybrid hardy geraniums bred by Alan Bremnar. The garden is a 2017 winner of *Gardeners' World* Britain's best challenging garden.

Open: Sunday 11 August, 11am - 4pm, admission £3.00, children free.

Directions: A964 from Kirkwall to Houton. Take ferry turning, straight across at first junction following tarmac road to a two-storey yellow house across the bay.

· *Friends of the Neuro Ward Aberdeen Royal Infirmary*

'Gardening may be
important in preventing
cognitive decline'
The Kings Fund, 2016

Caithness, Sutherland, Orkney & Shetland

THREE GARDENS NEAR DORNOCH
42 Astle IV25 3NH, Auchlea IV25 3HY, Skelbo House IV25 3QG
Fay Wilkinson, John & Fiona Garvie and Alison Bartlett

42 Astle IV25 3NH (Fay Wilkinson): Organic wildlife garden at the edge of boggy moorland. Mixed planting of trees, shrubs, also herbaceous perennials and fruit and vegetables, many on raised beds for improved drainage. There is a natural pond.

Auchlea Balnapolaig Muir IV25 3HY (John and Fiona Garvie): The creation of Auchlea garden from its natural state as a wetland of rushes and whins began in 1998 with the drainage and sowing of a lawn on introduced topsoil. The planting of trees, mostly around its periphery was also begun then. Extensive, herbaceous borders with a wide variety of colour and species have been gradually developed. There is also a sheltered vegetable garden, made more productive using raised beds, alongside is a recently replanted bog garden. The habitual, accumulated use of garden and household compost has progressively improved stony ground around the boundary, where a mixed hedge has made good progress.

Skelbo House Skelbo IV25 3QG (Alison Bartlett): Extensive woodland garden with spectacular views over Loch Fleet. Mixed herbaceous borders, rose garden and shrubberies surround the house. Lawns slope down to a small lochan and river walkway. Mature trees throughout. Large kitchen garden.

Open: Saturday 13 July, 10am - 4pm, admission £5.00, children free.

Directions: 42 Astle A9 from the south: Pass turn off to Dornoch, take first left after Tall Pines Restaurant, signposted *Astle*. After one and a half miles take left fork, cross river and no 42 is the second house on left. A9 from north: Turn right 100 yards before the Tall Pines Restaurant. As above. **Auchlea** Situated on B9168. This B road is on the right driving up the A9. Take B road and Auchlea is first house on right. **Skelbo House** From the south: On A9 take the small turning opposite Trentham Hotel (just past the Dornoch turn offs). At the side of Loch Fleet turn left, at the ruined castle take the second farm road which is fairly rough, and follow round to your right. If coming from the north take the Loch Fleet road signposted to *Embo* from the A9.

· Bumblebee Conservation Trust, Mary's Meals International & Mission Africa

Skelbo House, Three gardens near Dornoch

DUMFRIESSHIRE

Scotland's Gardens Scheme 2019 Guidebook is sponsored by **INVESTEC WEALTH & INVESTMENT**

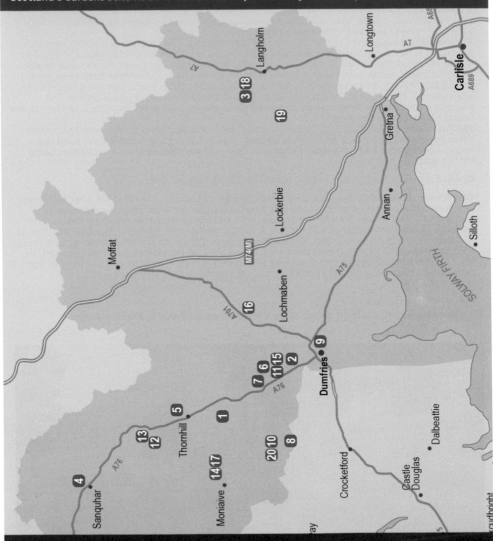

1. Barjarg Tower
2. Cowhill Tower
3. Craig
4. Crawick Multiverse
5. Dabton
6. Dalswinton House
7. Dalswinton Mill
8. Drumpark
9. Dumfries Station Garden
10. Dunesslin
11. Ellisland Farm, The Poet's Wild Garden
12. Holehouse
13. Kirkcaldy House
14. Peilton
15. Portrack, The Garden of Cosmic Speculation
16. Stanemuir
17. Townhead of Glencairn
18. Westerhall
19. Westwater Farm
20. Whiteside

DUMFRIESSHIRE

OUR VOLUNTEER ORGANISERS

District Organiser:	Sarah Landale	Dalswinton House, Dalswinton, Dumfries DG2 0XZ E: dumfriesshire@scotlandsgardens.org
Area Organisers:	Fiona Bell-Irving Guy Galbraith Liz Mitchell	Bankside, Kettleholm, Lockerbie DG11 1BY Stanemuir Parkgate, Dumfries DG1 3NE Drumpark, Irongray DG2 9TX
Treasurer:	Harold Jack	The Clachan, Newtonairds, Dumfries DG2 0JL

GARDENS OPEN ON A SPECIFIC DATE

Barjarg Tower, Auldgirth	Saturday/Sunday, 9/10 February
Craig, Langholm	Sunday, 17 February
Dumfries Railway Station Garden, Lovers Walk, Dumfries	Sunday, 28 April
Crawick Multiverse, Crawick, Sanquhar	Sunday, 5 May
Portrack, The Garden of Cosmic Speculation, Holywood	Sunday, 5 May
Dunesslin, Dunscore	Sunday, 12 May
Dalswinton House, Dalswinton	Sunday, 19 May
Ellisland Farm, The Poet's Wild Garden, Auldgirth, Dumfries	Sunday, 19 May
Holehouse, Near Penpont, Thornhill	Sunday, 26 May
Dabton, Thornhill	Sunday, 26 May
Westerhall, Bentpath, Langholm	Sunday, 26 May
Dalswinton Mill, Dalswinton, Dumfries	Sunday, 2 June
Whiteside, Dunscore	Sunday, 2 June
Stanemuir, Parkgate, Dumfriesshire	Sunday, 2 June
Drumpark, Irongray	Sunday, 9 June
Cowhill Tower, Holywood	Sunday, 16 June
Kirkcaldy House, Kirkcaldy, Burnsands, Thornhill	Sunday, 23 June
Dumfries Railway Station Garden, Lovers Walk, Dumfries	Sunday, 30 June
Townhead of Glencairn, Kirkland, by Moniaive	Sunday, 30 June
Whiteside, Dunscore	Sunday, 14 July
Dalswinton Mill, Dalswinton, Dumfries	Sunday, 4 August
Dumfries Railway Station Garden, Lovers Walk, Dumfries	Sunday, 8 September

GARDENS OPEN BY ARRANGEMENT

Craig, Langholm	10 February - 10 March
Peilton, Moniaive	13 April - 2 June
Westwater Farm, Langholm	1 June - 1 September
Kirkcaldy House, Kirkcaldy, Burnsands, Thornhill	17 June - 15 July

Dumfriesshire

BARJARG TOWER
Auldgirth DG2 0TN
Mary and Archie Donaldson
T: 01848 331545

Barjarg Tower lies on a gentle slope enjoying the lovely views of the surrounding Lowther hills. The original tower house dates back to the late 16th century but has had various cleverly designed additions over the years. The gardens have undergone considerable development over the last years, though the carpets of snowdrops in the surrounding woods remain a tribute to the care of earlier generations. While the gardens will be largely dormant at the chosen date, the spring bulbs should be poking through and the surrounding woods are sure to be thick with the annual display of these snowdrops.

Open: Saturday/Sunday, 9/10 February, 10am - 5pm for Snowdrops and Winter Walks, admission by donation. Teas are available in either Penpont, Auldgirth or Thornhill all located within a ten-minute drive.

Directions: Situated on the C125 half way between Auldgirth and Penpont. Driving from Auldgirth, the stone, arched entrance is on the left-hand side with Barjarg engraved on sandstone.

· *Alzheimer's Research UK*

Swathes of snowdrops at Barjarg Tower

Dumfriesshire

COWHILL TOWER
Holywood DG2 0RL
Mr and Mrs P Weatherall
T: 01387 720304 **E:** cmw@cowhill.co.uk

This is an interesting walled garden. There are topiary animals, birds and figures and a beautiful woodland walk. Splendid views can be seen from the lawn right down the Nith Valley. There are also a variety of statues from the Far East.

Open: Sunday 16 June, 2pm - 5pm, admission £5.00, children free.

Directions: Holywood is one and a half miles off A76, five miles north of Dumfries.

· *Maggie's*

The glasshouse at Cowhill Tower

CRAIG
Langholm DG13 0NZ
Mr and Mrs Neil Ewart
T: 013873 70230 **E:** nmlewart@googlemail.com

Craig snowdrops have evolved over the last 30 or so years. Round the house and policies, a large variety have been planted with a varied flowering season stretching from the start of January until April and peaking mid-February. Large drifts of *Leucojum vernum* (winter snowflake) have started to naturalise here, and along the riverbank a variety of snowdrops swept down by the river have naturalised in the adjacent woodland, known as the Snowdrop Walk.

Open: Sunday 17 February, 12pm - 4pm and also open by arrangement 10 February - 10 March for Snowdrops and Winter Walks. Admission £5.00, children free. The village hall serving teas is at Bentpath, one mile further towards Eskdalemuir. These will be available only on Sunday 17 February. For those wanting to visit in groups by arrangement, to see the earlier or later flowering snowdrops, there is access for minibuses or buses through the raceyard.

Directions: Craig is three miles from Langholm on the B709 towards Eskdalemuir. The village hall is at Bentpath, one mile further towards Eskdalemuir.

· *Kirkandrews Kirk Trust*

Dumfriesshire

CRAWICK MULTIVERSE
Crawick, Sanquhar DG4 6ET
Charles Jencks
T: 01659 50242 **E:** info@crawickmultiverse.co.uk
W: www.crawickmultiverse.co.uk

Crawick Multiverse is a major land art restoration project on the Duke of Buccleuch's Queensberry Estate in Dumfriesshire. Created by landscape architect Charles Jencks, the former open-cast coal mine has been transformed into a stunning representation of theories of the universe, linking the themes of space, astronomy and cosmology, using the ecology of the site, and the materials found within, to inspire its design.

Open: Sunday 5 May, 10am - 4pm, admission £5.00, children free. Please note that Portrack, The Garden of Cosmic Speculation, also designed by Charles Jencks, will be open on the same day.

Directions: From Sanquhar, head to Kirkconnel, turn right on the B740 Crawfordjohn, as you travel on the B740 after 250 yards you will pass under a viaduct (rail bridge) take the second exit on the left approximately 100 yards past the viaduct. See website for more details.

· *Maggie's*

DABTON
Thornhill DG3 5AR
The Duke and Duchess of Buccleuch
T: 01848 330467 **E:** phunter@buccleuch.com

Nineteenth-century house built of pink stone, with extensive walled garden. Ninety-five-yard-long herbaceous border, roses, island beds and shrubs, ponds surrounded by azaleas and primulas, woodland walk, vegetable garden and greenhouses.

Open: Sunday 26 May, 2pm - 5pm, admission £4.00, children free. The Upper Nithsdale Youth Pipeband will play throughout the afternoon. Holehouse is also open earlier this day and is only a 25 minute drive away.

Directions: Entrance off the A76 between Thornhill and Carronbridge.

· *Upper Nithsdale Youth Pipeband*

DALSWINTON HOUSE
Dalswinton DG2 0XZ
Mr and Mrs Peter Landale
T: 01387 740220 **E:** sarahlandale@gmail.com

Late 18th-century house sits on top of a hill surrounded by herbaceous beds and well established shrubs, including rhododendrons and azaleas, overlooking the loch. Attractive walks through woods and around the loch. It was here that the first steamboat in Britain made its maiden voyage in 1788 and there is a life-size model beside the water to commemorate this. Over the past years, there has been much clearing and development work around the loch, which has opened up the views considerably.

Open: Sunday 19 May, 2pm - 5pm, admission £5.00, children free. Ellisland, a home of Robbie Burns, on the opposite side of the River Nith, is also open on 19 May. Robbie Burns was a tenant of the then owner of Dalswinton, Patrick Miller.

Directions: Take A76 north from Dumfries to Thornhill. After seven miles, turn right to Dalswinton. Drive through Dalswinton village, past the orange church on the right and follow estate

Dumfriesshire

wall on the right. Entrance is by either the single lodge or double lodge entrance set in the wall.

· *Kirkmahoe Parish Church of Scotland*

DALSWINTON MILL
Dalswinton, Dumfries DG2 0XY
Colin and Pamela Crosbie
T: 01387 740070 **E:** colin.crosbie@talktalk.net

. . . .

A newly created plantsman's garden set around an 18th-century watermill with the Pennyland Burn running through it. The garden contains a wide range of perennials, trees and shrubs that favour the local climate and, throughout, a wide range of statuary can be found. It sits in a hollow and can be accessed only by steps; unfortunately, this makes the garden unsuitable for anyone with mobility requirements. We are also unable to offer disabled parking.

Open: Sunday 2 June and Sunday 4 August, 2pm - 6pm. Admission £4.00, children free.

Directions: Garden lies in Dalswinton, halfway between A76 and A701 on the Auldgirth to Kirkton Road. From Auldgirth take the first left after the Dalswinton Village Hall. The Mill is on the corner before the bridge.

· *IFDAS*

DRUMPARK
Irongray DG2 9TX
Mr and Mrs Iain Mitchell
T: 01387 820323 **E:** iain.liz.mitchell@googlemail.com

. . . .

Well contoured woodland garden and extensive policies nurture mature azaleas, rhododendrons and rare shrubs among impressive specimen trees. Water garden with primulas and meconopsis. Victorian walled garden with fruit trees and garden produce. There is also a beautiful herbaceous border. All planting is set in a natural bowl providing attractive vistas.

Open: Sunday 9 June, 2pm - 5pm, admission £5.00, children free.

Directions: From Dumfries bypass, head north on A76 for a half mile, turn left at the signpost to *Lochside Industrial Estates* and immediately right onto Irongray Road; continue for five miles; gates in sandstone wall on left (half mile after Routin' Brig).

· *Loch Arthur*

' Love your garden?
Why not share it with
others and open in 2020?'

Dumfriesshire

9

DUMFRIES STATION GARDEN
Dumfries Railway Station, Lovers Walk, Dumfries DG1 1LT
South West Railway Adopters Garden Group (Louis Wall)
T: 07769275971 **E:** stationgardener@live.co.uk
W: swragg.weebly.com

Dumfries Station Garden, on both sides of the station platform, is quite unusual. It is formally planted to reflect colour and interest all year round. There is a specialist wildlife garden planted with native wildflower species and also a Biblical garden, composed of many plants mentioned in the Bible. You will also see unique pieces of artwork depicting the *Flying Scotsman* and also the beautiful landscape of wild Galloway. The garden is co-ordinated by Louis Wall, holder of *Gardener of the Year Award* in 2018. He is assisted by a team of hard-working volunteers.

Open: Sunday 28 April, Sunday 30 June and Sunday 8 September, 11am - 4pm, admission by donation. Refreshments are available in the Station Cafe and in Dumfries.

Directions: The garden is located on both sides of the station platform at Dumfries Station on Lovers Walk in Dumfries. Most buses stop directly at the station, which is about a ten-minute walk from the town centre. There is ample parking spaces.

· *Donation to SGS Beneficiaries*

Dumfries Station Garden

Dumfriesshire

10

DUNESSLIN
Dunscore DG2 0UR
Iain and Zara Milligan
E: zaramilligan@gmail.com

Set in the hills with wonderful views and borrowed landscapes, the principal garden consists of a series of connecting rooms filled with a great and interesting variety of herbaceous plants, beautifully designed and maintained. There is a substantial rock garden with alpines and unusual plants and a very pretty pond. There is a short walk to three cairns by Andy Goldsworthy, through an evolving woodland garden.

Open: Sunday 12 May, 2pm - 5pm, admission £5.00, children free. Dunesslin is opening a month earlier than usual to afford a different perspective from previous years.

Directions: From Dunscore, follow the road to Corsock. About one and a half miles further on, turn right at the post box, still on the road to Corsock and at small crossroads half a mile on, turn left.

· Alzheimer Scotland

The beautifully designed grounds at Dunesslin

Dumfriesshire

ELLISLAND FARM, THE POET'S WILD GARDEN
Auldgirth, Dumfriesshire DG2 0RP
The Friends of Ellisland, Stuart Cochrane
T: 01387 740246 **E:** friends@ellislandfarm.co.uk
W: www.ellislandfarm.co.uk

The Ellisland Wild Garden celebrates the stunning scenery of Nithsdale and the poetry of Robert Burns. Now in its third year, the Wild Garden is the work of four of the Friends of Ellisland volunteers and is bursting with flowers and wildlife. The bluebells will be amongst the dancing campions in the Jewel Garden and Highland Mary's birk is bursting with primroses, foxgloves and comfrey.

Open: Sunday 19 May, 2pm - 5pm, admission £5.00, children free. The poetry of Burns which was inspired by the Nith will also feature on the day, performed, recited and even danced. Dalswinton House directly across the river will open on 19 May, too. Patrick Miller, the then of owner of Dalswinton owned Ellisland Farm at the time that Robbie Burns lived there. They were good friends and the joint opening is in recognition of this relationship.

Directions: Ellisland is signposted off the A76 half way between Holywood and Auldgirth. It is approximately six miles north of Dumfries and eight miles south of Thornhill.

· *The Friends of Ellisland*

HOLEHOUSE
Near Penpont, Thornhill DG3 4AP
Lord and Lady Norrie
T: 01848 600303

Holehouse has an established garden which has been beautifully and carefully landscaped. It has been developed in and around the farm steading over the past 15 years. Its secluded location high on a hillside offers some wonderful views over the Dumfries hills and nearby Drumlanrig Estate. It is a garden of great variety, which includes a labyrinth, pond, herbaceous plants, shrubs and maturing trees. There is also a vegetable garden and orchard.

Open: Sunday 26 May, 11am - 2pm, admission £5.00, children free. It is possible to make a day of it and visit this garden before visiting Dabton, only 25 minutes drive away.

Directions: From Penpont Village crossroads, take Sanquhar Rd. After about 2 miles. Pass triangle. Keep right. Continue about 1 mile downhill through wood. Take next unmarked left turn before reaching two white farm houses. Continue about a mile uphill to T junction and three white cottages. Turn right. Continue past farm on left. Holehouse is just under one mile on the right after the garden cottage.

· *Buccleuch And Queensberry Caledonia Pipe Band*

Dumfriesshire

KIRKCALDY HOUSE
Kirkcaldy, Burnsands, Thornhill DG3 4AL
Professor and Mrs Robert McClelland
E: rmcclell16@btinternet.com

The garden is set on a hillside with spectacular views over the Nith Valley and Lowther Hills. Although the foundations of the garden were in place, it has been extended over the past 12 years by the owners. It is a compact site with a variety of trees, shrubs, herbaceous plants, roses, a pond, decorative dykes and sculptures.

Open: Sunday 23 June, 2pm - 5pm. Also open by arrangement 17 June - 15 July. Admission £3.00, children free (Sunday 23 June) and by donation (17 June - 15 July). There will be light refreshments only. Good teas are available at Thomas Tosh in neighbouring Thornhill.

Directions: Take the A76 through Thornhill and Carronbridge and past the turning to Drumlanrig Castle. At the next turning left just before the *Picnic Area* (about four miles) turn left and then immediately left after crossing the Glenairlie Bridge. Kirkcaldy is the second house at the top of the hill.

· *Loch Arthur*

PEILTON
Moniaive DG3 4HE
Mrs A Graham
T: 01848 200363 **E:** amgatpeilton@gmail.com

This really very special and attractive woodland garden has a great variety of interesting rhododendrons, shrubs and flowering trees. Peilton is of particular interest for the real plantsman.

Open: Open by arrangement 13 April - 2 June, admission by donation. Tea and coffee is available in Moniaive close by.

Directions: Off A702 between Kirkland of Glencairn and Moniaive.

· *Marie Curie*

Dumfriesshire

15 **PORTRACK, THE GARDEN OF COSMIC SPECULATION**
Holywood DG2 0RW
John Jencks
W: www.gardenofcosmicspeculation.com

....

Forty major areas, gardens, bridges, landforms, sculpture, terraces, fences and architectural works. Covering 30 acres, The Garden of Cosmic Speculation, designed by Charles Jencks, uses nature to celebrate nature, both intellectually and through the senses, including the sense of humour.

Open: Sunday 5 May, 11am - 5pm, admission £10.00, children free. There is limited parking in the fields beside Portrack, so admission is via pre-paid ticket only. Please book your tickets online from 1 February at Eventbrite, www.eventbrite.co.uk (browse for 'Portrack' in the search box). There will also be limited tickets available in person at the Midsteeple in Dumfries for local people with no internet access. Please check ticket availability as we expect this event to sell out. Early entry before 11am will not be permitted and last entry is 4.30pm. We regret that there is no wheelchair access. Dogs must be kept on a lead at all times. Teas will be provided throughout the afternoon by The Usual Place, our local enterprise partner. The Upper Nithsdale Youth Pipe Band will perform near the tea area at 1.30pm and 3pm (weather permitting). Please note that the garden is not open to the public at any other time during the year. Further information is on the Scotland's Gardens Scheme website.

Directions: Holywood is one and a half miles off A76, five miles north of Dumfries.

· *Maggie's*

Portrack, The Garden of Cosmic Speculation. Top photo by © Ming Thein 2015

Dumfriesshire

16

STANEMUIR
Parkgate, Dumfriesshire DG1 3NE
Guy and Sarah Galbraith
T: 01387 860630 **E:** guy.stanemuir@gmail.com

A Garden in the making. The first trees round the house were planted in 2000 and the house (on a green field site) was completed in 2008. The adjacent woodland provided scope for a wild garden. A network of tracks provides good access to a woodland loch that is sheltered by mature Scots pine. This area has now been planted with rhododendron, azaleas and other acid-loving plants. The gardens at Stanemuir are a 'work in progress' and ideas for future development are much encouraged.

Open: Sunday 2 June, 2pm - 5pm, admission £5.00, children free. Stanemuir is opening this year in cooperation with SRUC Barony College which is a local agricultural and horticultural college. It lies right beside Stanemuir.

Directions: Stanemuir lies off the A701 Moffat to Dumfries road, eight miles north of Dumfries and 11 miles south of Moffat. At Parkgate on the A701 turn left at the signpost for *Barony College/ Lochmaben/Templand*. After a third of a mile you will see the drive to the left with the beginnings of a beech hedge. Turn up here and follow road bearing left. The house is on your right over a cattle grid.

· *Epilepsy Society*

17

TOWNHEAD OF GLENCAIRN
Kirkland, by Moniaive DG3 4HD
Mr Ian and Mrs Kate Craig
T: 01848 200461 **E:** tofglencairn@gmail.com

The south-facing house sits on a hill protected by mature trees. A burn has been diverted to run through the garden into a lochan surrounded by water-loving plants. To the side of the house, the flower beds are terraced and there are pergolas with old-fashioned climbing roses and clematis and a large Victorian greenhouse.

Open: Sunday 30 June, 2pm - 5pm, admission £5.00, children free.

Directions: On A702 betweeen Thornhill and Moniaive in the hamlet of Kirkland. Kirkland lies one and a half miles east of Moniaive and 6.5 miles west of Thornhill.

· *SGS Beneficiaries*

'Scotland's Gardens
Scheme welcomes all
varieties of garden'

Dumfriesshire

18 WESTERHALL
Bentpath, Langholm DG13 0NQ
Mrs Peter Buckley
E: mary.buckley@hotmail.co.uk

An extensive collection of azaleas, rhododendrons, rare shrubs and mature trees set in a landscape of follies, sculpture and stunning vistas. The redesigned walled garden contains a glasshouse with some exotic plants collected from around the world.

Open: Sunday 26 May, 2pm - 5pm, admission £5.00, children free. Selling plants this year will be Allan Clark, a rhododendron specialist, and there will also be a stall selling bedding plants. Homebaked cream teas will be available throughout the afternoon.

Directions: From Langholm take the B709 towards Eskdalemuir. After approximately five miles in village of Bentpath, turn right by white house. Go down through the village, over a small/narrow bridge and turn right by the church. Continue on this road for approximately one mile. Parking at farm which will be signed.

· *Westerkirk Parish Trust*

Townend of Glencairn

Dumfriesshire

19

WESTWATER FARM
Langholm DG13 0LU
Mr and Mrs Charlie Clapperton
T: 01387 381004 **E:** charlieclapperton@hotmail.com

In a wonderful, remote and romantic setting, the interesting walled garden adjacent to the house has both herbaceous plants and shrubs. There is also a woodland garden with a variety of bamboos and interesting trees. Dotted around the house and steadings are some fabulous pots.

Open: Open by arrangement 1 June - 1 September, admission by donation. The garden will also have a one-day, pop-up opening when the garden is looking at its very best in July. See our website for further details nearer the time.

Directions: Thirteen miles from Lockerbie on the B7068 Lockerbie to Langholm road (five miles from Langholm). Entrance is signed *Westwater* on the left coming from Lockerbie. Keep to left fork for house.

· *SGS Beneficiaries*

20

WHITESIDE
Dunscore DG2 0UU
John and Hilary Craig
T: 01387 820501 **E:** hjcraig19@gmail.com

The Garden, which extends to several acres, is 600 feet above sea level on a north-facing slope with views across to Queensberry and the Lowther Hills. There are some mature trees around the house but the rest of the garden is relatively new, having been created from a bare hillside since 2000. There are shrubs, young trees, a rowan avenue, a walled vegetable garden, orchard and courtyard garden. Several burns run through the property and there is a pond and two duck enclosures.

Open: Sunday 2 June and Sunday 14 July, 2pm - 5pm. Admission £5.00, children free.

Directions: From Dunscore, take the Corsock road. Continue two miles on, turn right opposite the postbox. Continue for one and three quarters miles, over the humpback bridge and past the white farmhouse on the left. *Whiteside* is signed on the left.

· *Music in Dumfries*

DUNBARTONSHIRE

Scotland's Gardens Scheme 2019 Guidebook is sponsored by **INVESTEC WEALTH & INVESTMENT**

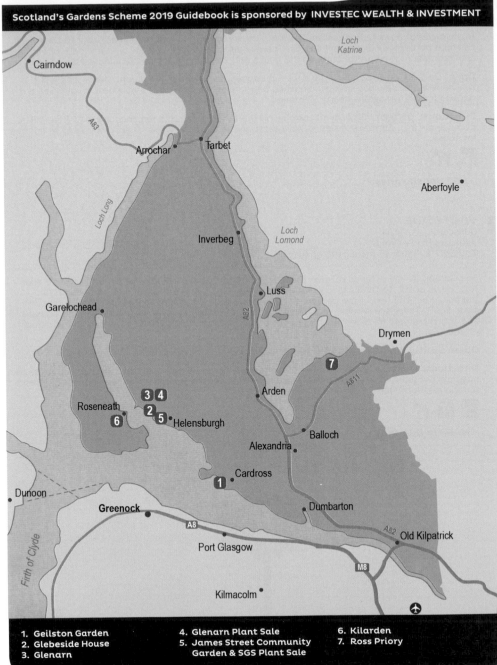

1. Geilston Garden
2. Glebeside House
3. Glenarn
4. Glenarn Plant Sale
5. James Street Community Garden & SGS Plant Sale
6. Kilarden
7. Ross Priory

OUR VOLUNTEER ORGANISERS

District Organiser:	Tricia Stewart	High Glenan, 24a Queen Street, Helensburgh G84 9LG E: dunbartonshire@scotlandsgardens.org
Area Organisers:	Joyce Goel Graham Greenwell	33 West Argyle Street, Helensburgh G84 8XR Avalon, Shore Road, Mambeg Garelochhead G84 0EN
Treasurer:	Kathleen Murray	4 Cairndhu Gardens, Helensburg, G84 8PG

GARDENS OPEN ON A SPECIFIC DATE

Kilarden, Rosneath	Sunday, 14 April
Glenarn Plant Sale, Glenarn Road, Rhu	Sunday, 28 April
Ross Priory, Gartocharn	Sunday, 19 May
Geilston Garden, Main Road, Cardross	Sunday, 9 June
Glebeside House, Spy's Lane, Rhu	Sunday, 23 June
James Street Community Garden Plant Sale, Helensburgh	Sunday, 8 September

GARDENS OPEN REGULARLY

Glenarn, Glenarn Road, Rhu, Helensburgh	21 March - 21 September

'Encouraging, promoting
and supporting garden
opening since 1931'

Dunbartonshire

GEILSTON GARDEN
Main Road, Cardross G82 5HD
The National Trust for Scotland
T: 01389 849187 **E:** geilstongarden@nts.org.uk
W: www.nts.org.uk/visit/places/Geilston-Garden/

Geilston Garden has many attractive features including the walled garden with the herbaceous border providing summer colour, tranquil woodland walks and a large working kitchen garden. This is the ideal season for viewing the Siberian iris in flower along the Geilston Burn and the Japanese azaleas.

Open: Sunday 9 June, 1pm - 5pm, admission details can be found on the garden's website. No dogs.

Directions: On the A814, one mile from Cardross towards Helensburgh.

*· **The National Trust for Scotland: Gelston Garden***

Laburnum arch at Glebeside House

Dunbartonshire

2 GLEBESIDE HOUSE
Spy's Lane, Rhu, Helensburgh G84 8RA
Francoise and Peter Proctor

Traditional Scottish house built in 1834 with a third of an acre of ground. A small garden surrounds the house and comprises a natural rockery, shrubs at the rear, an old wash house recently renovated, laburnum arch and four or five 'rooms' in the larger garden. A more recently added alteration is a French oak boat port with slated roof built over the entrance. To the front and side there are mixed herbaceous islands and borders, mature shrubs, lawn and greenhouse.

Open: Sunday 23 June, 2pm - 5pm, admission £3.00, children free. Teas and scones available and plant stall.

Directions: Take the A814 from Helensburgh to Rhu Marina. Turn right into Pier Road. Spy's Lane is up the hill on the left. Park on Pier Road.

· *Gareloch Group Riding For The Disabled Association SCIO*

3 GLENARN
Glenarn Road, Rhu, Helensburgh G84 8LL
Michael and Sue Thornley
T: 01436 820493 **E:** masthome@btinternet.com
W: www.gardens-of-argyll.co.uk

Glenarn survives as a complete example of a ten-acre garden which spans from 1850 to the present day. There are winding paths through miniature glens under a canopy of oaks and limes, sunlit open spaces, a vegetable garden with beehives, and a rock garden full of surprise and season-long colour, with views over the Gareloch. The famous collections of rare and tender rhododendrons and magnolias give way in midsummer to roses rambling through the trees and climbing hydrangeas, followed by the starry white flowers of hoherias and eucryphias to the end of the season.

Open: 21 March - 21 September, dawn - dusk, admission £5.00, children free.

Directions: On the A814, two miles north of Helensburgh, up Pier Road. Cars to be left at the gate unless passengers are infirm.

· *Donation to SGS Beneficiaries*

4 GLENARN PLANT SALE
Glenarn Road, Rhu, Helensburgh G84 8LL
Michael and Sue Thornley
T: 01436 820493 **E:** masthome@btinternet.com
W: www.gardens-of-argyll.co.uk

Magnolias, rhododendrons, maples, meconopsis and other ericaceous plants raised by cuttings from Glenarn plants or from specialist seed exchanges plus lots of other interesting plants.

Open: Sunday 28 April, 2pm - 5pm, admission £5.00, children free. Tea and coffee with a range of homemade scones available. Glenarn honey for sale.

Directions: On the A814, two miles north of Helensburgh. Cars to be left at the gate unless passengers are infirm.

· *Alzheimer Scotland: Helensburgh Dementia Resource Centre*

Dunbartonshire

JAMES STREET COMMUNITY GARDEN PLANT SALE
Helensburgh G84 8EY
The Gardeners of James Street

Developed from a derelict children's play ground, the Community Garden is a relaxed area for contemplation with mixed herbaceous beds, maze and young trees. The plant sale will include a wide selection of nursery-grown perennials and locally grown trees, shrubs, herbaceous, alpine and house plants.

Open: Sunday 8 September, 12pm - 4pm, admission by donation.

Directions: Travel west along Princes Street from Sinclair Street through Colquhoun Square, turn right up James Street and the Community Garden is on the left. Park on the street.

· James Street Community Garden

KILARDEN
Rosneath G84 0PU
Carol Rowe

Sheltered hilly ten acre woodland part of a 20-acre property with a notable collection of species and hybrid rhododendrons gathered over a period of 50 years by the late Neil and Joyce Rutherford as seen on *The Beechgrove Garden*. The collection has been augmented in the last 18 years by the current owner. Elsewhere during this time hurricane and severe storm-damaged trees and mature specimens of conifers have been cleared as have commercial conifers and *Rhododendron ponticum*. Fruit trees and bushes have been established, of which apples and blueberries are particularly successful, despite a far from favourable north-facing shady site.

Open: Sunday 14 April, 2pm - 5pm, admission £3.00, children free. Homemade teas in the church hall and music in the church. The Shandon Ukelele Band will be playing in the garden.

Directions: A quarter of a mile from Rosneath off the B833.

· Friends of St. Modan's, Rosneath

ROSS PRIORY
Gartocharn G83 8NL
University of Strathclyde

Mansion house with glorious views over Loch Lomond with adjoining garden. Wonderful rhododendrons and azaleas are the principal plants in the garden, with a varied selection of trees and shrubs throughout. Spectacular spring bulbs, border plantings of herbaceous perennials, shrubs and trees. Extensive walled garden with glasshouses, pergola and ornamental plantings. Children's play area and putting green beside the house.

Open: Sunday 19 May, 2pm - 5pm, admission £5.00, children free. Please note the house is not open to view. Plant stall and homemade teas in the walled garden. Dogs on leads are welcome except in the walled garden.

Directions: Gartocharn one and a half miles off the A811. The Balloch to Gartocharn bus leaves Balloch at 13:52.

· Friends Of Loch Lomond & The Trossachs & Children's Hospice Association Scotland

Dunbartonshire

Kilarden

'Gardening is a medicine
that has no prescription
and no limit on dosage'
Author unknown

EAST LOTHIAN

Scotland's Gardens Scheme 2019 Guidebook is sponsored by INVESTEC WEALTH & INVESTMENT

Dunbar

Stenton

East Linton

7 Tyninghame

North Berwick

2 Athelstaneford

Dirleton

Haddington

Gifford

1

Gullane

3

6 Stobshiel

A68

Humbie **4**

Longniddry

A1

FIRTH OF FORTH

Pencaitland

8

Tranent

Cockenzie and Port Seton

Prestonpans

Musselburgh

5

Dalkeith

Gorebridge

A7

1. Broadwoodside
2. Fairnielaw
3. Gullane House

4. Humbie Dean
5. Shepherd House
6. Stobshiel House

7. Tyninghame House and The
   Walled Garden
8. Winton Castle

EAST LOTHIAN

OUR VOLUNTEER ORGANISERS

District Organiser:	Joan Johnson	The Round House, Woodbush, Dunbar EH42 1HB
		E: eastlothian@scotlandsgardens.org
Area Organisers:	Becca Duncan	St Michael's Lodge, Inveresk EH21 7UA
	Frank Kirwan	Humbie Dean, Humbie EH36 5PW
	Ian Orr	6 Grannus Mews, Inveresk EH21 7TT
	Judy Riley	The Old Kitchen, Tyninghame House EH42 1XW
Treasurer:	Colin Wilson	5 Tenterfield Drive, Haddington EH41 3JF

GARDENS OPEN ON A SPECIFIC DATE

Shepherd House, Inveresk, Musselburgh	Saturday/Sunday, 23/24 February
Winton Castle, Pencaitland	Sunday, 7 April
Humbie Dean, Humbie	Sunday, 21 April
Humbie Dean, Humbie	Sunday, 28 April
Tyninghame House and The Walled Garden, Dunbar	Sunday, 12 May
Humbie Dean, Humbie	Sunday, 19 May
Humbie Dean, Humbie	Sunday, 26 May
Shepherd House, Inveresk, Musselburgh	Saturday/Sunday, 8/9 June
Fairnielaw, Fairnielaw House, Athelstaneford, North Berwick	Sunday, 9 June
Gullane House, Sandy Loan, Gullane	Saturday/Sunday, 22/23 June
Tyninghame House and The Walled Garden, Dunbar	Sunday, 30 June
Humbie Dean, Humbie	Sunday, 7 July
Broadwoodside, Gifford	Sunday, 28 July
Fairnielaw, Fairnielaw House, Athelstaneford, North Berwick	Sunday, 29 September

GARDENS OPEN REGULARLY

Shepherd House, Inveresk, Musselburgh	12 - 28 February (Tuesdays & Thursdays)
Shepherd House, Inveresk, Musselburgh	24 April - 11 July (Tuesdays & Thursdays)

GARDENS OPEN BY ARRANGEMENT

Stobshiel House, Humbie	1 March - 1 November

East Lothian

BROADWOODSIDE
Gifford EH41 4JQ
Anna and Robert Dalrymple
W: www.broadwoodside.co.uk

'I was spellbound by the wit and elegance at Broadwoodside,' wrote David Wheeler, the editor of *Hortus* 'a garden created in less than two decades by Anna and Robert Dalrymple from derelict yards surrounding an ancient agricultural steading in East Lothian'. 'A garden of singular style and wit … achieved with considerable aplomb and originality,' wrote Tim Richardson in the *Daily Telegraph*. Come and see but don't expect teas as we are not doing them this year.

Open: Sunday 28 July, 11am - 5pm, admission £6.00, children free.

Directions: On B6355 going out of Gifford towards Pencaitland, at the Golf Course junction.

· *Leuchie*

FAIRNIELAW
Athelstaneford, North Berwick EH395BE
Alison Johnston
T: 07747862841 **E:** alison@fairnielawhouse.co.uk

Fairnielaw is a two-and-a-half-acre garden set on a rocky ridge where the wind blows frequently through the Garleton Hills and hits us side on. To provide shelter we planted a mixed tree mini forest and created a series of 'rooms' enclosed by beech hedges and dry-stone walls. The garden is on several levels and is a mixture of both formal and wild areas with beautiful views towards Traprain Law and the Garleton Hills at the highest point.

Open: Sunday 9 June and Sunday 29 September, 10am - 5pm. Admission £5.00, children free.

Directions: Fairnielaw House is in the village of Athelstaneford set back from the road behind tall trees opposite the church. It is served by a bus service that runs between Haddington and North Berwick several times a day.

· *Trellis*

Formal planting at Fairnielaw

East Lothian

3 GULLANE HOUSE
Sandy Loan, Gullane EH31 2BH
William and Judy Thomson

A traditional walled garden of three acres. The front of the house looks onto rose-hedged twin herbaceous borders of delphinium, peonies and lupins followed by dahlias, phlox and salvias and preceded by tulips and alliums. A small lily pond leads to a newly made rose and lavender garden planted within established box hedging. The next 'room' is reached through a beech hedge and is full of soft fruit and vegetables. The garden also boasts several kinds of fruit trees and shrubs, a splendid elm and oak and woodland paths surround the formal areas providing plenty of places for hide and seek!
Champion Trees: Elm, Oak.

Open: Saturday/Sunday, 22/23 June, 2pm - 6pm, admission £6.00, children free.

Directions: Gullane House is situated on Sandy Loan about 30 yards from the main street in Gullane. Public transport: X5 and 124 buses from Edinburgh to North Berwick.

· *Save the Children UK & St Adrians Episcopal Church: Gullane*

4 HUMBIE DEAN
Humbie EH36 5PW
Frank Kirwan
T: 07768 996382 **E:** frank.kirwan@which.net

A two-acre ornamental and woodland garden sandwiched between two burns at 600 feet with interest throughout a long season. A limited palette of plants with hosta, hellebores, perennial geranium, primula, meconopsis, martagon lilies, spring bulbs, ground cover, herbaceous and shrub planting, bluebell meadow, mature and recent azalea and rhododendron planting.
A short woodland walk has been created, only accessible by a series of steps.

Open: Sunday 21 April, Sunday 28 April, Sunday 19 May, Sunday 26 May and Sunday 7 July, 10am - 2pm, admission £5.00, children free.

Directions: Enter Humbie from the A68, pass the school and village hall on the left then immediately turn right just before the Humbie Hub. Take second left and Humbie Dean is on the left between two small bridges. Limited parking.

· *Mamie Martin Fund*

East Lothian

SHEPHERD HOUSE
Inveresk, Musselburgh EH21 7TH
Sir Charles and Lady Fraser
T: 0131 665 2570 **E:** annfraser@talktalk.net
W: www.shepherdhousegarden.co.uk

A constantly evolving artist's garden that never stands still, with lots of surprises including a shell house built in 2014, lavender parterres, a rill and fountains. At its heart are the plants filling every border, spilling over arches and lining paths, which are the inspiration for Ann's paintings. The season starts with the snowdrop collection of over 70 cultivars, moves on through hellebores, tulips, irises and roses. The latest addition to the garden in 2017 is a mirror steel diamond sculpture to commemorate the Fraser's diamond wedding anniversary and 60 years in this garden.

Open: Saturday/Sunday, 23/24 February, 11am - 4pm and 12 February - 28 February (Tuesdays and Thursdays), 2pm - 4pm for Snowdrops and Winter Walks. Also open Saturday/Sunday, 8/9 June, 11am - 4pm. And open 24 April - 11 July (Tuesdays and Thursdays), 2pm - 4pm. Admission £5.00, children free. Artist's cards by Ann Fraser available.

Directions: The garden is near Musselburgh. From the A1 take the A6094 exit signed *Wallyford* and *Dalkeith* and follow signs to *Inveresk*.

· *The Scottish Battlefields Trust: The Battle of Pinkie Cleugh and Musselburgh Tapestry.*

STOBSHIEL HOUSE
Humbie EH36 5PD
Mr Maxwell and Lady Sarah Ward
T: 01875 833646 **E:** stobshiel@gmail.com

A walled formal garden with box-edged borders, a castellated yew, large greenhouse and rustic summerhouse. The garden was originally laid out at the turn of the 19th century. The planting has been changed and varied. It now comprises lots of spring bulbs, roses, lavender, agapanthus, iris, meconopsis etc within a formal frame work. Outside the wall there is a large pond, formal lily pond and walks through shrubberies of rhododendron, azalea, philadelphus, acer, cornus and many more. In the spring there are many daffodils, snowdrops, aconites , fritillary and tulips. There is a woodland garden with a burn running through it. There are many old and young trees which give an excellent show in the autumn.The garden is cared for by a small team and there are always weeds somewhere (merely plants in the wrong place)!

Open: Open by arrangement 1 March - 1 November, admission £5.00, children free. Teas by arrangement (£9.00 including entry).

Directions: On the B6368 Haddington/Humbie road; sign to *Stobshiel* one mile.

· *Circle Supporting Families in Scotland*

TYNINGHAME HOUSE AND THE WALLED GARDEN
Dunbar EH42 1XW
Mrs C Gwyn and Tyninghame Gardens Ltd

The formal walled garden combines the lawn, sculpture and yew hedges, an Apple Walk, extensive herbaceous planting including roses and peonies with an informal arboretum. Splendid 17th century sandstone Scottish baronial house, remodelled in 1829 by William Burn. The gardens include herbaceous border, formal rose garden, Lady Haddington's Secret Garden with old fashioned roses and an extensive Wilderness spring garden with rhododendrons, azaleas, flowering trees and bulbs. Grounds include a one mile beech avenue to the sea. The Romanesque ruin of St Baldred's Church commands views across the Tyne Estuary and Lammermuir Hills. Tyninghame

East Lothian

has been awarded 'Outstanding' for every category in the *Inventory of Gardens and Designed Landscapes of Scotland*.
Champion Trees: Two British and seven Scottish.

Open: Sunday 12 May and Sunday 30 June, 1pm - 5pm. Admission £5.00, children free.

Directions: Gates on the A198 at Tyninghame Village. Bus 120.

· *Lynton Day Centre (Sunday 12 May) & Tyninghame Village Hall (Sunday 30 June)*

WINTON CASTLE
Pencaitland EH34 5AT
Sir Francis Ogilvy Winton Trust
T: 01875 340222
W: www.wintoncastle.co.uk

The gardens continue to develop and improve. In addition to the natural areas around Sir David's Loch and the Dell, extensive mixed borders are taking shape for the terraces and walled garden. In spring a glorious covering of daffodils makes way for cherry and apple blossoms. Enjoy an informative tour of this historic house and walk off delicious lunches and home baking around the estate. A visit to Winton Castle is a wonderful family day out.

Open: Sunday 7 April, 12pm - 4:30pm, admission £5.00, children free. The open day is essentially a family event with bouncy castle, archery, falconry displays, Luca's ice cream sold from a vintage Bentley, tours of the house, games on the lawn, treasure hunts, face painting and more.

Directions: Entrance off the B6355 Tranent/Pencaitland Road.

· *Marie Curie*

The glasshouse at Stobshiel House

EDINBURGH, MIDLOTHIAN & WEST LOTHIAN

Scotland's Gardens Scheme 2019 Guidebook is sponsored by **INVESTEC WEALTH & INVESTMENT**

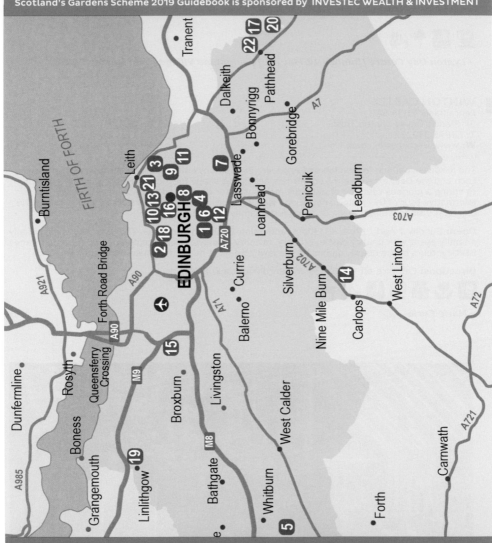

1. 101 Greenbank Crescent
2. 19 Gardiner Road
3. 39 Nantwich Drive
4. 41 Hermitage Gardens
5. 45 Northfield Crescent
6. 5 Greenbank Crescent
7. 89 Ravenscroft Street
8. Beech Lodge
9. Craigentinny Telferton Allotments
10. Dean Gardens
11. Dr Neil's Garden
12. Hunter's Tryst
13. Moray Place & Bank Gardens
14. Newhall
15. Newliston
16. Gardens Lower New Town
17. Preston Hall Walled Garden
18. Redcroft
19. Rivaldsgreen House
20. Silverburn Village
21. The Glasshouses at the RBG
22. Whitburgh House Walled Garden

EDINBURGH, MIDLOTHIAN & WEST LOTHIAN

OUR VOLUNTEER ORGANISERS

District Organiser:	Victoria Reid Thomas	Riccarton Mains Farmhouse, Currie EH14 4AR E: edinburgh@scotlandsgardens.org
Area Organisers:	Jerry & Christine Gregson Caroline Pearson	101 Greenbank Crescent, Edinburgh EH10 5TA 42 Pentland Avenue, Edinburgh EH13 0HY
Treasurer:	Michael Pearson	42 Pentland Avenue, Edinburgh EH13 0HY

GARDENS OPEN ON A SPECIFIC DATE

41 Hermitage Gardens, Edinburgh	Saturday/Sunday, 27/28 April
Dr Neil's Garden, Duddingston Village	Saturday/Sunday, 4/5 May
Moray Place and Bank Gardens, Edinburgh	Sunday, 5 May
Hunter's Tryst, 95 Oxgangs Road, Edinburgh	Sunday, 12 May
Redcroft, 23 Murrayfield Road, Edinburgh	Sunday, 12 May
101 Greenbank Crescent, Edinburgh	Sunday, 19 May
Rivaldsgreen House, 48 Friars Brae, Linlithgow	Saturday, 25 May
89 Ravenscroft Street, Edinburgh	Saturday, 8 June
Dean Gardens, Edinburgh	Sunday, 9 June
The Glasshouses at the Royal Botanic Garden Edinburgh	Sunday, 9 June
89 Ravenscroft Street, Edinburgh	Tuesday, 11 June
Beech Lodge, 10 Church Hill, Edinburgh	Sunday, 16 June
89 Ravenscroft Street, Edinburgh	Saturday, 22 June
19 Gardiner Road, Edinburgh	Sunday, 23 June
89 Ravenscroft Street, Edinburgh	Tuesday, 25 June
Open Gardens of the Lower New Town, 24 Fettes Row	Saturday, 29 June
5 Greenbank Crescent, Edinburgh	Sunday, 30 June
45 Northfield Crescent, Longridge, Bathgate	Saturday/Sunday, 27/28 July
Craigentinny Telferton Allotments, Telferton Road	Sunday, 28 July
39 Nantwich Drive, Edinburgh	Saturday, 3 August
Silverburn Village, Hopelands Road	Friday, 6 September

GARDENS OPEN REGULARLY

Newliston, Kirkliston	1 May - 2 June (not Mondays & Tuesdays)

GARDENS OPEN BY ARRANGEMENT

101 Greenbank Crescent, Edinburgh	13 April - 29 September
Preston Hall Walled Garden, Pathhead	1 May - 30 September
Newhall, Carlops	1 June - 31 August
Whitburgh House Walled Garden, Pathhead, Midlothian	19 August - 18 October

Edinburgh, Midlothian & West Lothian

1 101 GREENBANK CRESCENT
Edinburgh EH10 5TA
Jerry and Christine Gregson
T: 0131 447 6492 **E:** jerry_gregson@yahoo.co.uk

The garden is behind the house, on a steeply sloped site which looks over Braidburn Valley Park, with views to the Pentland hills. Winding paths and steps join a variety of distinct areas and terraces, each with a different character. In ten years of opening we have gradually changed and overhauled these, aiming to have colour, contrast and interest all year round.

Open: Sunday 19 May, 2pm - 5pm. Also open by arrangement 13 April - 29 September. Admission £4.00, children free.

Directions: From city centre take the A702 through Morningside. Continue uphill and turn right at Greenbank Church on to Greenbank Crescent. On 5 and 16 bus routes, the stop is for Greenbank Row.

· *Shelter Scotland*

2 19 GARDINER ROAD
Edinburgh. EH4 3RP
Ms Rae Renwick
E: rae_renwick@yahoo.com

This is a newly designed (and surprisingly large) south-facing garden which had been neglected for some years. While the design retains much of the original structure, a circular theme was introduced to help define grass, pond and seating areas. The hard landscaping is specifically designed to give a feeling of space and openness and effectively joins the living quarters of the house to the garden itself. Some established trees, hedges and shrubs were retained and some much loved trees and shrubs from a previous garden were incorporated. Mixed planting of evergreens and herbaceous plants help to ensure year-round interest. There are also raised beds, vegetable and fruit plots as well as a greenhouse. The front area is minimalist and deliberately low maintenance.

Open: Sunday 23 June, 2pm - 5pm, admission £4.00, children free.

Directions: Buses 43 from St Andrew's Square or 41 from Kings Buildings. Get off at Blackhall Post Office.

· *Alzheimer Scotland*

3 39 NANTWICH DRIVE
Edinburgh EH7 6RA
Michael and Susan Burns

Large wildlife friendly garden, run on organic principles. Includes mini orchard, pond, mixed borders, greenhouse and a secret garden. There are mini woodland walks and an allotment for vegetables, plus a compost area, worm bin and rotary bin.

Open: Saturday 3 August, 2pm - 5pm, admission £4.00, children free.

Directions: Bus 19 to Craigentinny Road or bus 26 to Kekewich Drive.

· *The Henry Doubleday Research Association*

Edinburgh, Midlothian & West Lothian

41 HERMITAGE GARDENS
Edinburgh EH10 6AZ
Dr and Mrs Tony Toft
E: toft41@hotmail.com

This relatively large city garden on the corner of Hermitage Gardens and Hermitage Drive is at its best in spring with its rock garden, rhododendrons, camellias, acers, tulips and mature trees.

Open: Saturday/Sunday, 27/28 April, 2pm - 5pm, admission £4.00, children free.

Directions: Buses 5, 11, 15, 16, 23.

· *Chest Heart & Stroke Scotland*

45 NORTHFIELD CRESCENT
Longridge, Bathgate EH47 8AL
Mr Jamie Robertson
T: 07885 701642 **E:** jamierobertson04@hotmail.co.uk

A delightful garden with a wide variety of shrubs, herbaceous, bedding and dozens of dahlia plants. Large pond with a small waterfall and a colourful decked area with an attractive selection of bedding plants. There is a vegetable patch with raised beds. A feature greenhouse shows award-winning pot plants. The garden is the current holder of the *Oatridge College* award and has won several gold medals. The owner has won the *West Lothian Gardener of the Year* prize four times and is Chairman of the *Livingston and District Horticultural Society*.

Open: Saturday/Sunday, 27/28 July, 2pm - 5pm, admission £3.00, children free.

Directions: From A71 turn right after Breith at traffic lights, go about a mile and turn right into Northfield Crescent. From Whitburn, take A706 Longridge Road to Longridge and last left into Northfield Crescent.

· *Worldwide Cancer Research*

5 GREENBANK CRESCENT
Edinburgh EH10 5TE
Sandy Corlett
T: 0131 440 2948 **E:** sandycorlett@hotmail.co.uk

South-facing, newly designed, sloping terraced garden with views over Braidburn Valley Park to the Pentlands. Colourful chaos of herbaceous plants, shrubs, roses and small trees. Hard features include a gazebo, pergola, greenhouse and water feature.

Open: Sunday 30 June, 2pm - 5pm, admission £4.00, children free.

Directions: From city centre take A702 through Morningside, continue uphill on Comiston Road, turn right at Greenback Church on to Greenbank Crescent. Buses 5, 16, 11.

· *Parkinsons UK*

Edinburgh, Midlothian & West Lothian

7

89 RAVENSCROFT STREET
Edinburgh EH17 8QS
Andrew and Alex Gray Muir

A large walled garden, full of surprises, in the old mining village of Gilmerton. Planting includes mature trees, roses and herbaceous borders. There is also a potager. Andrew and Alex Gray Muir have been there for over 50 years but say the garden is still a work in progress. There are plenty of seats so bring a thermos and sit and enjoy the garden.

Open: Saturday 8 June, Tuesday 11 June, Saturday 22 June and Tuesday 25 June, 2pm - 5pm, admission £4.00, children free.

Directions: Buses 29 and 3 come to the end of the street - look out for *Tanz* on the left and get off at next stop. It is a nine minute walk up Ravenscroft Street. Buses 7 and 11 come to Hyvots Bank. A short walk up Ravenscroft Place will bring you to Ravenscroft Street, where you turn right up a short stretch of unmetalled road. If you come by car, park on the public road and walk up last 50 yards. If necessary, passengers can be dropped off in the yard in front of house.

· *Scottish Association For Mental Health: Redhall Walled Garden*

Outdoor seating at 5 Greenbank Crescent

Edinburgh, Midlothian & West Lothian

BEECH LODGE
10 Church Hill, Edinburgh EH10 4BQ
Dr Anthony Ayles

Approximately one-acre garden concealed inside a high wall in Church Hill Edinburgh. The garden contains a large lawn, white box garden, and large pond with bridge. There is also a doocot and beehives.

Open: Sunday 16 June, 2pm - 5pm, admission £4.00, children free.

Directions: Turn east at the T junction off Morningside Road, initially along Church Hill Place which becomes Church Hill. It is two-thirds of the way down on the right, behind a high beech hedge.

· *The PF Counselling Service & Chest Heart & Stroke Scotland*

CRAIGENTINNY TELFERTON ALLOTMENTS
Telferton Road, off Portobello Road, Edinburgh EH7 6XG
The Gardeners of Craigentinny and Telferton
W: www.ctallotments.com

Established in 1923, this independent allotment site is a tranquil and charming space, hidden away in a built-up area, where the local community benefit from growing their own vegetables and fruit.

Open: Sunday 28 July, 2pm - 5pm, admission £4.00, children free. Yarn bombing of allotments. Display of scarecrows. Come and enjoy tea, home baking and chat with our friendly plot-holders.

Directions: Park on Telferton Road. Buses 15, 26, 45.

· *Craigentinny Telferton Allotments*

DEAN GARDENS
Edinburgh EH4 1QE
Dean Gardens Management Committee
W: www.deangardens.org

Nine acres of semi-woodland garden with spring bulbs on the steep banks of the Water of Leith in central Edinburgh. Founded in the 1860s by local residents, the Dean Gardens contain part of the great structure of the Dean Bridge, a Thomas Telford masterpiece of 1835. Lawns, paths, trees, and shrubs with lovely views to the weir in the Dean Village and to the St Bernard's Well. There is also a children's play area.

Open: Sunday 9 June, 2pm - 5pm, admission £4.00, children free.

Directions: Entrance at Ann Street or Eton Terrace.

· *St Columbas Hospice*

Edinburgh, Midlothian & West Lothian

DR NEIL'S GARDEN
Duddingston Village EH15 3PX
Dr Neil's Garden Trust
E: info@drneilsgarden.co.uk
W: www.drneilsgarden.co.uk

Wonderful, secluded, landscaped garden on the lower slopes of Arthur's Seat including conifers, heathers, alpines, a physic garden, herbaceous borders and ponds. Also Thompson's Tower with the Museum of Curling and beautiful views across Duddingston Loch.

Open: Saturday/Sunday, 4/5 May, 2pm - 5pm, admission £3.00, children free.

Directions: Park at kirk car park on Duddingston Road West and then follow signposts through the manse garden.

· *Dr. Neils Garden Trust*

HUNTER'S TRYST
95 Oxgangs Road, Edinburgh EH10 7BA
Jean Knox
T: 0131 477 2919 **E:** jean.knox@blueyonder.co.uk

Well stocked and beautifully designed, mature, medium-sized town garden comprising herbaceous and shrub beds, lawn, fruit and some vegetables, water features, seating areas and trees. This is a wildlife-friendly garden that has been transformed from a wilderness 30 years ago and continues to evolve. In 2017 two raised beds were added to the front garden. This hidden treasure of a garden was featured on *The Beechgrove Garden* in June 2015 and on *The Instant Gardener* in June 2016.

Open: Sunday 12 May, 2pm - 5pm, admission £4.00, children free.

Directions: From Fairmilehead crossroads head down Oxgangs Road to Hunter's Tryst roundabout, last house on the left. Take buses 4, 5, 18 or 27. The bus stop is at Hunter's Tryst and the garden is opposite.

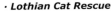

· *Lothian Cat Rescue*

MORAY PLACE AND BANK GARDENS
Edinburgh EH3 6BX
The Residents of Moray Place and Bank Gardens

Nearly six acres of secluded wild gardens with lawns, trees and shrubs with banks of bulbs down to the Water of Leith. Stunning vistas across the Firth of Forth. Private garden of three-and-a-half-acres in Georgian New Town. Shrubs, trees and beds offering atmosphere of tranquillity in the city centre.

Open: Sunday 5 May, 2pm - 5pm, admission £4.00, children free. Home baking.

Directions: Bank Gardens Enter by the gate at the top of Doune Terrace. **Moray Place** Enter by the north gate in Moray Place.

· *Euan Macdonald Centre for Motor Neurone Disease Research*

Edinburgh, Midlothian & West Lothian

NEWHALL
Carlops EH26 9LY
John and Tricia Kennedy
T: 01968 660206 **E:** tricia.kennedy@newhalls.co.uk

Traditional 18th century walled garden with huge herbaceous border, shrubberies, fruit and vegetables. Stunning glen running along the North Esk river in the process of restoration (stout shoes recommended). Large pond with evolving planting. Young arboretum and collection of *Rosa spinosissima*. Featured in *Good Gardens Guide 2010, Scottish Field, Gardens Monthly* and *Scotland on Sunday.*

Open: Open by arrangement 1 June - 31 August, admission £5.00, children free. Light lunches available if booked in advance.

Directions: On the A702 Edinburgh/Biggar, half a mile after Ninemileburn and a mile before Carlops. Follow signs.

· *SGS Beneficiaries*

NEWLISTON
Kirkliston EH29 9EB
Mr and Mrs R C Maclachlan
T: 0131 333 3231 **E:** newliston@gmail.com

18th-century-designed landscape with good rhododendrons and azaleas. The house, designed by Robert Adam, is also open.

Open: 1 May - 2 June (not Mondays & Tuesdays), 2pm - 5pm, admission £5.00, children free.

Directions: Four miles south of the Forth Road Bridge, entrance off B800.

· *Children's Hospice Association Scotland*

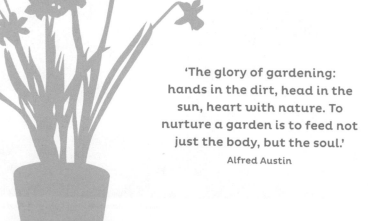

'The glory of gardening:
hands in the dirt, head in the
sun, heart with nature. To
nurture a garden is to feed not
just the body, but the soul.'
Alfred Austin

Edinburgh, Midlothian & West Lothian

OPEN GARDENS OF THE LOWER NEW TOWN
24 Fettes Row, Edinburgh EH3 6RH
The Gardeners of the Lower New Town

A variety of imaginative horticultural creations in New Town spaces bringing greenery and wildlife into the heart of the city. Comprising a steeply-terraced town garden, a densely-planted courtyard garden, charming back lane, patio and basement gardens, a hidden roof garden and a sunken oasis. Plus a unique gem on a doorstep, glorious mews lane planting and spectacular pot gardens. The collection provides year-round interest with a mix of seasonal planting and structural evergreens which the gardeners will be on hand to talk about.

Open: Saturday 29 June, 2pm - 5pm, admission £5.00, children free. Almost all gardens are visible from the road but only some gardens can be entered in a wheelchair.

Directions: Tickets and map of all gardens from Northumberland Street Lane NW, 24 Fettes Row and the allotments on Indian Place. Buses 23, 27, 29.

· *Médecins Sans Frontières*

India Place Allotments of the Open Gardens of Lower New Town

Edinburgh, Midlothian & West Lothian

17 PRESTON HALL WALLED GARDEN

Pathhead EH37 5UG
William and Henrietta Callander
T: 01875 320099 **E:** william@prestonhall.co.uk
W: www.prestonhall.co.uk

Preston Hall Walled Garden is a beautiful example of an 18th-century walled garden. The current restoration began in 2011 and wonderfully demonstrates what can be achieved in a few years. An imposing brick wall surrounds the two-acre garden, which features two impressive gazebo structures that give spectacular views of the garden, a rose garden, a partly restored Victorian greenhouse, fruit and vegetables patches, and a stunning flower garden.

Open: Open by arrangement 1 May - 30 September, admission £5.00, children free.

Directions: Located 12 miles south of Edinburgh on A68, one mile east of Pathhead village.

· **My Name'5 Doddie Foundation**

Preston Hall Walled Garden

18 REDCROFT

23 Murrayfield Road, Edinburgh EH12 6EP
James and Anna Buxton
T: 0131 337 1747 **E:** annabuxtonb@aol.com

Redcroft is a mature walled garden surrounding an attractive Arts and Craft house. It is a hidden haven off a busy road with a variety of different features and habitats: an orchard, a rockery, a pond, shrubberies, a large lawn and contrasting longer grass. It is well maintained with many clipped shrubs and some cloud pruning. Early May is very colourful with rhododendrons and many other flowering shrubs and wall plants, and the greenhouse is full of tender plants. There will be tulips in pots and many other bulbs. Some large conifers have recently been felled, letting in extra light and offering a new opportunity for planting.

Open: Sunday 12 May, 2pm - 5pm, admission £5.00, children free. Children are very welcome and there will be plentry for them to do.

Directions: Murrayfield Road runs north from Corstorphine Road to Ravelston Dykes. There is easy parking available which is free. Buses 12, 26, 31, get off at Murrayfield Stadium and 38 which goes down Murrayfield Road.

· **Royal Caledonian Horticultural Society: Greenhouse at Saughton**

Edinburgh, Midlothian & West Lothian

Abundant borders at Rivaldsgreen House

19 RIVALDSGREEN HOUSE
48 Friars Brae, Linlithgow EH49 6BG
Dr Ian Wallace
T: 01506 845700 **E:** Ianwjw1940@gmail.com

Mature two-acre garden with lovely mixed herbaceous, rose and tree planting.

Open: Saturday 25 May, 2pm - 5pm, admission £5.00, children free.

Directions: For final directions, if necessary, call the number listed above. There is car parking available.

· *St Peters Episcopal Church*

20 SILVERBURN VILLAGE
Hopelands Road   EH26 9LH
The Gardener's of Silverburn

For over 30 years various Silverburn village gardens have opened for SGS, proving that a wide variety of planting styles can be successful at an exposed location above 800 feet. Famous for our wonderful views of the Pentland Hills, lovely woodland walks and specialist plant stalls, we invite children to bring their grandparents, parents and minders to join us for a Family Friday Afternoon. Enjoy visiting a variety of gardens, following the nature trail in the Beechgrove Community Garden and tasting our delicious home bakes in the village hall.

Open: Friday 6 September, 2pm - 5pm, admission £5.00, children free.

Directions: A702 Edinburgh/ Biggar Road 13 miles south of Edinburgh. Bus 101/102 Edinburgh - Dumfries Service.

· *Mary's Meals*

Edinburgh, Midlothian & West Lothian

21

THE GLASSHOUSES AT THE ROYAL BOTANIC GARDEN EDINBURGH
20A Inverleith Row, Edinburgh EH3 5LR
Royal Botanic Garden Edinburgh
T: 0131 248 2909
W: www.rbge.org.uk

The Glasshouses with their ten climatic zones are a delight all year round. The Orchids and Cycads House brings together primitive cycads which dominated the land flora some 65 million years ago, and a diverse range of orchids, the most sophisticated plants in the world. In summer, giant water lilies, *Victoria amazonica*, are the star attraction in the Tropical Aquatic House. Plants with vibrant flowers and fascinating foliage thrive in the Rainforest Riches House and the complex ecosystems of life in the world's deserts are explored in the Arid Lands House. A large collection of gingers, *Zingiberaceae*, one of the largest collections of vireya rhododendrons in the world and a case housing carnivorous plants are among other attractions.

Open: Sunday 9 June, 2pm - 5pm, admission details can be found on the garden's website.

Directions: Located off the A902, one mile north of the city centre. Entrances at Inverleith Row and Arboretum Place. Lothian Buses 8, 23 and 27 stop close to the East Gate entrance on Inverleith Row. The Majestic Tour Bus stops at Arboretum Place.

· **Donation to SGS Beneficiaries**

22

WHITBURGH HOUSE WALLED GARDEN
Pathhead, Midlothian EH37 5SR
Mrs Elizabeth Salvesen
E: eesal39@gmail.com

This contemporary, stylish one-acre walled garden, 700 feet above sea level, is a lively forward-looking and unexpected gem. The solidity and graphic quality of clipped foliage act as a foil for the many perennials, grasses, annuals, fruit and vegetables. A spiral path leads through an acre of white birches. There is also a variety of ponds and fine sculptures spread around 14 acres of policies. Whitburgh garden has featured recently in *Gardens Illustrated* and other publications.

Open: ONLY by arrangement 19 August - 18 October, admission £6.00, children free.

Directions: From the north - half a mile south of Pathhead on the A68 turn left and follow the SGS signs. From the south - one mile north of Blackshiels on the A68 turn right at the sign to *Fala Dam* and follow SGS signs. Whitburgh House is about two miles from either turn off and south east of Pathhead.

· **Horatio's Garden**

'Findings suggest that gardening can promote relief from acute stress'
The Kings Fund, 2016

FIFE

Scotland's Gardens Scheme 2019 Guidebook is sponsored by INVESTEC WEALTH & INVESTMENT

1. 46 South Street
2. Backhouse at Rossie Estate
3. Balcarres
4. Boarhills Village Gardens
5. Crail
6. Dalgety Bay Gardens
7. Earlshall Castle
8. Fife Spring Trail
9. Fife Summer Trail
10. Glassmount House
11. Helensbank
12. Hidden Gardens of Newburgh
13. Hill of Tarvit Plant Sale
14. Kirklands
15. Lindores House
16. Logie House
17. Pittenweem
18. Rosewells
19. South Flisk
20. St Fort Woodland Garden
21. The Tower
22. Willowhill
23. Wormistoune House

FIFE

OUR VOLUNTEER ORGANISERS

District Organiser:	Louise Roger	Chesterhill, Boarhills, St Andrews KY16 8PP
		E: fife@scotlandsgardens.org
Area Organisers:	Alison Aiton	Craigview Cottage, Blebo Craigs, Cupar KY15 5UQ
	Jeni Auchinleck	2 Castle Street, Crail KY10 3SQ
	Oenone Baillie	St Andrews
	Pauline Borthwick	96 Hepburn Gardens, St Andrews KY16 9LP
	Evelyn Crombie	Keeper's Wood, Over Rankeilour, Cupar KY15 4NQ
	Anne Lumgair	Falside Cottage, Falside Mill, Kingsbarns KY16 8PT
	Caroline Macpherson	Edenside, Strathmiglo KY14 7PX
	Barbara Pickard	Straiton Farmhouse, Balmullo KY16 0BN
	April Simpson	The Cottage, Boarhills, St Andrews KY16 8PP
	Fay Smith	37 Ninian Fields, Pittenweem KY10 2QU
	Julia Young	South Flisk, Blebo Craigs, Cupar KY15 5UQ
Treasurer:	David Buchanan-Cook	Helensbank, 56 Toll Road, Kincardine FK10 4QZ

GARDENS OPEN ON A SPECIFIC DATE

Cambo Plant Fair	Sunday, 14 April
Fife Spring Trail	Tuesday - Friday, 16-19 April
Fife Spring Trail	Tuesday - Friday, 23-26 April
The Tower, 1 Northview Terrace, Wormit	Saturday, 27 April
Fife Spring Trail	Monday, 29 April - Friday, 3 May
Earlshall Castle, Leuchars	Sunday, 5 May
46 South Street, St Andrews	Sunday, 12 May
Balcarres, Colinsburgh	Sunday, 19 May
St Fort Woodland Garden, St Fort Farm, Newport-on-Tay	Sunday, 26 May
South Flisk, Blebo Craigs, Cupar	Sunday, 26 May
Kirklands, Saline	Sunday, 26 May
Earlshall Castle, Leuchars	Sunday, 2 June
Fife Summer Trail	Monday - Thursday, 3-6 June
Fife Summer Trail	Monday - Thursday, 10-13 June
Pittenweem: Gardens in the Burgh	Sunday, 23 June
Hidden Gardens of Newburgh, Newburgh	Sunday, 23 June
Backhouse at Rossie Estate, By Collessie	Sunday, 30 June
Boarhills Village Gardens, St Andrews	Sunday, 30 June
Crail: Small Gardens in the Burgh	Saturday/Sunday, 20/21 July
Dalgety Bay Gardens, Dalgety Bay	Saturday/Sunday, 20/21 July
The Tower, 1 Northview Terrace, Wormit	Saturday, 3 August
Willowhill, Forgan, Newport-on-Tay	Saturday, 3 August
Willowhill, Forgan, Newport-on-Tay	Saturday, 10 August
Willowhill, Forgan, Newport-on-Tay	Saturday, 17 August
Willowhill, Forgan, Newport-on-Tay	Saturday, 24 August
Willowhill, Forgan, Newport-on-Tay	Saturday, 31 August
Hill of Tarvit Plant Sale and Autumn Fair, Hill of Tarvit, Cupar	Sunday, 29 September

FIFE

GARDENS OPEN REGULARLY

Glassmount House, By Kirkcaldy   1 April - 30 September (not Sundays)

GARDENS OPEN BY ARRANGEMENT

Lindores House, By Newburgh	17 March - 31 May
Kirklands, Saline	1 April - 30 September
The Tower, 1 Northview Terrace, Wormit	1 April - 30 September
Rosewells, Pitscottie	1 April - 30 September
St Fort Woodland Garden, St Fort Farm, Newport-on-Tay	1 April - 31 October
South Flisk, Blebo Craigs, Cupar	1 May - 30 June
Logie House, Crossford, Dunfermline	1 May - 30 September (not Wednesdays, Saturdays & Sundays)
Helensbank, Kincardine	1 June - 31 July
Wormistoune House, Crail	1 June - 30 August

Japanese garden features at Helensbank

Fife

1 46 SOUTH STREET
St Andrews KY16 9JT
Mrs June Baxter
T: 01334 474 995

Renowned town garden in medieval long rig, with orchard, spring bulbs and many spring-flowering shrubs. Clematis clothes the surrounding high walls. An historic and unique feature in St Andrews, but also a wonderfully planted space where different styles of planting complement the range of plants used. Historic doocot.

Open: Sunday 12 May, 2pm - 5pm, admission £5.00, children free. Fife Committee of The Art Fund are providing the teas.

Directions: Entry for the garden is off South Street.

· **The Art Fund**

2 BACKHOUSE AT ROSSIE ESTATE
By Collessie KY15 7UZ
Caroline Thomson and Andrew Thomson
E: caroline.thomson@rofsie-estate.com
W: www.backhouserossie.co.uk

A series of arches at the heart of the walled garden smothered by rambling roses over a DNA pathway form the longest interrupted Rose Archway in Scotland. A formal pond, water feature, grass labyrinth, yew-backed herbaceous borders with wispy grasses and unusual perennials, potager filled with roses, cut flowers, soft fruits and herbs. Old espalier fruit trees trained against the walls, new orchard and Victorian glass house complete the walled garden. Alpine scree and gravel plantings, walk to covenanters' tomb, short Bear Walk for little children, nine hole family putting. Heritage and Education Centre Exhibition.
National Plant Collection: *Narcissus* (Backhouse cvs).

Open: Sunday 30 June, 2pm - 5pm, admission £5.00, children free.

Directions: Between Auchtermuchty and Collessie off the A91 at the Backhouse Rossie banner and the single sign to *Charlottetown*. 300 yards down single track road turn right into Backhouse Rossie Estate.

· **Suzy Lamplugh Trust - National Stalking Helpline**

Fife

BALCARRES

Colinsburgh KY9 1HN
The Earl and Countess of Crawford and Balcarres
T: 01333 340205 (Estate Office)

The gardens at Balcarres are outstanding in the spring and will be bursting into life with a great array of interesting plants and trees. Many of the magnolias and rhododendrons will be in full bloom and the borders will be bursting into life with daffodils, tulips, snowdrops, primroses, primulas and polyanthus. The woodland area and Chapel Walk will also be at their best with many different hostas, trilliums and other interesting and diverse plants, shrubs and trees.

Open: Sunday 19 May, 2pm - 5pm, admission £6.00, children free.

Directions: Half a mile north of Colinsburgh off A942. Bus to Colinsburgh.

· *East Fife and Scooniehill Riding for the Disabled SCIO*

Formal planting at Balcarres

BOARHILLS VILLAGE GARDENS

St Andrews KY16 8PP
The Gardeners of Boarhills
T: 01334 880 238

Eight delightfully varied village gardens exhibiting a range of styles: colourful, richly planted herbaceous borders surrounding a magnificent lawn at Kenly Green Farm; traditional mixed cottage garden style at The Dirdale and No 2 Old Edinburgh, with kitchen gardens and orchard; spectacular bedding and sweet peas at No 5 Old Edinburgh; clever use of different levels and existing built features at The Cottage, Sea View and No 1 Old Edinburgh, where the design beautifully complements stunning ranges of herbaceous and shrub planting, and lovely views; beautiful new rockery and water feature in the hidden garden of Byways.

Open: Sunday 30 June, 2pm - 5pm, admission £5.00, children free. Teas in the village hall.

Directions: Enter the Village off the A917. Parking at Kenly Green Farm.

· *Fife Young Carers SCIO*

FIFE

OUR VOLUNTEER ORGANISERS

District Organiser:	Louise Roger	Chesterhill, Boarhills, St Andrews KY16 8PP
		E: fife@scotlandsgardens.org
Area Organisers:	Alison Aiton	Craigview Cottage, Blebo Craigs, Cupar KY15 5UQ
	Jeni Auchinleck	2 Castle Street, Crail KY10 3SQ
	Oenone Baillie	St Andrews
	Pauline Borthwick	96 Hepburn Gardens, St Andrews KY16 9LP
	Evelyn Crombie	Keeper's Wood, Over Rankeilour, Cupar KY15 4NQ
	Anne Lumgair	Falside Cottage, Falside Mill, Kingsbarns KY16 8PT
	Caroline Macpherson	Edenside, Strathmiglo KY14 7PX
	Barbara Pickard	Straiton Farmhouse, Balmullo KY16 0BN
	April Simpson	The Cottage, Boarhills, St Andrews KY16 8PP
	Fay Smith	37 Ninian Fields, Pittenweem KY10 2QU
	Julia Young	South Flisk, Blebo Craigs, Cupar KY15 5UQ
Treasurer:	David Buchanan-Cook	Helensbank, 56 Toll Road, Kincardine FK10 4QZ

GARDENS OPEN ON A SPECIFIC DATE

Cambo Plant Fair	Sunday, 14 April
Fife Spring Trail	Tuesday - Friday, 16-19 April
Fife Spring Trail	Tuesday - Friday, 23-26 April
The Tower, 1 Northview Terrace, Wormit	Saturday, 27 April
Fife Spring Trail	Monday, 29 April - Friday, 3 May
Earlshall Castle, Leuchars	Sunday, 5 May
46 South Street, St Andrews	Sunday, 12 May
Balcarres, Colinsburgh	Sunday, 19 May
St Fort Woodland Garden, St Fort Farm, Newport-on-Tay	Sunday, 26 May
South Flisk, Blebo Craigs, Cupar	Sunday, 26 May
Kirklands, Saline	Sunday, 26 May
Earlshall Castle, Leuchars	Sunday, 2 June
Fife Summer Trail	Monday - Thursday, 3-6 June
Fife Summer Trail	Monday - Thursday, 10-13 June
Pittenweem: Gardens in the Burgh	Sunday, 23 June
Hidden Gardens of Newburgh, Newburgh	Sunday, 23 June
Backhouse at Rossie Estate, By Collessie	Sunday, 30 June
Boarhills Village Gardens, St Andrews	Sunday, 30 June
Crail: Small Gardens in the Burgh	Saturday/Sunday, 20/21 July
Dalgety Bay Gardens, Dalgety Bay	Saturday/Sunday, 20/21 July
The Tower, 1 Northview Terrace, Wormit	Saturday, 3 August
Willowhill, Forgan, Newport-on-Tay	Saturday, 3 August
Willowhill, Forgan, Newport-on-Tay	Saturday, 10 August
Willowhill, Forgan, Newport-on-Tay	Saturday, 17 August
Willowhill, Forgan, Newport-on-Tay	Saturday, 24 August
Willowhill, Forgan, Newport-on-Tay	Saturday, 31 August
Hill of Tarvit Plant Sale and Autumn Fair, Hill of Tarvit, Cupar	Sunday, 29 September

FIFE

GARDENS OPEN REGULARLY

Glassmount House, By Kirkcaldy   1 April - 30 September (not Sundays)

GARDENS OPEN BY ARRANGEMENT

Lindores House, By Newburgh	17 March - 31 May
Kirklands, Saline	1 April - 30 September
The Tower, 1 Northview Terrace, Wormit	1 April - 30 September
Rosewells, Pitscottie	1 April - 30 September
St Fort Woodland Garden, St Fort Farm, Newport-on-Tay	1 April - 31 October
South Flisk, Blebo Craigs, Cupar	1 May - 30 June
Logie House, Crossford, Dunfermline	1 May - 30 September (not Wednesdays, Saturdays & Sundays)
Helensbank, Kincardine	1 June - 31 July
Wormistoune House, Crail	1 June - 30 August

Japanese garden features at Helensbank

Fife

1 46 SOUTH STREET
St Andrews KY16 9JT
Mrs June Baxter
T: 01334 474 995

Renowned town garden in medieval long rig, with orchard, spring bulbs and many spring-flowering shrubs. Clematis clothes the surrounding high walls. An historic and unique feature in St Andrews, but also a wonderfully planted space where different styles of planting complement the range of plants used. Historic doocot.

Open: Sunday 12 May, 2pm - 5pm, admission £5.00, children free. Fife Committee of The Art Fund are providing the teas.

Directions: Entry for the garden is off South Street.

· *The Art Fund*

2 BACKHOUSE AT ROSSIE ESTATE
By Collessie KY15 7UZ
Caroline Thomson and Andrew Thomson
E: caroline.thomson@rofsie-estate.com
W: www.backhouserossie.co.uk

A series of arches at the heart of the walled garden smothered by rambling roses over a DNA pathway form the longest interrupted Rose Archway in Scotland. A formal pond, water feature, grass labyrinth, yew-backed herbaceous borders with wispy grasses and unusual perennials, potager filled with roses, cut flowers, soft fruits and herbs. Old espalier fruit trees trained against the walls, new orchard and Victorian glass house complete the walled garden. Alpine scree and gravel plantings, walk to covenanters' tomb, short Bear Walk for little children, nine hole family putting. Heritage and Education Centre Exhibition.
National Plant Collection: *Narcissus* (Backhouse cvs).

Open: Sunday 30 June, 2pm - 5pm, admission £5.00, children free.

Directions: Between Auchtermuchty and Collessie off the A91 at the Backhouse Rossie banner and the single sign to *Charlottetown*. 300 yards down single track road turn right into Backhouse Rossie Estate.

· *Suzy Lamplugh Trust - National Stalking Helpline*

Fife

BALCARRES
Colinsburgh KY9 1HN
The Earl and Countess of Crawford and Balcarres
T: 01333 340205 (Estate Office)

The gardens at Balcarres are outstanding in the spring and will be bursting into life with a great array of interesting plants and trees. Many of the magnolias and rhododendrons will be in full bloom and the borders will be bursting into life with daffodils, tulips, snowdrops, primroses, primulas and polyanthus. The woodland area and Chapel Walk will also be at their best with many different hostas, trilliums and other interesting and diverse plants, shrubs and trees.

Open: Sunday 19 May, 2pm - 5pm, admission £6.00, children free.

Directions: Half a mile north of Colinsburgh off A942. Bus to Colinsburgh.

· *East Fife and Scooniehill Riding for the Disabled SCIO*

Formal planting at Balcarres

BOARHILLS VILLAGE GARDENS
St Andrews KY16 8PP
The Gardeners of Boarhills
T: 01334 880 238

Eight delightfully varied village gardens exhibiting a range of styles: colourful, richly planted herbaceous borders surrounding a magnificent lawn at Kenly Green Farm; traditional mixed cottage garden style at The Dirdale and No 2 Old Edinburgh, with kitchen gardens and orchard; spectacular bedding and sweet peas at No 5 Old Edinburgh; clever use of different levels and existing built features at The Cottage, Sea View and No 1 Old Edinburgh, where the design beautifully complements stunning ranges of herbaceous and shrub planting, and lovely views; beautiful new rockery and water feature in the hidden garden of Byways.

Open: Sunday 30 June, 2pm - 5pm, admission £5.00, children free. Teas in the village hall.

Directions: Enter the Village off the A917. Parking at Kenly Green Farm.

· *Fife Young Carers SCIO*

Fife

5

CRAIL: SMALL GARDENS IN THE BURGH
2 Castle Street, Crail KY10 3SQ
Mrs J Auchinleck
T: 01333 450 538 **E:** sueellen.jerdan@gmail.com
W: www.crailfestival.com

Several new gardens this year! A number of gardens in varied styles: cottage, historic, plantsman's and bedding. The stunning coastal location of the gardens presents some challenges for planting but also allows a great range of more tender species to flourish.

Open: Saturday/Sunday, 20/21 July, 1pm - 5pm, admission £5.50, children free. Ticket and maps available on the day from Mrs Jeni Auchinleck, 2 Castle Street or from the Crail Festival Box Office, Town Hall, Marketgate.

Advance ticket sales available from www.crailfestival.com (if purchasing in advance please present your ticket at any of the gardens to receive your map and sticker). Crail gardens open in association with Crail Festival, 17 – 27 July.

Directions: Approach Crail from either St Andrews or Anstruther via the A917. Parking available in Marketgate.

· *Crail Preservation Society*

6

DALGETY BAY GARDENS
Dalgety Bay KY11 9HH
Sybil Cobban and Dalgety Bay Horticultural Society (DBHS)
E: Michaeljg@btinternet.com

17 Inchview Gardens KY11 9SA (Mrs Sybil Cobban): This compact garden was designed and created by Sybil, who won *Fife Garden Competition* in 2006. Having held seven annual garden parties for Marie Curie Nurses and three for her local church, Sybil is now opening for SGS! The garden has a selection of herbaceous and bedding plants. She does not have a favourite flower, but top of her list are heucheras, acers and hostas.
DBHS Allotments Western Approach Road, KY11 9HH: The allotment site has grown and developed over the last 44 years. All allotments are taken and it is really nice to see them in production in the month of July. The Annual Show is in September and a lot of the produce you see will be on the show benches. Allotment holders will be on site to chat and you may get the secret of the huge marrow or gigantic cabbage.

Open: Saturday/Sunday, 20/21 July, 2pm - 5pm, admission £5.00, children free. Teas will be served at 17 Inchview Gardens, and refreshments at the allotments. Entry charge includes teas. A donation for refreshments at the allotments will be requested.

Directions: Inchview Gardens are accessed off Moray Way South. The allotments are behind Peter Vardy Vauxhall, Western Approach Road, Dalgety Bay.

· *Marie Curie*

Fife

EARLSHALL CASTLE
Leuchars KY16 0DP
Paul and Josine Veenhuijzen
T: 01334 839205

Extensive, exquisitely designed garden, which perfectly complements the Castle also restored by Sir Robert Lorimer in the 1890s. Fascinating topiary lawn, the finest in Scotland and for which Earlshall is renowned, rose terrace, croquet lawn with herbaceous borders, shrub border, box garden, orchard, kitchen and herb garden. Spectacular spring bulbs.

Open: Sunday 5 May and Sunday 2 June, 2pm - 5pm. Admission £5.00, children free.

Directions: On Earlshall Road, three quarters of a mile east of Leuchars Village (off A919). Bus/train to Leuchars.

· Royal Scots Dragoon Guards Regimental Trust (Sunday 5 May) & Leuchars St Athernase Parish Church (Sunday 2 June)

FIFE SPRING TRAIL
Various locations across Fife
The Fife Gardeners
E: fife@scotlandsgardens.org

The Fife Spring Trail comprises six unique gardens and one plant fair, at Cambo Gardens. Visitors can enjoy visiting a wide variety of gardens, with special collections of endangered species from the Southern Hemipshere (Cedar Cottage) or a tulip-adorned walled garden and bluebell-covered Millennium Wood (Teasses). It's a wonderful opportunity to explore a plantsman's garden undergoing gradual redevelopment (Rosemount Cottage) and spring woodland with terraced walled garden (Kirklands). And Balcaskie's rhododendrons and magnolias will be at their magnificent best.

Balcaskie Pittenweem KY10 2RE (The Anstruther Family)
Open Fridays: 19 and 26 April and 3 May, 1pm - 4pm
Cambo Plant Fair Kingsbarns KY16 8QD (Trustees of Cambo Heritage Trust)
Open Sunday 14 April, noon - 3pm
Cedar Cottage Mill Road, Craigrothie KY15 5PZ (Mr Ian Douglas)
Open Thursdays: 18 and 25 April and 2 May, 1pm - 4pm
Kirklands Saline KY12 9TS (Peter & Gill Hart)
Open Wednesdays: 17 and 24 April and 1 May, 2pm - 5pm
Rosemount Cottage 21 Main Street, Ceres KY15 5NA (Gavin and Sarah Anderson)
Open Monday 29 April, Wednesday 1 May and Thursday 2 May, 2pm - 5pm
Strathkinness Community Garden and Orchard Bonfield Road KY16 9RR (Strathkinness Community Trust)
Open Tuesdays: 16, 23 and 30 April, 2pm - 4pm
Teasses Gardens near Ceres KY8 5PG (Sir Fraser and Lady Morrison)
Open Fridays: 19 and 26 April and 3 May, 10am - 4pm

Open: The Fife Spring Trail offers various dates and times over the last two weeks in April and first week in May. See the description for the specific openings for each garden. Admission £25.00, children free, pre-sales tickets available from Eventbrite (browse 'SGS Fife Spring Trail') or at the gardens on the day. Gardens can be visited individually, and tickets purchased at the garden for £5.00. See pages 14-15 for further details.

Directions: Directions to each garden will be provided with the tickets.

· East Neuk First Responders & The Rotary Club of St Andrews: Arclight Eye Project

Fife

9

FIFE SUMMER TRAIL
Various locations across Fife
The Fife Gardeners
E: fife@scotlandsgardens.org

Garden open season is in full swing, and this year gardeners of Fife are throwing open their garden gates for a Summer Trail. There will be eight gardens open over the fortnight, showcasing very different and wonderful designs. From a baby Victorian walled garden with mixed borders and fruit trees at Gordonshall Farm, to a later Edwardian landscaped garden with stunning views, rockeries and water features, including a granite grotto with waterfall pool (The Tower). The air will be heavily perfumed by the English roses at Straiton Farmhouse, which flourish alongside their tree peonies. Visitors can enjoy meandering among the island beds and overflowing borders (Kenly Green Farm), down a crab-apple-and-rose tunnel or pleached lime avenue in the walled garden at Millfield House.

Glenbeg South Road, Cupar KY15 5JG (Lilias and Alistair Smith)
Open Mondays: 3 and 10 June, 1pm - 4pm
Gordonshall Farm Carnbee, Anstruther KY10 2RU (Mihai and Louisa Cocris)
Open Wednesdays: 5 and 12 June, 10am - 4pm
Greenhead Farmhouse Greenhead of Arnot, Leslie KY6 3JQ (Mr and Mrs Malcolm Strang Steel)
Open Tuesday:, 4 and 11 June, 4pm - 8pm
Kenly Green Farm Boarhills KY16 8PP (Frank and Bernice Roger)
Open Thursdays: 6 and 13 June, 1pm - 4pm
Millfield House Falkland KY15 7BN (Sarah Marshall)
Open Tuesdays: 4 and 11 June, 4pm - 8pm
Straiton Farmhouse Straiton Farm, Balmullo KY16 0BN (Mrs Barbara Pickard)
Open Mondays: 3 and 10 June, 10am - 1pm
The Tower 1 Northview Terrace, Wormit DD6 8PP (Peter and Angela Davey)
Open Mondays: 3 and 10 June, 4pm - 8pm
Wormistoune House Crail KY10 3XH (Baron and Lady Wormiston)
Open Thursdays: 6 and 13 June, 10am - 4pm with plants for sale

Open: The Fife Summer Trail offers various dates and times over the first two weeks of June. See the description for the specific openings for each garden. Admission £25.00, children free, pre-sales tickets available from Eventbrite (browse 'SGS Fife Summer Trail') or at the gardens on the day. Gardens can be visited individually, and tickets purchased at the garden for £5.00. See pages 16-17 for further details.

Directions: Directions to each garden will be provided with the tickets.

· *East Neuk First Responders & The Rotary Club of St Andrews: Arclight Eye Project*

Raised beds at Glenbeg, Fife Summer Trail

Fife

Mackenzie & Moncur greenhouse at Glassmont House

10 GLASSMOUNT HOUSE
By Kirkcaldy KY2 5UT
Peter, James and Irene Thomson
T: 01592 890214 **E:** mcmoonter@yahoo.co.uk

Densely planted walled garden with surrounding woodland. An A-listed sun dial, Mackenzie & Moncur greenhouse and historical doocot are complemented by a number of newer structures. Daffodils are followed by a mass of candelabra and cowslip primula, meconopsis and *Cardiocrinum giganteum*. Hedges and topiary form backdrops for an abundance of bulbs, clematis, rambling roses and perennials, creating interest through the summer into September. The garden is now extending beyond the walls, with new areas of naturalistic planting blending the boundary between the surrounding fields and the woodland.

Open: 1 April - 30 September (not Sundays), 2pm - 5pm, admission £5.00, children free.

Directions: From Kirkcaldy, head west on the B9157. Turn left immediately after the railway bridge on the edge of town. Follow the single track road for one and a half miles and cross the crossroads. Glassmount House is the first turning on your right.

· *Parkinsons UK*

11 HELENSBANK
Kincardine FK10 4QZ
David Buchanan-Cook and Adrian Miles
T: 07739 312912 **E:** Helensbank@aol.com

An 18th-century walled garden, with main feature a Cedar of Lebanon, reputedly planted in 1750 by the sea captain who built the house. It provides challenges for planting in terms of shade and

Fife

needle fall. Distinctive garden 'rooms' in part of the garden comprise a perennial blue and white cottage garden, a formal rose garden and an Italian Garden with citrus trees in pots. A 'hot' courtyard contains exotics such as bananas, acacias, iochromas, melianthus and brugmansia. A shaded walk along the bottom of the garden leads to a Japanese pagoda. A large conservatory/greenhouse houses various climbing plants including varieties of passiflora.

Open: Open by arrangement 1 June - 31 July, admission £4.00, children free. Cream teas and lunches available on request for small or large groups.

Directions: On request.

· Scottish Veterans Residences

HIDDEN GARDENS OF NEWBURGH
Newburgh KY14 6AJ
Judith Laughlan
T: 07763 340362   **E:** judilaugh@gmail.com
....

Hidden behind the 18th-century facades of Newburgh High Street is a jumble of wonderful old gardens, some of them dating back centuries, and many with spectacular views of the Tay estuary. We are opening for the second time, and the gardens will include some of last year's along with some new – including a converted church garden fronting onto the main street, and the beautiful gardens of the local care home. Those which are opening for the second time will be significantly developed and as before there will be a wide mix of flowers, vegetables, herbaceous borders, orchards, and a fair few hens and ducks.

Open: Sunday 23 June, 12pm - 5pm, admission £5.00, children free. Admission includes tea/coffee. Newburgh, at the northern end of the Fife coastal path, sits on a hill; and access to some of the gardens is up closes and down vennels. Some allow for disabled access but not all.

Directions: On the A913 between Perth and Cupar. There is a car park at each end of the village with tickets and teas available nearby.

· Newburgh Community Trust

HILL OF TARVIT PLANT SALE AND AUTUMN FAIR
Hill of Tarvit, Cupar KY15 5PB
The National Trust for Scotland/Scotland's Gardens Scheme - Fife
E: fife@scotlandsgardens.org
....

This long-established plant sale is a fantastic opportunity to purchase bare root and potted plants from an enormous selection on offer. We welcome donations of plants before the sale. Please deliver to Hill of Tarvit on the Friday or Saturday. A number of invited specialist nurseries and bulb suppliers will also be taking part. Hill of Tarvit is one of Scotland's finest Edwardian mansion houses. The surrounding woodland offers lovely walks, with autumn colours on show.

Open: Sunday 29 September, 10:30am - 2:30pm, admission £2.00, children free.

Directions: Two miles south of Cupar on A916.

· SGS Beneficiaries

Fife

14

KIRKLANDS
Saline KY12 9TS
Peter and Gill Hart
T: 01383 852737 **E:** gill@i-comment360.com
W: www.kirklandshouseandgarden.co.uk

Kirklands, built in 1832 on the site of an older house, has been the Hart family home for 41 years (and now Hart/Dawson family since our daughter and family moved back). Over the years we have re-instated the walled garden from a paddock and constructed terraces and raised beds with 18 espalier apple trees, box hedging and a display of red and yellow tulips. A woodland garden starts with snowdrops and bluebells, rhododendrons, trilliums, fritillaries, meconopsis, erythroniums, Candelabra primulas follow. The garden is constantly being added to, with herbaceous borders, a rockery with dwarf rhododendrons and azaleas, a bog garden by the Saline Burn, and 20 acres of woodland with walks. To keep the grandchildren occupied, Peter has built a tree house, zip wire and rope swing, though we hope they will take an interest in gardening too!

Open: Sunday 26 May, 2pm - 5pm. Also open by arrangement 1 April - 30 September. Admission £5.00, children free.

Directions: Junction 4, M90, then B914. Parking in the centre of the village, then a short walk to the garden. Limited disabled parking at Kirklands.

· *Saline Environmental Group*

15

LINDORES HOUSE
By Newburgh KY14 6JD
Mr and Mrs R Turcan
T: 01337 840369

Lindores House overlooks the loch. Woodland walk beside the loch and stunning views from the garden. Herbaceous borders, wonderful snowdrops, leucojums, trilliums, primula, rhododendrons and species trees including *Nothofagus* and *Davidia involucrata*, the handkerchief tree, and a 17th-century yew, believed to be the largest in Fife.

Open: Open by arrangement 17 March - 31 May, admission £5.00, children free.

Directions: Off A913 two miles east of Newburgh. Bus from Cupar.

· *Bumblebee Conservation Trust*

16

LOGIE HOUSE
Crossford, Dunfermline KY12 8QN
Mr and Mrs Jonathan Hunt
T: 07867 804020

Central to the design of this walled garden is a path through a double mixed border. Long rows of vegetables and fruit also contribute to colour and design when seen from the house and terrace. A long border of repeat flowering roses and rose and annual beds contribute to an extended season of colour and interest. There is a magnificent and very productive Mackenzie & Moncur greenhouse in excellent condition with fully working vents and original benches and central heating system. The garden is surrounded by a belt of mixed woodland with walks.

Open: Open by arrangement 1 May - 30 September (Monday-Tuesday and Thursday-Friday), admission £5.00, children free.

Fife

Directions: M90 exit 1 for Rosyth and Kincardine Bridge (A985). After about two miles turn right to Crossford. At traffic lights, turn right and the drive is on the right at the end of the village main street.

· *Scottish Veterans Residences*

PITTENWEEM: GARDENS IN THE BURGH
Pittenweem KY10 2PQ
The Gardeners of Pittenweem
T: 01333 311988

A great variety in garden design: from well-established traditional, to open-aspect landscaped, a hidden raised walled garden, existing and newly participating 'make over' projects. The nearby refurbished Crazy Golf circuit, next to the West Braes car park remains an attraction for the children.

Open: Sunday 23 June, 11am - 5pm, admission £5.00, children free. Tickets and maps obtainable at 3 Seaview Row, Pittenweem (near West Braes car park), 24 Milton Road (east side of Pittenweem) and from several gardens. Refreshments are available in pubs, coffee shops and some gardens. Disabled access for some gardens.

Directions: On the A917 coast road enter Pittenweem following the signs to the *West Braes car park* next to the Crazy Golf. For traffic from the east, stop and park at Milton Road.

· *Pittenweem Community Library and Information Centre*

One of the gardens on Pittenweem

Fife

18 ROSEWELLS
Pitscottie KY15 5LE
Birgitta and Gordon MacDonald
E: birgittamac@hotmail.co.uk

Rosewells, designed by the garden owners, has developed over the last 25 years with an underlying theme that each part of the garden should work in relation to the rest to create one overall effect. The design centres on texture and foliage to provide a lively effect with structure and shape all year. The winter 'bones' are provided with trees and shrubs with features such as contorted stems and peeling or coloured bark. In spring and summer, texture and coloured foliage of shrubs and perennials add to the overall design. Birgitta sees flowers as an added bonus with scent and colour being important and combinations of yellow, blue and white colour schemes are preferred. The garden has many varieties of cornus, magnolias, trilliums, meconopsis, agapanthus, rhododendrons, primulas, auriculas, fritillaries, erythroniums, peonies and acers, which are favourites.

Open: Open by arrangement 1 April - 30 September, admission £5.00, children free.

Directions: B940 between Pitscottie and Peat Inn, one mile from Pitscottie. Rosewells is the ochre-coloured house.

· *Save the Children UK*

Rosewells

Fife

19

SOUTH FLISK
Blebo Craigs, Cupar KY15 5UQ
Mr and Mrs George Young
T: 01334 850859 **E:** julia@standrewspottery.co.uk
W: www.standrewspottery.co.uk

....

The spectacular views over Fife to Perthshire and Angus and the large flooded quarry full of fish and planted with impressive marginals make the garden at South Flisk very special in the area. Flights of old stone steps, cliffs, huge boulders, exotic ferns and mature trees form a backdrop for carpets of primroses, bluebells, spring bulbs and woodland plants like trilliums, camassia and colourful primulas. There are different rhododendrons in flower in the garden from March until July. In front of the house is a charming, mature walled garden with traditional cottage-garden planting and next to the house is the St Andrews Pottery where George will be demonstrating his pottery skills for those who need a break from the garden!

Open: Sunday 26 May, 2pm - 5pm. Also open by arrangement 1 May - 30 June. Admission £5.00, children free.

Directions: Six miles west of St Andrews off the B939 between Strathkinness and Pitscottie. There is a small stone bus shelter opposite the road into the village and a small sign saying *Blebo Craigs*. Or check out the map on our website. Bus to Blebo Craigs.

· *Book Aid International*

20

ST FORT WOODLAND GARDEN
St Fort Farm, Newport-on-Tay DD6 8RE
Mr and Mrs Andrew Mylius
T: 07974 083110
W: www.stfort.co.uk

....

Inspired by a visit to Ruskin's woodland garden at Brantwood. Azaleas and specimen rhododendrons are the principal plants. Created from an area of mixed woodland, the garden has been further enlarged in 2018 by the addition of two acres of new planting. The rhododendrons include a wide selection of both specimen and hybrids. Azaleas are mainly *Azalea pontica* chosen for scent and autumn colour. Around 30 acres, theNorthwood is home to red squirrels, and offers spectacular views northwards over the River Tay. Also of interest are eucryphia, cercidiphyllum, tulip tree, various red acers, rowans, liquidambar, metasequoia and magnolias. Spectacular late autumn foliage, when the garden potentially surpasses its spring glory in terms of colours!

Open: Sunday 26 May, 1pm - 5pm. Also open by arrangement 1 April - 31 October. Admission £5.00, children free.

Directions: One and three quarters miles south of the Tay Road Bridge off the A92, between the Forgan and Five Roads roundabouts. St Fort is approached with a woodland walk of about 400 metres from the car park and garden entrance.

· *Brooke Action for Working Horses & Donkeys*

Fife

Views from The Tower

21

THE TOWER
1 Northview Terrace, Wormit DD6 8PP
Peter and Angela Davey
T: 01382 541635 **M:** 07768 406946 **E:** adavey541@btinternet.com

Situated four miles south of Dundee, this one-acre Edwardian landscaped garden has panoramic views over the River Tay. Set on a hill, a series of paths meander around ponds and a small stream, rockeries featuring hellebores and low-level planting, a curved lawn and larger borders. Original woodland paths lead to a granite grotto with waterfall pool. At the rear of the house the vegetable garden features raised beds made from granite sets. We have recently removed rhododendrons to create more space for seating and flower beds.

Open: Saturday 27 April and Saturday 3 August, 1pm - 5pm. Also open by arrangement 1 April - 30 September. Admission £4.00, children free.

Directions: From B946 park on Naughton Road outside Spar shop and walk up path on left following signs.

 · *Amnesty International (UK Section) Charitable Trust*

Fife

WILLOWHILL
Forgan, Newport-on-Tay DD6 8RA
Eric Wright and Sally Lorimore
T: 01382 542890 **E:** e.g.wright@dundee.ac.uk
W: www.willowhillgarden.weebly.com

An evolving three acre garden. The house is surrounded by a series of mixed borders designed with different vibrant colour combinations for effect all season. Spectacular mix of roses, herbaceous perennials and annuals planted through the wide borders are a highlight in late summer.

Open: Saturdays in August (3, 10, 17, 24 and 31), 2pm - 5pm, admission £5.00, children free.

Directions: One and a half miles south of Tay Road Bridge. Take the B995 to Newport off the Forgan roundabout. Willowhill is the first house on the left hand side next to the Forgan Arts Centre.

· Forgan Arts Centre SCIO

WORMISTOUNE HOUSE
Crail KY10 3XH
Baron and Lady Wormiston
T: Katherine Taylor, Head Gardener 07905 938449 **E:** ktaylor.home@googlemail.com

The ongoing restoration and transformation of this 'pocket' estate's 17th century Scot's tower house and gardens continues to evolve and delight. Within the walled garden, imaginatively clipped yew hedges enclose 'rooms' filled with luxuriantly planted herbaceous borders, a productive potager garden, wildflower meadows, an intricate box parterre, water features and a magical shade garden which is home to four of Scotland's largest *Griselinia littoralis* specimens. In recent years planting has extended into the wider woodland policies and highlights include a new Nuttery (inspired by Sissinghurst), extensive wildflower meadows and waterside plantings surrounding an impressively landscaped pond.

Open: Open by arrangement 1 June - 30 August, admission £5.00, children free. Please note, for large groups only (more than 10 people).

Directions: One mile north of Crail on the A917 Crail to St Andrews road. Crail/St Andrews bus.

· Maggies Centre

'Gardening is a great way
to make friends with people
with similar hobbies'

GLASGOW & DISTRICT

Scotland's Gardens Scheme 2019 Guidebook is sponsored by INVESTEC WEALTH & INVESTMENT

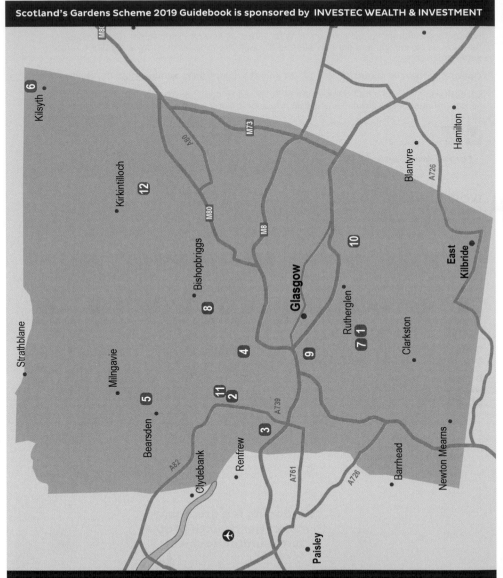

1. Berridale Allotments and
    Gardens Association
2. Gartnaval Secret Garden
3. Horatio's Gardens

4. Kew Terrace Gardens:
    Back to Front
5. Kilmardinny Gardens
6. Kilsyth Gardens
7. Merrylee Spring Plant Sale

8. Milton Community Gardens
9. Strathbungo Garden
10. The Good Life Gardens
11. Whittingehame Drive
    Gardens
12. Woodbourne House

OUR VOLUNTEER ORGANISERS

District Organiser:	Heidi Stone	4 Arrowsmith Avenue, Glasgow G13 2SX
		E: glasgow@scotlandsgardens.org
Area Organisers:	Caroline Anderson	64 Partickhill Road, Glasgow G11 5NB
	Mary Marshall	14 Hughenden Gardens, Glasgow G12 9XW
	Audrey Mason	Hillend House, Drakemyre, Dalry KA24 5JR
	Jim & Anne Murray	44 Gordon Road, Netherlee, Glasgow G44 3TW
	Margaret & John Redmond	68 Kilmardinny Crescent, Bearsden G61 3NW
Treasurer:	John Mason	Hillend House, Drakemyre, Dalry, KA24 5JR

GARDENS OPEN ON A SPECIFIC DATE

Merrylee Spring Plant Sale, Merrylee Plots, Quadrant Road	Saturday, 4 May
Gartnaval Secret Garden, Gartnavel Royal Hospital	Sunday, 12 May
Whittingehame Drive Gardens, Glasgow	Saturday, 1 June
Kilsyth Gardens, Allanfauld Road, Kilsyth	Sunday, 2 June
Berridale Allotments and Gardens, Delvin Road, Glasgow	Saturday, 22 June
Kew Terrace Gardens; Back to Front, Kew Terrace Lane, Glasgow	Saturday, 29 June
Milton Community Garden, Liddesdale Square, Milton, Glasgow	Sunday, 7 July
Gartnaval Secret Garden, Gartnavel Royal Hospital	Sunday, 14 July
Strathbungo Garden, March Street, Glasgow	Sunday, 21 July
Kilmardinny Gardens, Glasgow	Sunday, 28 July
Woodbourne House, Seven Sisters, Lenzie, Glasgow	Sunday, 18 August
The Good Life Gardens, Cambuslang, Glasgow	Sunday, 25 August
Horatio's Gardens, Queen Elizabeth University Hospital	Sunday, 1 September

GARDENS OPEN BY ARRANGEMENT

Kilsyth Gardens, Allanfauld Road, Kilsyth	1 April - 30 August

Glasgow & District

 BERRIDALE ALLOTMENTS AND GARDENS
Delvin Road, Cathcart, Glasgow G44 3AB
Berridale Allotments and Gardens Association
E: berridaleaa@gmail.com

There have been allotments at Berridale since before the Second World War. The site has 51 plots, most with huts and/or greenhouses, and is a green oasis in an urban setting with the River Cart running along one side of our site. There is a large variety of vegetables, flowers and fruit cultivated, and over the years we have regularly had individual plotholders winning prizes for the top plots in Glasgow. Our site is privately owned, run and managed and there is a constant and high demand from folk wishing to become members. Come and have a look around our site and chat with some of our members. We have a large hut so even if it's wet you can stay dry.

Open: Saturday 22 June, 2pm - 5pm, admission £5.00, children free.

Directions: The allotments are very close to public transport. Buses run along Clarkston Road, which is about 100 yards from our site. The allotments are about 50 yards east from the Delvin Road exit from Cathcart Railway Station. Although there is plenty of on-street parking in the area there is no parking on Delvin Road.

· *Berridale Allotments*

 GARTNAVAL SECRET GARDEN
Gartnavel Royal Hospital, 1055 Great Western Road, Glasgow G12 0XH
Gartnavel Royal Hospital Volunteers
T: 07977 406900

Gartnavel's hidden walled garden forms part of the original, 200-year-old-hospital, and was originally the private garden of the hospital's superintendent. It was restored about six years ago by the Green Exercise Partnership and is run by a loyal group of volunteers as an oasis of calm for hospital patients, staff and visitors. We do a little bit of everything at Gartnavel, growing both edibles and ornamentals and, as a hospital garden, we feature lots of sensory and medicinal plants too.

Open: Sunday 12 May, 12pm - 5pm. Also open Sunday 14 July, 2pm - 5pm. Admission £6.00, children free.

Directions: From Great Western Road (car, bus or foot): Enter Gartnavel Hospital site and turn right at the traffic lights onto Shelley Road. Follow yellow *Garden Open* signs, continue past pond and car park and at the fork bear left up the hill. Continue up the hill to T junction, turn right along the front of West House and park in the spaces there. Once parked continue to follow the signs to the gardens at the rear of West House.

· *TCV Scotland, The Conservation Volunteers Scotland*

Glasgow & District

HORATIO'S GARDENS
National Spinal Injuries Unit, Queen Elizabeth University Hospital
1325 Govan Road, Glasgow G51 4TF
E: sallie@horatiosgarden.org.uk
W: Horatiosgarden.org.uk

Opened in 2016, award-winning Horatio's Garden at the Scottish National Spinal Injuries Unit, was designed by acclaimed garden designer and RHS judge, James Alexander-Sinclair. This fully accessible garden creates a sanctuary through planting, seasonality in every corner and in a wealth of variety and colour. Visit to see how this high profile national charity has created a beautiful, cleverly designed, contemporary, accessible garden in the heart of Greater Glasgow and Clyde NHS for the benefit of patients, relatives, staff and all visitors.

Open: Sunday 1 September, 2pm - 5pm, admission £6.00, children free. Guests will be guided around the courtyard and woodland gardens by our knowledgeable Head Gardener and volunteer team. Children's crafts and activities available. Plants and beautifully selected charity merchandise will be on sale.

Directions: From the east or west of the city on the M8 motorway to Junction 25, follow signs for the Clyde Tunnel (A739) for three quarters of a mile, then follow signs for the Queen Elizabeth Hospital. Turn left into Govan Road and the hospital is on the left. From north of the River Clyde go through the Clyde tunnel (A739) and follow signs for the hospital. A map can be found on our website indicating where the garden is situated on the hospital site.

· *Horatio's Garden*

KEW TERRACE GARDENS: BACK TO FRONT
Kew Terrace Lane, Glasgow G12 0TE
Professor George G Browning and other Owners

The opening under Scotland's Gardens Scheme is for some of the south-facing rear gardens. As last year was a good year for roses, in both the back and front gardens the 2019 opening has been moved to later in the year, hoping to catch the roses at their flowering peak. Access to these is from the delightful cobbled, tree-lined and partially gardened Kew Lane. Funds from openings are used to plant and maintain the terrace front gardens on Great Western Road.

Open: Saturday 29 June, 2pm - 5pm, admission £7.00, children free. Includes homemade teas in a marque in the communal west end garden.

Directions: From the M8 take Junction 17 (A82) and turn west onto Great Western Road. Drive west to the junction of Byres Road and Great Western Road, recognisable by the main entrance to the Botanic Gardens. Continue west on Great Western Road to the next traffic lights at Kirklee and turn left into Horslethill Road. You are now in the Downhill controlled parking area, where parking spaces are usually available especially on Horselethill Road after it swings left. Access to Kew Terrace (G12 0TE) is down the first road on the left.

· *Kew on Great Western Road Garden Fund*

'Hundreds of
gardens open
with us annually'

Glasgow & District

KILMARDINNY GARDENS
Glasgow G61 3NW
The Gardeners of Kilmardinny Gardens

···

The gardens are well established and have a good display of mature trees, shrubs and planting:
64 Kilmardinny Crescent G61 3NW (Colin and Joan McMinn): The garden is dominated by a large lawn with a flower bed with mixed planting. There is also a mature lime, lilac and cherry trees. There is a border with a profusion of mixed planting including lavatera, fuchsias, pampas grass and hydrangeas. Overlooking the lawn is a 'sitooterie'. At the rear of the property is a delightful bijou courtyard garden.
68 Kilmardinny Crescent G61 3NW (John and Margaret Redman): The front garden has a curved lawn which has borders of mixed trees, shrubs perennials and annual plants including a scented path. Statues are delightfully placed in the garden. There are various pots in the gravel area and the lower patio area. The borders either side of the house contain peonies hellebores, hostas, shrubs and a magnolia tree.
70 Kilmardinny Crescent G61 3NW (John and Nancy Heath): The front garden contains a colourful variety of shrubs and trees. There is an eye-catching carved wooden sculpture of an eagle surrounded by shrubs which include berberis, pieris, azaleas and hostas. The small lawn at the front of the house is bordered with shrubs. There is a water feature at the corner of the lawn.
8 Carse View Drive G61 3NJ (Gerry and Sandra Connolly): The garden is the setting for a 1930s Art Deco/International style house in Bearsden. There is a large lawn with an informal planting scheme of trees and shrubs. There are many unusual plants including a pineapple tree and a pink variety of cornus.

Open: Sunday 28 July, 2pm - 5pm, admission £7.00, children free. There will be a well stocked plant stall at 68 Kilmardinny Crescent. Cream teas will be served at 64 Kilmardinny Crescent.

Directions: From Glasgow via Canniesburn Toll Roundabout take the A81 (Milngavie Road). Just past Kilmardinny Estate Self Catering Cottages on the right-hand side take a left into Kilmardinny Avenue then second left into Kilmardinny Crescent. By bus 60A from Glasgow or 10A Balfron bus. Bus stop near junction of Milngavie Road and Kilmardinny Avenue. By train to Hillfoot station then a short bus ride.

· *Children's Hospice Association Scotland: Robin House, Balloch*

'Scotland's Gardens
Scheme is supported
by 150 wonderful
volunteers'

Glasgow & District

KILSYTH GARDENS
Allanfauld Road, Kilsyth G65 9DE
Mr & Mrs George Murdoch and Mr & Mrs A Patrick
T: 07743 110908 **E:** alan.patrick3@googlemail.com

Aeolia (Mr and Mrs George Murdoch): A third-of-an-acre woodland garden developed since 1960 and designed to have something in flower every month of the year. The garden contains a large variety of mature specimen trees and shrubs, maples, primulas, hardy geraniums and herbaceous plants. Spring bulbs provide early colour and lilies and dahlias provide late season interest. There are a couple of small ponds for wildlife, two greenhouses and a fruit production area. The owners are members of the *Scottish Rhododendron Society* and have a collection of over 100 specimens, some grown from seed. Areas of the garden are often under development to provide something new to see and provide material for the extensive plant sale, which is all home grown.
Blackmill (Mr and Mrs A Patrick): Across the road from Aeolia, Blackmill is a garden of two parts in that the Garrel Burn runs through the property. On one side is an acre of mature specimen trees, rhododendrons and shrubs on the site of an old waterpowered sickle mill. There is an ornamental pond and a rock pool built into the remains of the mill building. On the other side is a further two acres of woodland glen with paths along the Garrel Burn with views to many cascading waterfalls, one with a 23 foot drop. New is a large area of wildflowers alongside the burn, a microhydro scheme is on view along with many different types of dry stone walls.

Open: Sunday 2 June, 2pm - 5pm. Also open by arrangement 1 April - 30 August. Admission £7.00, children free. Includes entry to both gardens and homemade teas. Well-stocked plant stall with a good variety of home grown plants. There is a minimum of six visitors for the 'by arrangement' openings. W/C (not suitable for disabled).

Directions: Turn off the A803 into Parkburn Road up to crossroads (parking attendant will advise you on parking). Bus: 89 Glasgow-Kilsyth has a stop up at the crossroads a couple of minutes walk to the gardens. Trains: the nearest station is Croy connection, bus 147 or 344 to Kilsyth.

· **Strathcarron Hospice**

8 Carse View Drive, Kilmardinny Gardens

Glasgow & District

MERRYLEE SPRING PLANT SALE
Merrylee Plots, Quadrant Road, Newlands, Glasgow G43 2QQ
Merrylee Plotholders Association
T: 07768 964027 **E:** merryleeplots@yahoo.co.uk

The annual Merrylee Plant Sale is delighted to open the gates for 2019 to the public for the first time. Previously a members-only event, the plant sale is a firm favourite in the gardening calendar. The stalls are situated in the courtyard at Merrylee Plotholders Association allotments in the heart of Glasgow's Southside - a two kilometre square hidden gem in the city. Our bank holiday, early season sale includes a wide selection of home-grown perennials, shrubs, bedding plants, and vegetable seedlings like leeks, tomatoes, brassicas and salads.

Open: Saturday 4 May, 11:30am - 3:30pm, admission £4.00, children free. There are some gravel paths. The courtyard cafe will be serving teas with delicious home baking. Tours of the grounds will be available with plotholders on hand to give planting advice. There's also a traditional side show attraction for the kids and plenty of free on-street parking nearby.

Directions: From Glasgow, follow the M8 west, joining the M77, leave at Junction 2, turning left onto Barrhead Road. Follow for two and a half miles via Nether Auldhouse Road, then turn left onto Langside Drive, then Merrylee is on the right at Quadrant Road. By Rail from Glasgow Central Newton line, alight at Langside then walk for half a mile to Merrylee Plots. Merrylee is on the left at Quadrant Road. Bus from Glasgow City Centre, towards First Bus to Crookfur. Catch buses 38, 38b, 38c, 38e to Calderwood Road. Walking south on Kilmarnock Road, left onto Merrylee Road and along Langside Drive; go in on the left (ten-minute walk).

· *Merrylee Plotholders Association*

MILTON COMMUNITY GARDEN
Liddesdale Square, Milton, Glasgow G22 7BT
North Glasgow Community Food Initiative
T: 07422 375524 **E:** gardens@ngcfi.org.uk
W: www.ngcfi.org.uk

This community garden is a wildlife- and visitor- friendly organic growing space in the heart of Milton. It offers a peaceful environment for the local community to walk through or sit in, to volunteer to help develop the space or to spend time with our gardener and landscaper to learn how to 'grow your own' or build things from recycled wood. It features a pond, a green roof, a Ridan composter, a children's garden complete with mud kitchen and willow sculptures as well as lots of raised beds bursting with fruit, vegetables and flowers.

Open: Sunday 7 July, 2pm - 5pm, admission by donation.

Directions: From the M8 leave at Junction 15 onto Springburn Road (A803). After two miles turn left into Colston Road then at the T junction turn right onto Ashgill Road. At the roundabout take the first left into Shillay Street then left into Liddesdale Place. Turn left into Liddesdale Square, garden is at the opposite corner. Parking in the square or there is on street parking. By bus take the 75 bus to Ashgill Road, get off at the back of St Augustine's Church and the square is a short walk through an alley-way.

· *Milton Community Garden and Food Hub*

Glasgow & District

STRATHBUNGO GARDEN
March Street, Glasgow G41 2PX
Frank Burns
W: Facebook (Strathbungo Garden)

Nestled behind Glasgow's busy main road artery to the Southside, you will happen upon a hidden walled terrace garden which marks the historical boundary to Strathbungo. It's an unexpected and interesting cottage-style city garden, showing what can be turned into a lovely colourful space for all the occupants of the terrace to enjoy. Inventive container planting is a key feature of this distinct urban retreat, which holds year-round interest. There's a range of fruit trees, some of which are trained as minarettes and stepovers. Why not visit Strathbungo Garden on Facebook and see what's been happening in the garden over the past months?

Open: Sunday 21 July, 2pm - 5pm, admission £4.00, children free.

Directions: From the south take the M74 to Junction 1A Polmadie. Turn left onto Polmadie Road, then turn right at the next traffic lights onto Calder Street. Proceed to Nithsdale Drive, then turn left into March Street where ample parking can be found. From the north take the M8 and join the M74, turn right into Polmadie Road at Junction 1A.

· *ALVO Rural South Lanarkshire*

Meconopsis at Strathbungo Garden

Glasgow & District

10 THE GOOD LIFE GARDENS
Cambuslang, Glasgow G72 8BJ
Paul and Sheona Brightey, Andy and Amanda Bateman

Two gardens of around a third-of-an-acre each.
12 Chatelherault Avenue (Paul and Sheona Brightey): The front garden of No 12 is split into a gravel garden and a small white woodland garden. Go through the gate and you will find a garden the aim of which is to grow as many different edibles as possible, herbs, fruit arches, vegetable beds and edible hedging. There are herbaceous perennials and a cut-flower bed, a wildlife pond, a pizza oven and around the corner a food smoker.
14 Chatelherault Avenue (Andy and Amanda Bateman): An established garden that has been revived since the owners arrived four years ago. As the overgrowth was removed more and more beautiful surprises emerged. The garden is now a lovely calm sanctuary, artistically planted with a wide range of herbaceous perennials surrounded by beautiful trees.

Open: Sunday 25 August, 2pm - 5pm, admission £6.00, children free.

Directions: M74 Glasgow to Cambuslang at Junction two, exit onto Cambuslang Road/A724 towards Rutherglen. At the roundabout, take the first exit and stay on Cambuslang Road/A724. Continue to follow A724. Turn right onto Buchanan Drive, then right onto Richmond Drive, which turns left and becomes Chatelherault Avenue.

· *FAST Romania*

11 WHITTINGEHAME DRIVE GARDENS
Glasgow G12 0XS
The Whittingehame Drive Gardeners

12 Whittingehame Drive (Mike and Gill Craig): A small garden, originally laid out in the early 1900's. Front garden and a small private back garden, re-modelled in 2011 when two patios and raised beds were created. A selection of flowering shrubs, herbaceous plants and pots create a colourful palette.
20 Whittingehame Drive (Bob and Connie Simpson): A delightful and intriguing small town garden. Colourful shrubs and flowers include enkianthus, eucryphia, philadelphus, rhododendrons and Corsican broom. Shrub and climbing roses include *Rosa mundi* and the apothecary's rose. A herb garden, raised beds, a chamomile seat and an impressive, flourishing fig tree. A breakfast patio with hostas, hanging baskets, window boxes and a green wall with ivy, clematis, honeysuckle and flowering annuals. Look for the novel way to grow a fig tree.
22 Whittingehame Drive (Robert and Helen Jamieson): The garden was laid out in the 1960s by a *Beechgrove Garden* presenter. A strong structure of garden rooms, some overlapping, prevails. Ericaceous plants abound, poppies and meconopsis feature with about 40 clematis often used in companion planting. Much use is made of pots displaying Asiatic and oriental lilies, alliums, begonias and garlic. A cedar greenhouse contains cacti and other succulents and grows vegetables, tomatoes and chilies.
5 and 5a Whittinghame Drive
(Jane & Peter Craig and Jock & Margaret Fleming) The soil is well suited to camellias, magnolias, poppies, heathers and there is extensive herbaceous planting. With a waterfall and small pond surrounded by water loving plants it is an oasis within the West End.

Open: Saturday 1 June, 2pm - 5pm, admission £6.50, children free.

Directions: Take the M8 Junction 17; from A82 (Great Western Road), past Gartnavel Hospital and the next left is Whittingehame Drive.

· *Vine Trust & Beatson Cancer Charity*

Glasgow & District

12 WOODBOURNE HOUSE
Seven Sisters, Lenzie, Glasgow G66 3AW
Alice May

This is a landscaped garden on several levels; about the size of half a football pitch and roughly triangular with the house in the middle. While it has the traditional lawns you'd expect of a Victorian villa, rare and unusual perennials, including cold-hardy tropicals, have been added to the existing planting. On one side, a woodland-style border gives way to a bog garden and exotic slope, while a path to its side rises up to decking and gravel planting to the rear.

Open: Sunday 18 August, 2pm - 5pm, admission £6.00, children free.

Directions: From the M80 exit Junction 3 onto the A806. After two mini roundabouts turn left onto Woodilee Road at the Old Gatehouse pub. Park in the pub. Walk back onto Woodilee Road and turn left along it, then left again onto Seven Sisters and continue right to the very end to Woodbourne House.

· *David Sheldrick Wildlife Trust*

Woodbourne House

INVERNESS, ROSS, CROMARTY & SKYE

Scotland's Gardens Scheme 2019 Guidebook is sponsored by INVESTEC WEALTH & INVESTMENT

1. 2 Durnamuck
2. 5 Knott
3. Abriachan Garden Nursery
4. Attadale
5. Aultgowrie Mill
6. Balmeanach House
7. Brackla Wood
8. Dundonnell House
9. Dunvegan Castle and Gardens
10. Field House
11. Glenkyllachy
12. Gorthleck House Garden
13. Highland Liliums
14. House of Aigas and Field Centre
15. House of Gruinard
16. Kilcoy Castle
17. Kiltarlity Gardens
18. Leathad Ard
19. Old Allangrange
20. Oldtown of Leys Garden
21. Shanvall
22. The Lookout
23. Torcroft

INVERNESS, ROSS, CROMARTY & SKYE

OUR VOLUNTEER ORGANISERS

District Organiser: Lucy Lister-Kaye — House of Aigas, Aigas, Beauly IV4 7AD
E: inverness@scotlandsgardens.org

Area Organiser: Emma MacKenzie — Glenkyllachy, Tomatin IV13 7YA

Treasurer: Sheila Kerr — Lilac Cottage, Struy, By Beauly IV4 7JU
T: 01463 782443

GARDENS OPEN ON A SPECIFIC DATE

Dundonnell House, Little Loch Broom, Wester Ross	Thursday, 18 April
Old Allangrange, Munlochy	Sunday, 19 May
Dundonnell House, Little Loch Broom, Wester Ross	Thursday, 30 May
Gorthleck House Garden, Stratherrick	Friday/Saturday/Sunday, 31/1/2 May/June
House of Gruinard, Laide, by Achnasheen	Wednesday, 5 June
Field House, Belladrum, Beauly	Sunday, 9 June
Brackla Wood, Culbokie, Dingwall	Wednesday, 12 June
Torcroft, Balnain, Glenurquhart	Saturday/Sunday, 22/23 June
House of Aigas and Field Centre, By Beauly	Sunday, 30 June
2 Durnamuck, Little Loch Broom, Wester Ross	Sunday, 21 July
Kiltarlity Gardens, Aird View, Foinaven & Highland Liliums, Kiltarlity	Sunday, 21 July
House of Aigas and Field Centre, By Beauly	Sunday, 28 July
Kilcoy Castle, Redcastle, by Muir of Ord	Sunday, 18 August
Dundonnell House, Little Loch Broom, Wester Ross	Thursday, 22 August
2 Durnamuck, Little Loch Broom, Wester Ross	Sunday, 25 August
Old Allangrange, Munlochy	Sunday, 1 September

GARDENS OPEN REGULARLY

Highland Liliums, 10 Loaneckheim, Kiltarlity	1 January - 31 December
Oldtown of Leys Garden, Inverness	1 January - 31 December
Abriachan Garden Nursery, Loch Ness Side	1 February - 30 November
Attadale, Strathcarron	1 April - 31 October
Dunvegan Castle and Gardens, Isle of Skye	1 April - 15 October
Glenkyllachy, Tomatin	1 April - 30 October (Mondays only)
Leathad Ard, Upper Carloway, Isle of Lewis	1 May - 28 September (not Sundays)
Balmeanach House, Balmeanach, nr Struan, Isle of Skye	2 May - 10 October (Mondays & Thursdays)
The Lookout, Kilmuir, North Kessock	1 June - 31 August (Sundays only)
5 Knott, Clachamish, Portree, Isle of Skye	27 June - 20 September (Thursdays & Fridays)
Torcroft, Balnain, Glenurquhart	1 July - 26 August (Mondays only)

GARDENS OPEN BY ARRANGEMENT

Old Allangrange, Munlochy	1 January - 31 December
2 Durnamuck, Little Loch Broom, Wester Ross	1 April - 30 September
Aultgowrie Mill, Aultgowrie, Urray, Muir of Ord	1 April - 1 September
Glenkyllachy, Tomatin	1 April - 30 October
House of Aigas and Field Centre, By Beauly	1 April - 31 October
Leathad Ard, Upper Carloway, Isle of Lewis	1 April - 30 April (not Sundays)
The Lookout, Kilmuir, North Kessock	1 April - 30 September
5 Knott, Clachamish, Portree, Isle of Skye	1 June - 30 September
Shanvall, Glentruim, Newtonmore	1 June - 31 August

View from 2 Durnamuck

Inverness, Ross, Cromarty & Skye

2 DURNAMUCK
Little Loch Broom, Wester Ross IV23 2QZ
Will Soos and Susan Pomeroy
T: 01854 633761 **E:** sueandwill@icloud.com

Our garden is situated on the edge of Little Loch Broom and is south-east facing. It is a coastal plantsman's garden with a rich mix of herbaceous borders, trees and shrubs, vegetables, drystone wall planting, South African plants, Mediterranean plants, a wild meadow and stunning views. Many of the plants have been collected from all over the world and growing them in Durnamuck has provided the obvious challenges but with an overall pleasing outcome. We were lucky enough to be featured on *Gardeners' World* in 2016 and *Garden Magazine* and *Country Life* in 2017.

Open: Sunday 21 July and Sunday 25 August, 12pm - 5pm. And open by arrangement 1 April - 30 September. Admission £4.00, children free. Tea and cakes on 25th August only.

Directions: On the A832, between Dundonnell and Ullapool, take the turning along the single-track road signed *Badcaul*, continue to the yellow salt bin, turn right, go to the bottom of the hill and 2 Durnamuck is the house with the red roof. There is parking down by the house if needed.

· **The Aspinall Foundation**

5 KNOTT
Clachamish, Portree, Isle of Skye IV51 9NZ
Brian and Joyce Heggie
T: 01470 582213 **E:** jbheggie@hotmail.co.uk
W: knottcottageselfcatering.co.uk

An informal, organic garden on a gently sloping half-acre site. Perimeter hedging has enabled a sheltered, tranquil oasis to be created. Winding paths meander through densely planted borders filled with a diverse range of perennials, annuals and shrubs. The house overlooks a sheltered bay with regular sightings of otters, sea eagles and harbour porpoises. There is a separate vegetable and herb area with a large polytunnel and raised beds. Garden seating in several locations. The garden is situated in an easily reached, particularly quiet and scenic area of Skye.

Open: 27 June - 20 September (Thursdays and Fridays), 2pm - 5pm. Also open by arrangement 1 June - 30 September. Admission £3.00, children free. Groups by prior arrangement.

Directions: From Portree, take the A87 to Uig/Dunvegan. After approximately three miles, take the A850 towards Dunvegan. Six miles on, past the *Treaslane* sign, look for the red phone box on the right. Turn right on the bend at the signpost for Knott.

· **Crossroads Care Skye & Lochalsh**

'Join a crew of over
150 volunteers. We are
always looking for a
range of skills.'

Inverness, Ross, Cromarty & Skye

ABRIACHAN GARDEN NURSERY
Loch Ness Side IV3 8LA
Mr and Mrs Davidson
T: 01463 861232 **E:** info@lochnessgarden.com
W: www.lochnessgarden.com

This is an outstanding garden with over four acres of exciting plantings with winding paths through native woodlands. Seasonal highlights include snowdrops, hellebores, primulas, meconopsis, hardy geraniums and colour-themed summer beds. Views over Loch Ness.

Open: 1 February - 30 November, 9am - 7pm, including for Snowdrops and Winter Walks, admission £3.00, children free.

Directions: On the A82 Inverness/Drumnadrochit road, about eight miles south of Inverness.

· *Highland Hospice*

ATTADALE
Strathcarron IV54 8YX
Mr Ewen Macpherson
T: 01520 722603 **E:** info@attadalegardens.com
W: www.attadalegardens.com

The Gulf Stream, surrounding hills and rocky cliffs, creates a microclimate for 20 acres of outstanding water gardens, old rhododendrons, unusual trees and a fern collection in a geodesic dome. There is also a sunken fern garden developed on the site of an early 19th-century drain, a waterfall into a pool with dwarf rhododendrons, sunken garden, Peace Garden and kitchen garden. Other features include a conservatory, Japanese Garden, sculpture collection and giant sundial.

Open: 1 April - 31 October, 10am - 5:30pm, admission £8.00, children £1.00. Self-service teas with home baking.

Directions: On the A890 between Strathcarron and South Strome.

· *Strathcarron Project*

AULTGOWRIE MILL
Aultgowrie, Urray, Muir of Ord IV6 7XA
Mr and Mrs John Clegg
T: 01997 433699 **E:** john@johnclegg.com

Aultgowrie Mill is an 18th century converted water mill set in gardens, river and woodlands of 13 acres. Features include a wooded island, a half-acre wildflower meadow and a wildlife pond, all with outstanding views of the surrounding hills. The maturing gardens have terraces, lawns, two mixed orchards and raised vegetable beds with glasshouse and a third-of-a-mile river walk. *The Beechgrove Garden* featured this garden in July 2014.

Open: Open by arrangement 1 April - 1 September, admission £4.50, children free. Teas available by arrangement.

Directions: From the south, turn left at Muir of Ord Distillery, Aultgowrie Mill is then about three miles. From the north and west, after Marybank Primary School, Aultgowrie Mill is about one-and-a-half miles up the hill.

· *RNLI*

Inverness, Ross, Cromarty & Skye

6

BALMEANACH HOUSE
Balmeanach, nr Struan, Isle of Skye IV56 8FH
Mrs Arlene Macphie
T: 01470 572320 **E:** info@skye-holiday.com
W: www.skye-holiday.com

During the late 1980s, a third-of-an-acre of croft land was fenced in to create a garden. Now there is a glorious herbaceous border, bedding-plants area and a small azalea and rhododendron walk. In addition, there is a woodland dell with fairies, three ponds and a small shrubbery. Lots of seating areas are provided and visitors are welcome to rest, or even picnic, remembering please to take all litter away.

Open: 2 May - 10 October (Mondays and Thursdays), 10:30am - 3pm, admission £3.00, children free.

Directions: A87 to Sligachan, turn left, Balmeanach is five miles north of Struan and five miles south of Dunvegan.

· *Scottish SPCA*

7

BRACKLA WOOD
Culbokie, Dingwall IV7 8GY
Susan and Ian Dudgeon
T: 01349 877765 **E:** smdbrackla@aol.com

Mature one-acre plot consisting of woodland, wildlife features, ponds, mixed borders, a kitchen garden, rockery and mini-orchard. Spring bulbs and hellebores, rhododendrons, wisteria and roses followed by crocosmia, clematis and deciduous trees provide continuous colour and interest throughout the seasons. There is always the chance to see red squirrels.

Open: Wednesday 12 June, 2pm - 4:30pm, admission £3.00, children free. Homemade teas £2.50. No dogs, except Guide dogs.

Directions: From the north, take the A9 turn to Culbokie. At the end of the village, turn right to Munlochy. A mile up the road, turn right into *No Through Road* to Upper Braefindon. From the south, take the A9 to Munlochy. At the end of the village, turn right and then sharp left up road signposted *Culbokie and Killen*. After about four and a half miles turn left on to road signposted *Upper Braefindon*. Brackla Wood is the first house on the left.

· *Macmillan Cancer Support: Black Isle*

Inverness, Ross, Cromarty & Skye

8

DUNDONNELL HOUSE
Little Loch Broom, Wester Ross IV23 2QW
Dundonnell Estates
T: 07789 390028

Camellias, magnolias and bulbs in spring, rhododendrons and laburnum walk in this ancient walled garden. Exciting planting in new borders gives all year colour centred around one of the oldest yew trees in Scotland. A new water sculpture, midsummer roses, recently restored unique Victorian glass house, riverside walk, arboretum - all in the valley below the peaks of An Teallach. Champion Trees: Yew and Holly.

Open: Thursday 18 April and Thursday 30 May, 2pm - 5pm. And open Thursday 22 August, 2pm - 5pm. Admission £4.00, children free. Teas on 30 May only.

Directions: Turn off the A835 at Braemore on to the A832. After 11 miles take the Badralloch turn for a half mile.

· *MND Scotland & Compassion in World Farming*

9

DUNVEGAN CASTLE AND GARDENS
Isle of Skye IV55 8WF
Hugh Macleod of Macleod
T: 01470 521206 **E:** info@dunvegancastle.com
W: www.dunvegancastle.com

Five acres of formal gardens dating from the 18th century. In contrast to the barren moorland of Skye, the gardens are an oasis featuring an eclectic mix of plants, woodland glades, shimmering pools fed by waterfalls and streams flowing down to the sea. After the water garden with its ornate bridges and islands replete with a rich and colourful plant variety, wander through the elegant surroundings of the formal round garden. The walled garden is worth a visit to see its colourful herbaceous borders and recently added Victorian-style glasshouse. In what was formerly the castle's vegetable garden, there is a garden museum and a diverse range of plants and flowers which complement the features including a waterlily pond, a neoclassical urn and a larch pergola. Replanting and landscaping have taken place over the last 30 years to restore and develop the gardens.

Open: 1 April - 15 October, 10am - 5:30pm, admission details can be found on Dunvegan Castle's website.

Directions: One mile from Dunvegan Village, 23 miles west of Portree. Follow the signs for Dunvegan Castle.

· *Donation to SGS Beneficiaries*

10

FIELD HOUSE
Belladrum, Beauly IV4 7BA
Mr and Mrs D Paterson
W: www.dougthegarden.co.uk

An informal country garden in a one-acre site with mixed borders, ponds and some unusual plants - a plantsman's garden. Featured on the *The Beechgrove Garden*.

Open: Sunday 9 June, 2pm - 4:30pm, admission £4.00, children free.

Inverness, Ross, Cromarty & Skye

Directions: Four miles from Beauly on the A833 Beauly to Drumnadrochit road, then follow signs to *Belladrum*.

· *Friends of Autism Highland*

GLENKYLLACHY
Tomatin IV13 7YA
Mr and Mrs Philip Mackenzie
E: emmaglenkyllachy@gmail.com

....

In a magnificent Highland glen, at 1200 feet above sea level, Glenkyllachy offers a glorious garden of shrubs, herbaceous plants, rhododendrons, trees and spectacular views down the Findhorn River. There are some rare specimens and a newly planted arboretum. Rhododendrons and bulbs flower in May/June, herbaceous plants bloom through July/August. Experience the wildflower meadow in summer and glorious autumn colours from September. Original sculptures and a Highgrove-inspired wall provide year-round interest. As featured on *The Beechgrove Garden* 2018.

Open: 1 April - 30 October (Mondays only), 2pm - 5pm. Also open by arrangement 1 April - 30 October. Admission £5.00, children free. Individuals and groups welcome by arrangement .

Directions: Turn off the A9 at Tomatin and take the Coignafearn/Garbole single-track road down the north side of the River Findhorn, there is a cattle grid and gate on the right 500 yards AFTER the humpback bridge and the sign to *Farr*.

· *Marie Curie*

Autum colour at Glenkyllachy

Inverness, Ross, Cromarty & Skye

12

GORTHLECK HOUSE GARDEN
Stratherrick IV2 6UJ
Steve and Katie Smith
T: 07710 325903 **E:** visit@gorthleckgarden.co.uk

An unusual 20-acre woodland garden built in an unlikely place, on and around an exposed rocky ridge. The layout of the garden works with the natural features of the landscape rather than against them, with numerous paths, hedges and shelter belts creating clearly defined spaces that enable a large collection of plants and trees to thrive. It has extensive collections of rhododendrons and bamboos. The ridge offers long views of the surrounding countryside in the 'borrowed landscape' tradition of Japanese gardens. The garden didn't exist a dozen years ago and is very much a work in progress.

Open: Friday 31 May (10am - 8pm), Saturday 1 June (2pm - 5pm) and Sunday 2 June (2pm - 8pm), admission £5.00, children free.

Directions: From the A9, join the B862. Go through the village of Errogie where there is a sharp left-hand bend on the road. After approximately one mile, there is a small church on the left. The Gorthleck drive is directly opposite the church and the house can be seen on the hill to the left as you follow the drive to the left of the new house. Visitors can park on the verges at the top of the drive.

· *Maggies Centre*

13

HIGHLAND LILIUMS
10 Loaneckheim, Kiltarlity IV4 7JQ
Neil and Frances Macritchie
T: 01463 741365 **E:** accounts@highlandliliums.co.uk
W: www.highlandliliums.co.uk

Highland Liliums is a working retail nursery with spectacular views over the Beauly valley and Strathfarrar hills. A wide selection of home grown plants available including alpines, ferns, grasses, herbaceous, herbs, liliums, primulas and shrubs.

Open: Daily, 9am - 5pm, admission by donation. Also open on Sunday 21 July as part of the Kiltarlity Gardens opening.

Directions: Signposted from Kiltarlity village, which is just off the Beauly to Drumnadrochit road (A833), approximately 12 miles from Inverness.

· *Donation to SGS Beneficiaries*

14

HOUSE OF AIGAS AND FIELD CENTRE
By Beauly IV4 7AD
Sir John and Lady Lister-Kaye
T: 01463 782443 **E:** sheila@aigas.co.uk
W: www.aigas.co.uk

The House of Aigas has a small arboretum of named Victorian specimen trees and modern additions. The garden consists of extensive rockeries, herbaceous borders, ponds and shrubs. Aigas Field Centre rangers lead regular guided walks on nature trails through woodland, moorland and around a loch.
Champion Trees: Douglas fir, Atlas cedar and *Sequoiadendron giganteum*.

Open: Sunday 30 June and Sunday 28 July, 2pm - 5pm. And open by arrangement 1 April - 31 October. Admission £4.00, children free.

Inverness, Ross, Cromarty & Skye

Directions: Four and a half miles from Beauly on the A831 Cannich/Glen Affric road.

· *Highland Hospice: Aird branch*

HOUSE OF GRUINARD
Laide, by Achnasheen IV22 2NQ
The Hon Mrs A G Maclay
T: 01445 731235 **E:** office@houseofgruinard.com

Superb hidden and unexpected garden developed in sympathy with stunning west coast estuary location. Wide variety of interesting herbaceous and shrub borders with water garden and extended wild planting.

Open: Wednesday 5 June, 2pm - 5pm, admission £4.00, children free.

Directions: On A832 12 miles north of Inverewe and nine miles south of Dundonnell.

· *Macmillan Cancer Support*

KILCOY CASTLE
Redcastle, by Muir of Ord IV6 7RX
Kilcoy Castle Estate
T: 07766445511

To the front of the castle are steps which lead on to grass terraces surrounded by shrubs and trees: the walled garden leads off to the east. The area farthest from the castle has been restyled based on the poem *Solitude* by Thomas Merton. The shape is rhomboid with a central point taken from which the design radiates planted with pleached hornbeam, underplanted with willow. Box holly and yew hedges are still to grow to fruition. Work is ongoing with new herbaceous border and different planting using annuals and herbaceous plants; the garden will host a further vibrant display of colourful plants within the walled garden along with a greenhouse in full production.

Open: Sunday 18 August, 2pm - 4:30pm, admission £6.00, children under 12 free.

Directions: From the Tore roundabout, take the A832, go past Fettes Sawmill on the left. Turn right at Kilcoy Kindergarten (an old church) heading towards Kilcoy. Go along the single road for about a quarter mile and you will see the Kilcoy Castle entrance on the left.

· *ENF; EN Foundation: The Haven Project*

'Creating an inspiring, rewarding and enjoyable experience for volunteers and visitors alike'

Inverness, Ross, Cromarty & Skye

KILTARLITY GARDENS
Kiltarlity IV4 7JQ
Sheila Ross, Sue Mullins, and Neil & Frances Macritchie
T: 01463 741365 **E:** accounts@highlandliliums.co.uk
W: www.highlandliliums.co.uk

Aird View 30a Camault Muir IV4 7JH (Sheila Ross): The garden at Aird View offers a mix of borders, a water feature, an arbour and a newly added herbaceous border. There are also fruit trees and vegetable beds.

Foinaven Loaneckheim, Beauly IV4 7JQ (Sue Mullins): The garden is approximately half an acre in size, and is blessed with several mature Scots pine trees. The garden is a 'plantaholics' garden with many different varieties of shrubs, trees and herbaceous plants. There is a natural pond and the garden has untamed areas for wildlife and pollinators. Wildlife is well catered for by the selection of plants with flowers for pollinators, and the birds are fed well by the resultant berries.

Highland Liliums 10 Loaneckheim IV4 7JQ (Neil and Frances Macritchie): Highland Liliums is a working retail nursery with spectacular views over the Beauly valley and Strathfarrar hills. A wide selection of home-grown plants is available including alpines, ferns, grasses, herbaceous plants, herbs, lilies, primulas and shrubs. The garden is also open on a daily basis, see their individual entry for details.

Open: Sunday 21 July, 12pm - 5pm, admission £3.00, children free. Admission tickets available at any of the gardens. Teas and discounted plants at Highland Liliums.

Directions: For **Aird View**, take the A833 Beauly to Drumnadrochit road, pass Brockies Lodge. Turn right at the bus shelter and follow single track road to junction at school. Turn left up the hill to the top at junction. Aird View is on the right. For **Foinaven** and **Highland Liliums**, turn up Post Office Brae in Kiltarlity then turn right after the Free Church. Follow the road towards Highland Liliums. Foinaven is about a half mile from the church. (sixth house on the right-hand side) and Highland Liliums slightly further up the hill.

All gardens will be well signposted from Kiltarlity village, which is just off the Beauly to Drumnadrochit road (A833), approximately 12 miles from Inverness.

· *Highland Hospice: Aird branch*

The bee friendly garden at Old Allangrange

Inverness, Ross, Cromarty & Skye

18

LEATHAD ARD
Upper Carloway, Isle of Lewis HS2 9AQ
Rowena and Stuart Oakley
T: 01851 643204 **E:** stuart.oakley1a@gmail.com
W: www.leathadard.org.uk

A one-acre sloping garden with stunning views over East Loch Roag. It has evolved along with the shelter hedges that divide the garden into a number of areas giving a new view at every corner. With shelter and raised beds, the different conditions created permit a wide variety of plants to be grown. Features include herbaceous borders, cutting borders, bog gardens, grass garden, exposed beds, patios, a pond and vegetables and fruit grown both in the open ground and the Keder greenhouse. Some of the vegetables are grown to show standards.

Open: 1 May - 28 September (not Sundays), 10am - 6pm. Also open by arrangement 1 April - 30 April (not Sundays). Admission £4.00, children free.

Directions: On A858 Shawbost-Carloway, first right after Carloway football pitch, and first house on right. By bus take the Westside circular bus, exit Stornoway, head for Carloway football pitch.

· *British Red Cross*

A riot of colour at Leathad Ard

19

OLD ALLANGRANGE
Munlochy IV8 8NZ
J J Gladwin
T: 01463 811304 **E:** office@blackislebeegardendesign.com

A 17th-century lime-washed house is the backdrop to a formal(ish) garden with many fine old trees including an ancient stand of yews. We use sculpted hedges to play with perspective. There is an ice house, vegetable garden, a mound, orchard and two large polytunnels where we grow vegetables biodynamically. We are establishing a nursery where plants attractive to invertebrates are grown. We plant particularly for wildlife so wildflowers and beneficial weeds are encouraged. New beds planted in 2017 along with significant additional planting in the orchard.
Champion Trees: Yew.

Open: Sunday 19 May, 12pm - 5pm. Also open Sunday 1 September, 2pm - 5pm. And open by arrangement. Admission £7.50, children free. Entrance fee includes homemade teas.

Directions: From Inverness head four miles north on the A9, and follow the directions for *Black Isle Brewery*. Park in the brewery car park and you will be given directions in the shop.

· *Black Isle Bee Gardens*

Inverness, Ross, Cromarty & Skye

20 OLDTOWN OF LEYS GARDEN
Inverness IV2 6AE
David and Anne Sutherland
T: 01463 238238 **E:** ams@oldtownofleys.com

Large garden established in 2003 on the outskirts of Inverness and overlooking the town. Herbaceous beds with lovely rhododendron and azalea displays in spring. There are specimen trees, three ponds surrounded by waterside planting and a small woodland area. A new rockery area was created in 2015 and is still developing.

Open: Daily, dawn - dusk, admission by donation.

Directions: Turn off southern distributor road (B8082) at Leys roundabout towards Inverarnie (B861). At the T-junction turn right. After 50 yards turn right into Oldtown of Leys.

· *Local Charities*

21 SHANVALL
Glentruim, Newtonmore PH20 1BE
George and Beth Alder
T: 01540 673213 **E:** beth.alder@yahoo.co.uk

The garden is two-thirds of an acre at 900 feet above sea level, surrounding a 19th century cottage. On the south side of the River Spey, it has lovely views of the Creag Dubh and Creag Meagaidh mountains. There are ruined buildings of an old township within the garden. To the south is a garden of roses and perennials. Within a stone wall, there are fruit cages, a small orchard and organic vegetable beds which have been cultivated for about 200 years. The garden on the north slopes has trees, shrubs, herbaceous border, wildflowers, a pond and is rich with wildlife, including woodpeckers and red squirrels.

Open: Open by arrangement 1 June - 31 August, admission £5.00, children free. Price includes teas.

Directions: Shanvall is on the minor road running along the south side of the Spey, linking the A9 south of Newtonmore at Glentruim and the A889 at Catlodge. The garden gate is on the right about one and a half miles from the A9. Further details on request.

· *Newtonmore Church of Scotland*

Inverness, Ross, Cromarty & Skye

22

THE LOOKOUT
Kilmuir, North Kessock IV1 3ZG
David and Penny Veitch
T: 01463 731489 **E:** david@veitch.biz

A three-quarter-acre elevated coastal garden with incredible views over the Moray Firth which is only for the sure-footed. This award-winning garden, featured on the *The Beechgrove Garden* has been created out of a rock base with shallow pockets of ground, planted to its advantage to encourage all aspects of wildlife. There is a small sheltered courtyard, raised bed vegetable area, pretty cottage garden, scree and rock garden, rose arbour, rhododendrons, flowering shrubs, bamboos, trees and lily pond with waterside plants.

Open: 1 June - 31 August (Sundays only), 12pm - 4pm. Also open by arrangement 1 April - 30 September. Admission £3.00, children free.

Directions: From Inverness, take North Kessock left turn from A9, and third left at roundabout to go on underpass then sharp left onto Kilmuir Road. From Tore, take slip road for North Kessock and immediately right for Kilmuir. Follow signs for *Kilmuir* (three miles) until you reach the shore. The Lookout is near the far end of the village with a large palm tree on the grass in front.

· *Alzheimer Scotland*

23

TORCROFT
Balnain, Glenurquhart IV63 6TJ
Barbara Craig

This garden is about three-quarters of an acre on a hillside overlooking Loch Meiklie in Glen Urquhart. It is a wild garden, with its own character and style. There are weeds, cardamine for the orange tip butterflies, a nettle patch, but most of all there are plants in profusion from acer, anemone and astrantia to veronicastrum, verbascum, weigela and water lilies. A natural stream comes into the garden and meanders into various small ponds. In the spring there are masses of bog primula of all types and colours. There is a fern bed, a rockery, herbs, wooded area. New in 2018 was a stumpery, beds and another pond.

Open: Saturday/Sunday, 22/23 June, 2pm - 5pm. Also open 1 July - 26 August (Mondays only), 2pm - 5pm. Admission £6.00, children free (Saturday/Sunday, 22/23 June) and £3.00, children free (1 July - 26 August). Garden openings on 22/23 June includes teas.

Directions: From Inverness turn right at Drumnadrochit and go towards Cannich. After four miles, sign *Balnain*, there is a very sharp right-hand bend with a high retaining wall on the right. At the end of the wall take the turning to right signposted *Torcroft Lodges*.

· *Munlochy Animal Aid & Send a Cow*

KINCARDINE & DEESIDE

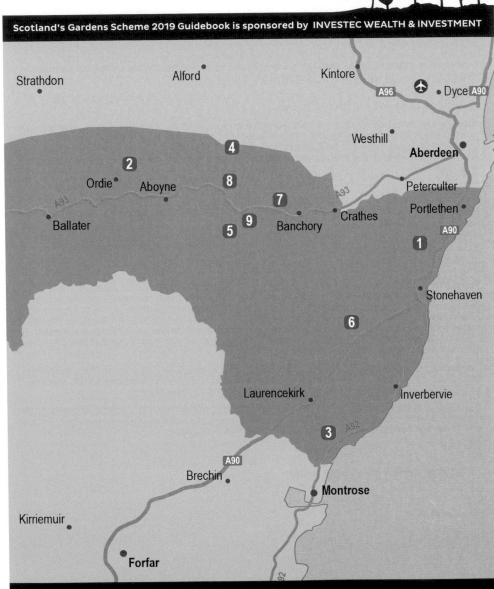

Scotland's Gardens Scheme 2019 Guidebook is sponsored by INVESTEC WEALTH & INVESTMENT

Strathdon

Alford

Kintore

A96 ✈ Dyce A90

Westhill

Aberdeen

4

2

Ordie Aboyne

Peterculter

Portlethen

A93

8

A93

7

Crathes

9

Ballater

5

Banchory

1

A90

Stonehaven

6

Laurencekirk

Inverbervie

3 A92

A90

Brechin

Montrose

Kirriemuir

Forfar

1. Clayfolds
2. Douneside House
3. Ecclesgreig Castle
4. Findrack
5. Finzean House
6. Glenbervie House
7. Inchmarlo Retirement Village Garden
8. Kincardine Castle
9. Woodend House Garden

KINCARDINE & DEESIDE

OUR VOLUNTEER ORGANISERS

District Organisers:	Catherine Nichols	Westerton Steading, Dess, Aboyne AB34 5AY
	Julie Nicol	Cedarwood Lodge, Rhu-Na-Haven Rd AB34 5JB
		E: kincardine@scotlandsgardens.org
Area Organisers:	Wendy Buchan	Inneshewen, Dess, Aboyne AB34 5BH
	Gavin Farquhar	Ecclesgreig Castle, St Cyrus DD10 0DP
	Hillary Greensill	Broomhill, Tarland, Aboyne AB34 4UJ
	Tina Hammond	Sunnybank, 7 Watson Street, Banchory AB31 5UB
	David & Patsy Younie	Bealltainn, Ballogie, Aboyne AB34 5DL
Treasurer:	Tony Coleman	Templeton House, Arbroath DD11 4QP

GARDENS OPEN ON A SPECIFIC DATE

Ecclesgreig Castle, St Cyrus	Sunday, 3 March
Inchmarlo Retirement Village Garden, Inchmarlo, Banchory	Sunday, 19 May
Woodend House Garden, Banchory	Sunday, 2 June
Kincardine Castle, Kincardine O'Neil	Sunday, 9 June
Finzean House, Finzean, Banchory	Sunday, 23 June
Findrack, Torphins	Sunday, 30 June
Douneside House, Tarland	Sunday, 7 July
Glenbervie House, Drumlithie, Stonehaven	Sunday, 4 August

GARDENS OPEN BY ARRANGEMENT

Clayfolds, Bridge of Muchalls, Stonehaven	3 April - 7 August

Kincardine & Deeside

CLAYFOLDS
Bridge of Muchalls, Stonehaven AB39 3RU
Andrea Sinclair
E: andreaysinclair@outlook.com

An informal country garden extending to a half-acre, with a further six acres of wildflowers, native trees and a pond. The main garden is laid out with lawn and mixed borders, which are filled with shrubs and a wide range of hardy perennials and includes a 'hot' border with various flaxes and a variety of 'hot'-coloured plants. Small cottage-style garden to the front of the house. Follow the tracks through the recently developed six-acre Wilderness Garden and see what native fauna and flora you can spot.

Open: Open by arrangement 3 April - 7 August, admission £4.00, children free. Teas available by request.

Directions: SatNav - AB39 3RU but travel inland a further one and a half miles to Clayfolds. Travelling in either direction on the A92, three miles north of Stonehaven, take the road signposted *Netherley 3*, continue travelling inland for approximately one-and-a-half miles and you will then be directed where to park.

· *Scottish SPCA*

DOUNESIDE HOUSE
Tarland AB34 4UD
The MacRobert Trust
W: www.dounesidehouse.co.uk

Douneside is the former home of Lady MacRobert, who developed these magnificent gardens in the early to mid 1900s. Ornamental borders and water gardens surround a spectacular infinity lawn overlooking the Deeside hills. A large walled garden supplies vegetables and cut flowers and also houses a large ornamental greenhouse. A new arboretum displays over 130 trees amongst mown grass paths and walking trails behind Douneside, which offer breathtaking views across the Howe of Cromar and beyond.

Open: Sunday 7 July, 2pm - 5pm, admission £5.00, children free. Concessions £3.00. There will be a local pipe band and raffle.

Directions: On the B9119 towards Aberdeen. Tarland one mile.

· *Perennial*

ECCLESGREIG CASTLE
St Cyrus DD10 0DP
Mr Gavin Farquhar
T: 01224 214301 **E:** enquiries@ecclesgreig.com
W: www.ecclesgreig.com

Ecclesgreig Castle, Victorian Gothic on a 16th-century core, is internationally famous as an inspiration for Bram Stoker's *Dracula*. The snowdrop walk (150+ varieties of snowdrop) starts at the castle, meanders around the estate, along woodland paths and the pond, ending at the garden. In the Italian balustraded gardens there is a 140-foot-long herbaceous border, classical statues and stunning shaped topiary with views across St Cyrus to the sea. Started from a derelict site, development continues. Also to be found in the grounds is the well of St Cyrus.

Open: Sunday 3 March, 1pm - 4pm for the Snowdrops and Winter Walks, admission £4.00, children free.

Kincardine & Deeside

Directions: *Ecclesgreig* will be signposted from the A92 Coast Road and from the A937 Montrose/ Laurencekirk Road.

· *Girl Guiding Montrose*

FINDRACK
Torphins AB31 4LJ
Mr Hal Salvesen

Findrack is a large mixed garden on a working estate with snapshot views to Clachna Ben. Woodland gardens, ponds, burn bed, sunken garden, vegetable garden, orchard and woodland walks, plus croquet and many other lawns may take some time to fully explore. The walled garden has herbaceous borders with varying themes, which are currently going through rejuvenation works. This garden has something for everyone, with a children's trail and family-friendly features throughout the gardens waiting to be enjoyed.

Open: Sunday 30 June, 2pm - 5pm, admission £5.00, children free.

Directions: Leave Torphins on the A980 to Lumphanan after half a mile turn off, signposted *Tornaveen*. There is a stone gateway one mile up on the left.

· *The Bread Maker*

FINZEAN HOUSE
Finzean, Banchory AB31 6NZ
Mr and Mrs Donald Farquharson

Finzean House was the family home of Joseph Farquharson, the Victorian landscape painter, and the garden was the backdrop for several of his paintings. The garden has lovely views over the historic holly hedge to the front of Clachnaben. There is a spring woodland garden, extensive lawns with herbaceous and shrub borders and a working cut flower garden for late summer alongside a recently restored pond area.

Open: Sunday 23 June, 2pm - 5pm, admission £5.00, children free, OAP's £4.00.

Directions: On the B976, South Deeside Road, between Banchory and Aboyne.

· *Forget Me Not Care & Counselling*

Kincardine & Deeside

6
GLENBERVIE HOUSE
Drumlithie, Stonehaven AB39 3YA
Mr and Mrs A Macphie

The nucleus of the beautiful present-day house dates from the 15th century with additions in the 18th and 19th centuries. A traditional Scottish walled garden on a slope with roses, herbaceous and annual borders along with fruit and vegetables. One wall is taken up with a Victorian-style greenhouse with many species of pot plants and climbers including peach and figs. A woodland garden by a burn is punctuated with many varieties of plants, primula to name but one.

Open: Sunday 4 August, 2pm - 5pm, admission £5.00, children free. Please note some steep pathways and tree roots can make walking difficult in places. Gravel pathways are not accessible for electric wheelchairs. Please no dogs. Garden visits available by arrangement, apply in writing.

Directions: Drumlithie one mile. Garden is one and a half miles off the A90.

· *Scotland's Charity Air Ambulance*

Winding paths through Glenbervie House

7
INCHMARLO RETIREMENT VILLAGE GARDEN
Inchmarlo, Banchory AB31 4AL
Skene Enterprises (Aberdeen) Ltd
T: 01330 826242 **E:** info@inchmarlo-retirement.co.uk
W: www.inchmarlo-retirement.co.uk

Beautiful five-acre woodland garden filled with azaleas and rhododendrons beneath ancient Scots pines, Douglas firs and silver firs (some over 140 feet tall). Also beeches, rare and unusual trees including pindrow firs, Pere David's maple, Erman's birch and a mountain snowdrop tree. The Oriental Garden features a Kare Sansui, a dry slate stream designed by Peter Roger, a RHS Chelsea gold medal winner. The Rainbow Garden, within the keyhole-shaped purple *Prunus cerasifera* hedge, has been designed by Billy Carruthers, an eight-times gold medal winner at the RHS Scottish Garden Show.

Open: Sunday 19 May, 1:30pm - 4:30pm, admission £5.00, children free.

Directions: From Aberdeen via North Deeside Road on the A93, one mile west of Banchory turn right at the main gate to the Inchmarlo Estate.

· *Alzheimer Scotland & Forget Me Not Care & Counselling*

Kincardine & Deeside

8

KINCARDINE CASTLE
Kincardine O'Neil AB34 5AE
Mr and Mrs Andrew Bradford

A superb series of gardens around a Victorian castle with great views across Deeside. Walled garden with a world-class laburnum walk, a mixture of herbaceous and shrub borders, vegetables and fruit trees. Extensive lawns, wildflower meadows and a thought-provoking Planetary Garden. A woodland garden with 120 varieties of rhododendrons and azaleas, many of recent planting, set amongst mature trees. Sculpture by Lyman Whittaker of Utah. A great day out.

Open: Sunday 9 June, 1:30pm - 5pm, admission £5.00, children free.

Directions: Kincardine O'Neil on the A93. Gates and lodge are opposite the village school.

· *Christ Church, Kincardine O'neil & Children 1st*

9

WOODEND HOUSE GARDEN
Banchory AB31 4AY
Mr and Mrs J McHardy

Tucked away in a secluded woodland location. Mature rhododendrons and azaleas with extensive lawns create a stunning backdrop for Woodend House set on the banks of the River Dee. There is a small walled cottage garden and a glorious riverside walk amongst the cowslips and wildflowers giving way to ancient and majestic beech trees.

Open: Sunday 2 June, 2pm - 5pm, admission £5.00, children free.

Directions: Four miles west of Banchory on the A93 (Banchory to Aboyne road).

· *Sandpiper Trust*

Woodend House Garden

KIRKCUDBRIGHTSHIRE

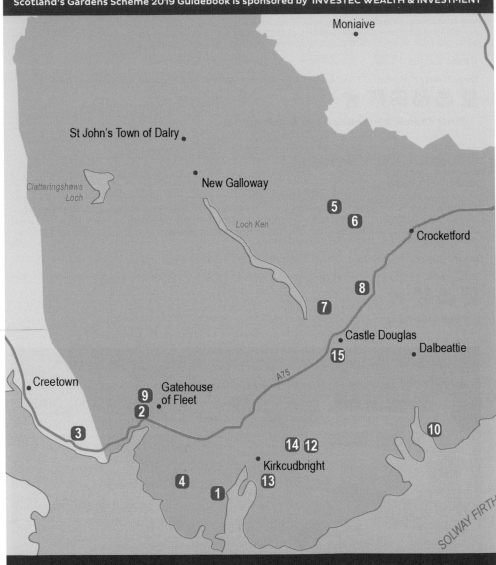

Scotland's Gardens Scheme 2019 Guidebook is sponsored by INVESTEC WEALTH & INVESTMENT

Moniaive

St John's Town of Dalry

Clatteringshaws
Loch

New Galloway

Loch Ken

5

6

Crocketford

8

7

Castle Douglas

15

Dalbeattie

Creetown

9

Gatehouse
of Fleet

2

3

A75

10

14 12

Kirkcudbright

4

13

1

SOLWAY FIRTH

1. 3 Millhall
2. Anwoth Old Schoolhouse
3. Barholm Castle
4. Barmagachan House
5. Corsock House
6. Crofts

7. Danevale Park
8. Kings Grange House
9. Luckie Harg's
10. Seabank
11. Southwick House
12. Stockarton

13. The Limes
14. The Waterhouse Gardens
     at Stockarton
15. Threave Garden

KIRKCUDBRIGHTSHIRE

OUR VOLUNTEER ORGANISERS

District Organisers:	Theodora & Julian Stanning	Seabank, Merse Road, Rockcliffe, Dalbeattie DG5 4QH
		E: kirkcudbrightshire@scotlandsgardens.org
Area Organisers:	Hedley Foster	Deer Park, Fleet Forest, Gatehouse of Fleet DG7 2DN
	Norman McClure	142 Cotton Street, Castle Douglas DG7 1DG
	Lesley Pepper	Anwoth Old Schoolhouse, Gatehouse of Fleet DG7 2EF
	Vivien Scott	14 Castle Street, Kirkcudbright DG6 4JA
	Audrey Slee	Holmview, New Galloway, Castle Douglas DG7 3RN
	George Thomas	Savat, Meikle Richorn, Dalbeattie DG5 4QT
Treasurer:	Duncan Lofts	Balcary Tower, Auchencairn, Castle Douglas DG7 1QZ

GARDENS OPEN ON A SPECIFIC DATE

Danevale Park, Crossmichael	Sunday, 24 February
3 Millhall, Shore Road, Kirkcudbright	Sunday, 14 April
Corsock House, Corsock, Castle Douglas	Sunday, 26 May
Seabank, The Merse, Rockcliffe	Sunday, 2 June
The Limes, Kirkcudbright	Sunday, 9 June
Barmagachan House, Borgue, Kirkcudbright	Sunday, 16 June
Threave Garden, Castle Douglas	Sunday, 23 June
Southwick House, Southwick	Sunday, 30 June
Kings Grange House, Castle Douglas	Sunday, 7 July
Crofts, Kirkpatrick Durham, Castle Douglas	Sunday, 21 July
3 Millhall, Shore Road, Kirkcudbright	Sunday, 1 September

GARDENS OPEN BY ARRANGEMENT

Stockarton, Kirkcudbright	1 January - 31 December
The Limes, Kirkcudbright	1 January - 31 December
Barholm Castle, Gatehouse of Fleet	15 February - 15 October
Anwoth Old Schoolhouse, Anwoth, Gatehouse of Fleet	15 February - 15 November
Luckie Harg's, Anwoth, Gatehouse of Fleet, Castle Douglas	1 April - 31 July
Corsock House, Corsock, Castle Douglas	1 April - 30 June
The Waterhouse Gardens at Stockarton, Kirkcudbright	1 May - 30 September

Kirkcudbrightshire

3 MILLHALL
Shore Road, Kirkcudbright DG6 4TQ
Mr Alan Shamash
T: 01557 870352 **E:** shamash@freeuk.com

Impressive five-acre garden with a large collection of mature shrubs, including over 200 rhododendron species, many camellias, perennials, over 300 hydrangeas and many rare Southern Hemisphere plants. The garden has several interesting paths and is on a hillside running along the rocky shore of the Dee Estuary in Kirkcudbright Bay.

Open: Sunday 14 April and Sunday 1 September, 2pm - 5pm. Admission £4.00, children free.

Directions: On the B727 between Kirkcudbright and Borgue on the west shore of the Dee Estuary. Parking at Dhoon beach public car park, about three miles south of Kirkcudbright. There is a five-minute walk to the house.

· *Kirkcudbright Hospital League Of Friends & Alzheimer's Research UK*

ANWOTH OLD SCHOOLHOUSE
Anwoth, Gatehouse of Fleet DG7 2EF
Mr and Mrs Pepper
T: 01557 814444 **E:** lesley.pepper@btinternet.com

Two acres of delightful cottage-style gardens behind the old schoolhouse and cottage in a picturesque setting opposite Anwoth Old Church (in ruins) and graveyard. Winding paths alongside a burn, informally planted with unusual woodland perennials and shrubs. Wildlife pond, fish pond, rock garden, vegetable garden, wildflower area and viewpoint.

Open: Open by arrangement 15 February - 15 November, admission £3.00, children free.

Directions: Driving west on the A75, take the Anwoth turnoff about half a mile after Gatehouse of Fleet. Anwoth Church is about half a mile along the road and Anwoth Old Schoolhouse is a little further along, opposite Anwoth Old Church (in ruins).

· *Dogs for Good*

3 Millhall

Kirkcudbrightshire

3 **BARHOLM CASTLE**
Gatehouse of Fleet DG7 2EZ
Drs John and Janet Brennan
E: barholmcastle@gmail.com

Barholm Castle, a 16th-century tower, was restored from a ruin in 2006. Since then the gardens surrounding the tower have mostly been developed from scratch and are now mature. There is a small but densely planted walled garden, with a gate designed by the artist-blacksmith Adam Booth; a courtyard garden; a wooded ravine with huge hybrid rhododendrons from Benmore, a pond and a large fernery with over 60 varieties of fern, including very large tree ferns; a large Victorian-style greenhouse filled with succulents and tender perennials; and a large open garden with island beds of shrubs and perennials and a pond. Directly around the castle are rockeries and shrub borders. Views over Wigtown Bay are magnificent. The garden is planted for year-round colour, from February, when the castle ravine is a river of snowdrops, to October, when autumn colour is splendid.

Open: Open by arrangement 15 February - 15 October including for Snowdrop and Winter Walks, admission £4.00, children free.

Directions: Off the A75 at the Cairn Holy turn off, fork right three times up a steep narrow road for half a mile.

· *Home-Start Wigtownshire*

4 **BARMAGACHAN HOUSE**
Borgue, Kirkcudbright DG6 4SW
Andy and Carolyn McNab
T: 01557 870225

This garden, developed since 2009, surrounds an 18th-century house on a rocky knoll overlooking Wigtown Bay. It is profusely planted with a large variety of alpines, perennials and shrubs. Two themes are plants from SW China and Australasia e.g. meconopsis, arisaema, Asian primulas, eucryphia and leptospermum. Planting is informal and naturalistic and designed to encourage wildlife. And there is a productive vegetable garden, soft fruit cage and developing orchard. Visitors may also explore the wood and motte.

Open: Sunday 16 June, 2pm - 5pm, admission £4.00, children free.

Directions: From Borgue follow the coast (Carrick) road up hill past the church and down. Take the first and only right turn and follow the lane winding past farms for about half a mile. Barmagachan House is on the left by a wood.

· *The Architectural Heritage Society of Scotland: Dumfries and Galloway Group*

'A good bit of digging is
fabulous exercise and there's
nothing like pulling weeds for
keeping you in touch
with your toes!
Argyll Gardener

Kirkcudbrightshire

CORSOCK HOUSE
Corsock, Castle Douglas DG7 3DJ
The Ingall family
T: 01644 440250

Corsock House garden includes an amazing variety of designed landscape, from a strictly formal walled garden, through richly planted woodlands full of different vistas, artfully designed water features and surprises to manicured lawns showing off the Bryce baronial mansion. This is an Arcadian garden with pools and temples, described by Ken Cox as 'perhaps my favourite of Scotland's many woodland gardens'.

Open: Sunday 26 May, 2pm - 5pm. Also open by arrangement 1 April - 30 June. Admission £5.00, children free. Additional fee for arranged larger guided tours.

Directions: Off A75 Dumfries 14 miles, Castle Douglas ten miles, Corsock village is a half mile on A712.

· *Corsock & Kirkpatrick Durham Church Of Scotland*

Pergoda at Corsock House

Kirkcudbrightshire

CROFTS

Kirkpatrick Durham, Castle Douglas DG7 3HX
Mrs Andrew Dalton
T: 01556 650235 **E:** jenniedalton@mac.com

Victorian country-house garden with mature trees, a walled garden with fruit and vegetables and glasshouses, hydrangea garden and a pretty water garden. Delightful woodland walk, colourfully planted with bog plants, and a stream running through.

Open: Sunday 21 July, 2pm - 5pm, admission £4.00, children free.

Directions: A75 to Crocketford, then three miles on A712 to Corsock and New Galloway.

· *Corsock & Kirkpatrick Durham Church Of Scotland*

DANEVALE PARK

Crossmichael DG7 2LP
Mrs M R C Gillespie
T: 01556 670223 **E:** danevale@tiscali.co.uk

First opening for snowdrops in 1951, these mature grounds have a wonderful display of snowdrops as well as aconites and many other wild flowers. Walks through the woods and alongside the River Dee make this a memorable afternoon!

Open: Sunday 24 February, 1pm - 4pm for Snowdrops and Winter Walks, admission £3.00, children free.

Directions: On the A713 two miles from Castle Douglas and one mile short of Crossmichael.

· *Earl Haig Fund Poppy Scotland*

Snowdrops at Danvale Park

Kirkcudbrightshire

KINGS GRANGE HOUSE
Castle Douglas DG7 3EU
Christine and Peter Hickman

An extensive garden surrounded by mature trees and shrubberies, with views to the southwest over the surrounding countryside. Originally Victorian, the garden is being restored by the present owners with a colourful variety of herbaceous mixed borders, beds and rockeries, mainly to the front of the house.

Open: Sunday 7 July, 2pm - 5pm, admission £4.00, children free.

Directions: Take the B794 north off the A75, two miles west of Castle Douglas. Kings Grange House is approximately one mile on the left.

· Marie Curie & Better Lives Partnership: Castle Douglas

Kings Grange House

Kirkcudbrightshire

6 CROFTS

Kirkpatrick Durham, Castle Douglas DG7 3HX
Mrs Andrew Dalton
T: 01556 650235 **E:** jenniedalton@mac.com

Victorian country-house garden with mature trees, a walled garden with fruit and vegetables and glasshouses, hydrangea garden and a pretty water garden. Delightful woodland walk, colourfully planted with bog plants, and a stream running through.

Open: Sunday 21 July, 2pm - 5pm, admission £4.00, children free.

Directions: A75 to Crocketford, then three miles on A712 to Corsock and New Galloway.

· *Corsock & Kirkpatrick Durham Church Of Scotland*

7 DANEVALE PARK

Crossmichael DG7 2LP
Mrs M R C Gillespie
T: 01556 670223 **E:** danevale@tiscali.co.uk

First opening for snowdrops in 1951, these mature grounds have a wonderful display of snowdrops as well as aconites and many other wild flowers. Walks through the woods and alongside the River Dee make this a memorable afternoon!

Open: Sunday 24 February, 1pm - 4pm for Snowdrops and Winter Walks, admission £3.00, children free.

Directions: On the A713 two miles from Castle Douglas and one mile short of Crossmichael.

· *Earl Haig Fund Poppy Scotland*

Snowdrops at Danvale Park

Kirkcudbrightshire

KINGS GRANGE HOUSE
Castle Douglas DG7 3EU
Christine and Peter Hickman

An extensive garden surrounded by mature trees and shrubberies, with views to the southwest over the surrounding countryside. Originally Victorian, the garden is being restored by the present owners with a colourful variety of herbaceous mixed borders, beds and rockeries, mainly to the front of the house.

Open: Sunday 7 July, 2pm - 5pm, admission £4.00, children free.

Directions: Take the B794 north off the A75, two miles west of Castle Douglas. Kings Grange House is approximately one mile on the left.

· *Marie Curie & Better Lives Partnership: Castle Douglas*

Kings Grange House

Kirkcudbrightshire

LUCKIE HARG'S
Anwoth, Gatehouse of Fleet, Castle Douglas DG7 2EF
Drs Carole and Ian Bainbridge
T: 01557 814141 **E:** luckiehargs@btinternet.com

....

A new and developing garden on the outskirts of Gatehouse. A rock and spring herbaceous garden with a wide range of alpines, Himalayan and New Zealand plants, rock garden, crevices, troughs, large alpine house and bulb frame. Under the extension new beds and woodland area are being developed. Small productive vegetable and fruit garden, plus a bluebell bank in May.

Open: Open by arrangement 1 April - 31 July, admission £4.00, children free.

Directions: From Gatehouse High Street, turn north onto Station Road, immediately west at the Fleet Bridge (by Ship Inn). After almost one mile turn left (signed to *Anwoth Old Church*). Luckie Harg's is first on right after 400 yards. Nearest bus stop on Gatehouse High Street, walk about 15 minutes to Luckie Harg's.

· *Scottish Rock Garden Club*

SEABANK
The Merse, Rockcliffe DG5 4QH
Julian and Theodora Stanning
T: 01556 630244

....

The one-and-a-half-acre garden extends to the high water mark with fine views across the Urr Estuary, Rough Island and beyond. Mixed shrub and herbaceous borders surround the house and there is a new walled garden for fruit and vegetables. A plantswoman's garden with a range of interesting and unusual plants.

Open: Sunday 2 June, 2pm - 5pm, admission £4.00, children free.

Directions: Park in the public car park at Rockcliffe. Walk down the road about 50 yards towards the sea and turn left along The Merse, a private road. Seabank is the sixth house on the left.

· *Marie Curie: DG5 Fundraising Group*

SOUTHWICK HOUSE
Southwick DG2 8AH
Mr and Mrs R H L Thomas

....

The extensive gardens at Southwick House comprise three main areas. The first is a traditional formal walled garden with potager and large glasshouse producing a range of fruit, vegetables and cutting flowers. Adjacent to this is a hedged formal garden with herbaceous, shrub and rose beds centred around a lily pond, with roses predominately as an interesting feature. Outwith the formal gardens there is a large water garden with two connected ponds with trees, shrubs and lawns running alongside the Southwick Burn.

Open: Sunday 30 June, 2pm - 5pm, admission £5.00, children free.

Directions: On A710 near Caulkerbush. Dalbeattie seven miles, Dumfries 17 miles.

· *Loch Arthur*

Kirkcudbrightshire

STOCKARTON
Kirkcudbright DG6 4XS
Lt. Col and Mrs Richard Cliff
T: 01557 330430

This garden was started in 1995 by Carola Cliff, a keen and knowledgeable plantswoman, and contains a collection of unusual shrubs and small trees, which are growing well. Our aim has been to create different informal gardens around a Galloway farm house, leading down to a lochan. Above the lochan there is a sweet cottage, used for holiday retreats, with its own interesting garden. In 1996 a three-acre arboretum was planted as a shelter belt and it now contains some rare oak trees.

Open: Open by arrangement, admission £4.00, children free.

Directions: On B727 Kirkcudbright to Gelston Road. Kirkcudbright three miles, Castle Douglas seven miles.

· Great Ormond Street Hospital Children's Charity

The clear waters at Stockarton

Kirkcudbrightshire

THE LIMES
Kirkcudbright DG6 4XD
David and Carolyn McHale
E: carolyn.mchale@btinternet.com

This one-and-a-quarter-acre plantsman's garden has a variety of different plant habitats: woodland, dry sunny gravel beds, rock garden, crevice garden and mixed perennial and shrub borders. There is also a large productive vegetable garden. The McHales like to grow most of their plants from seed obtained through various international seed exchanges. You can expect to see a large number of unusual and exciting plants. In June the meconopsis should be at their best.

Open: Sunday 9 June, 2pm - 5pm. Also open by arrangement. Admission £4.00, children free.

Directions: In Kirkcudbright go straight along St Mary Street towards Dundrennan. The Limes is on the right, about half a mile from the town centre crossroads, on the edge of the town.

· *Friends Of Kirkcudbright Swimming Pool*

THE WATERHOUSE GARDENS AT STOCKARTON
Kirkcudbright DG6 4XS
Martin Gould and Sharon O'Rourke
T: 01557 331266 E: waterhousekbt@aol.com
W: www.waterhousekbt.co.uk

One acre of densely planted terraced-cottage-style gardens attached to a Galloway cottage. Three ponds surround the oak-framed eco-polehouse 'The Waterhouse'. Climbing roses, clematis and honeysuckles are a big feature as well as a pond-side walk. Over 50 photos on their website. Featured on *The Beechgrove Garden* in 2007.

Open: Open by arrangement 1 May - 30 September, admission £4.00, children free.

Directions: On the B727 Kirkcudbright to Gelston - Dalbeattie road. Kirkcudbright three miles, Castle Douglas seven miles.

· *Loch Arthur*

THREAVE GARDEN
Castle Douglas DG7 1RX
The National Trust for Scotland
T: 01556 502 575 E: rapolley@nts.org.uk
W: www.nts.org.uk/visit/places/Threave-Garden-and-Estate

Threave Garden, The Training Centre for future Professional Gardeners, is home to the School of Heritage Gardening. A place of education and plantsmanship, the garden has been developed by generations of students since 1960, resulting in a series of 'rooms' within the garden, each showcasing year-round interest; from beautiful spring daffodils, striking autumnal colour and a multitude of summer herbaceous displays. Threave also boasts a fully productive working walled garden that yields a large bounty of home-grown produce each year for sale to the public and use in the on-site terrace cafe. Champion Trees: *Acer platanoides* 'Princeton Gold'.

Open: Sunday 23 June, 10am - 5pm, admission £5.00, children free.

Directions: Off A75, one mile west of Castle Douglas.

· *The National Trust for Scotland: School of Heritage Gardening*

LANARKSHIRE

Scotland's Gardens Scheme 2019 Guidebook is sponsored by INVESTEC WEALTH & INVESTMENT

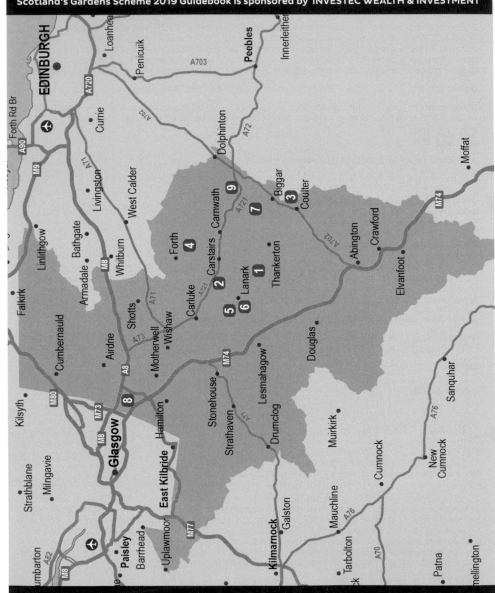

1. **Carmichael Mill**
2. **Cleghorn**
3. **Culter Allers**
4. **Dippoolbank Cottage**
5. **Old Farm Cottage**
6. **St Patrick's House**
7. **The Walled Garden, Shieldhill**
8. **Viewpark Allotments**
9. **Wellbutts**

LANARKSHIRE

OUR VOLUNTEER ORGANISERS

District Organiser:	Vanessa Rogers	1 Snowberry Field, Thankerton ML12 6RJ
		E: lanarkshire@scotlandsgardens.org
Area Organisers:	Nicky Eliott Lockhart	Stable House, Cleghorn Farm, Lanark ML11 7RW
	Janis Sinclair	2 Meadowflatts Cottage, Meadowflatts Rd ML12 6NF
Treasurer:	Shelia Munro Tulloch	Castlegait House, Strathaven ML10 6FF

GARDENS OPEN ON A SPECIFIC DATE

Cleghorn, Stable House, Cleghorn Farm, Lanark	Saturday, 9 March
Dippoolbank Cottage, Carnwath	Sunday, 16 June
Wellbutts, Elsrickle, by Biggar	Sunday, 21 July
Viewpark Allotments, Bairds Avenue, Viewpark	Sunday, 28 July
The Walled Garden, Shieldhill, Quothquan, Biggar	Sunday, 4 August
Culter Allers, Coulter, Biggar	Sunday, 18 August

GARDENS OPEN BY ARRANGEMENT

Carmichael Mill, Hyndford Bridge, Lanark	1 January - 31 December
Old Farm Cottage, The Ladywell, Nemphlar, Lanark	1 January - 31 December
St Patrick's House, Lanark	1 May - 31 May

Lanarkshire

1 **CARMICHAEL MILL**
Hyndford Bridge, Lanark ML11 8SJ
Chris, Ken and Gemma Fawell
T: 01555 665880 **E:** ken.fawell@btinternet.com

Gardens developed over the last 30 years surrounding the last workable water mill in Clydesdale. Water wheel will be rotating, river levels permitting. A large collection of over 200 different ornamental trees with shrubs and herbaceous plants, as well as a large vegetable and fruit garden. The mill lade (stream) flows through the centre, providing diverse habitats including Candelabra primula in late May. Large collection of tulips and narcissus in early spring followed by glorious display of flowering cherry and crab apples. Wildlife protection and enhancement are priorities. Also visible are archaeological remains of the medieval grain milling, flax processing and a foundry. (The bell in Carmichael village was made here.) A vote of thanks following a visit from the Hardy Plant Society: 'You have a fantastic garden Ken, but the best part about it is the small water feature on the side' - he meant the River Clyde!

Open: Open by arrangement, admission £5.00, children free.

Directions: Just off the A73 Lanark to Biggar road a half mile east of the Hyndford Bridge.

· **Donation to SGS Beneficiaries**

Cherry blossom and daffodils at Carmichael Mill

2 **CLEGHORN**
Stable House, Cleghorn Farm, Lanark ML11 7RN
Mr and Mrs R Eliott Lockhart
T: 01555 663792 **E:** eliottlockhart.nicky@gmail.com
W: www.cleghornestategardens.com

Eighteenth-century garden which is gradually being renovated. Attractive walks through mature trees and shrubs. Recent replanting of a valley below a 12th-century dam. Abundant snowdrops and visitors are welcome to return when the daffodils are in flower.

Open: Saturday 9 March, 2pm - 4pm for the Snowdrops and Winter Walks. Also open by arrangement. Admission by donation. Prize-winning book title trail for both adults and children.

Directions: Cleghorn Farm is situated two miles north of Lanark off the A706.

· **Marie Curie**

Lanarkshire

CULTER ALLERS
Coulter, Biggar ML12 6PZ
The McCosh family

The grounds of Culter Allers centre around its traditional one-and-a-half-acre walled garden, within which lies a productive vegetable and fruit garden with espalier fruit trees and berry bushes lining the walls. There are cut-flower beds, an apple-tree lined walk, a 'secret' herb garden, a wishing well and wide herbaceous borders revolving around an ornamental cherry and lawn. The policies of the house include winding woodland walks, fairy doors, a giant (small one) and an avenue of 125-year-old lime trees leading to the village kirk.

Open: Sunday 18 August, 2pm - 5pm, admission £4.00, children free.

Directions: In the village of Coulter, three miles south of Biggar on A702.

· *Coulter Public Library Trust*

DIPPOOLBANK COTTAGE
Carnwath ML11 8LP
Mr Allan Brash

Artist's intriguing cottage garden. Vegetables are grown in small beds. There are herbs, fruit, flowers and a pond in woodland area with treehouse and summerhouse. The fernery was completed in 2007. This is an organic garden that was mainly constructed with recycled materials.

Open: Sunday 16 June, 2pm - 6pm, admission £4.00, children free.

Directions: Off B7016 between Forth and Carnwath near the village of Braehead on the Auchengray road. Approximately eight miles from Lanark. Well signposted.

· *The Little Haven (Forth)*

OLD FARM COTTAGE
The Ladywell, Nemphlar, Lanark ML11 9GX
Ian and Anne Sinclair
T: 01555 663345 **M:** 07833 204 180 **E:** anniesinclair58@gmail.com

This delightful garden has something of interest all-year-round. Spring bulbs, shrubs and small trees attractive for their flowers, fruit and autumn foliage are complemented by herbaceous plantings. The garden also offers a wild flower area, a pond, an apiary and small orchard. Around an acre in size it has a large grassed area with a putting green, which it is particularly suitable for families. There are lots of child-friendly nooks and crannies for discovery and play. Visitors are welcome to bring a picnic as there are many sheltered places to sit and enjoy views over the Clyde Valley and district. Cover available if wet.

Open: Open by arrangement, admission by donation. Close to the Nemphlar spur of the Clyde Walkway. Walking groups welcome.

Directions: Leave A73 at Cartland Bridge (Lanark to Carluke Road) or A72 (Clyde Valley Road) at Crossford. Both routes well signposted.

· *Guide Dogs*

Lanarkshire

6

ST PATRICK'S HOUSE
Lanark ML11 9EH
Mr and Mrs Peter Sanders
T: 01555 663800 **E:** peterjeansanders@gmail.com

A May visit to St Patrick's House garden will be rewarded with a stunning display of rhododendrons, azaleas, heathers and shrubs. Created over a 50-year period, the grounds of this five-acre garden slope down to the River Clyde. Natural springs have been harnessed to create water features, a large contemporary pond with an arbour begs you to sit a while. Paths wind between beds of varied plantings and perennials, rockeries, and woodland plants, which all add to the magic of this unexpected gem.

Open: Open by arrangement 1 May - 31 May, admission £4.00, children free.

Directions: A73 into Lanark, after Police Station turn right into Friars Lane. At bottom of hill turn right onto St. Patrick Road. Garden a quarter of a mile on the left.

· *Lanark Community Development Trust*

7

THE WALLED GARDEN, SHIELDHILL
Quothquan, Biggar ML12 6NA
Mr and Mrs Gordon
T: 01899 221961 **E:** nicolagord@gmail.com

This 200-year-old walled garden was completely redesigned and planted in 2014/15 with contemporary features within a classic design. The garden incorporates a modern rill and banks of colour with perennial flowers in a variety of borders. The resident bees enjoy the large area of traditional meadow flowers as well as the rose garden planted with lavenders, salvias and stocks. Outside the wall you will find mature woodland including a giant sequoia and a wildlife pond. If you are interested in fruit and vegetables, take a look at the raised beds and the peach tree and vine in the greenhouse.

Open: Sunday 4 August, 2pm - 5pm, admission £5.00, children free.

Directions: Turn off the B7016 between Biggar and Carnwath towards Quothquan. After about a mile, look for signs and turn right at the lodge.

· *Médecins Sans Frontières (UK)*

8

VIEWPARK ALLOTMENTS
Bairds Avenue, Viewpark G71 6HJ
Viewpark Allotments Association
T: 07967 153798
W: www.viewparkgardensallotmentsassociation.btck.co.uk

Viewpark is a thriving community of contemporary allotments. These not only provide the opportunity to garden and grow but also offer enjoyment, education and therapy for local groups, families and individuals. Each plot has its own character. Crops grown range from potatoes to peaches, godetia to grapes. Inspiration can be found everywhere, from planting combinations, irrigation methods, use of small spaces, unusual crops, etc. Environmental awareness is high on the agenda with a stunning wildflower meadow, hedgehog houses, bug hotels, group orchard and the use of recyclable materials.

Open: Sunday 28 July, 12pm - 4:30pm, admission £4.00, children free. Our 'moth man' will be in attendance and there will be children's activities throughout the afternoon. Light lunches and refreshments available from 12.00pm.

Lanarkshire

Directions: On the A721, New Edinburgh Road between Bellshill and Viewpark.

· *Parkinsons UK*

WELLBUTTS
Elsrickle, by Biggar ML12 6QZ
Nick and Lillian Slater

We started our croft garden 19 years ago on an exposed hill site of approximately two acres at an altitude of 960 feet. Our priority then was hedging, shrub and tree planting, keeping open views but creating windbreaks for herbaceous gardens, spring fed natural duck ponds and a rill fed 'boggery'. Now established the beds are reshaped, enlarged and replanted with an extensive collection of perennials. Greenhouses and covered areas provide protection for more than 70 hanging baskets and our collection of pot grown begonias.

Open: Sunday 21 July, 1pm - 5pm, admission £4.00, children free. We have plants for sale in the garden and seating areas under cover where we serve cream teas in vintage china with the help of our special team of garden open day friends.

Directions: Parking on the main road (A721) then walk to the garden (approximately 200 yards). Adjacent field parking may be available dependent on the weather, see signs on the day.

· *Alzheimer Scotland*

Productive plots at Viewpark Allotments

MORAY & NAIRN

Scotland's Gardens Scheme 2019 Guidebook is sponsored by INVESTEC WEALTH & INVESTMENT

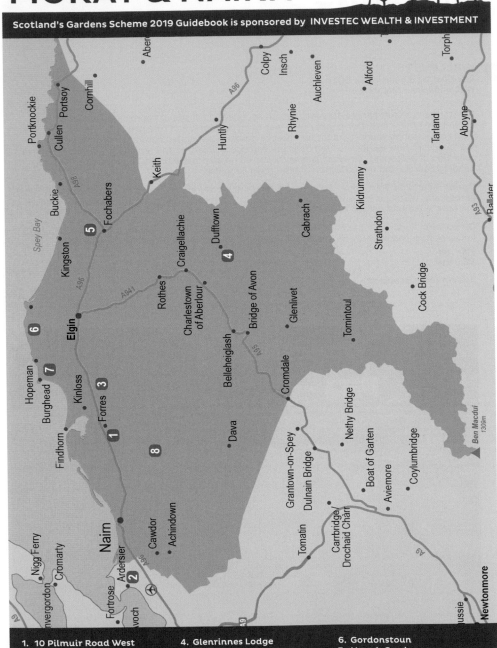

1. **10 Pilmuir Road West**
2. **10 Stuart Avenue**
3. **Burgie**
4. **Glenrinnes Lodge**
5. **Gordon Castle Walled Garden**
6. **Gordonstoun**
7. **Haugh Garden**
8. **Logie House**

MORAY & NAIRN

OUR VOLUNTEER ORGANISERS

District Organiser:	James Byatt	Lochview Cottage, Pitgaveny, Elgin IV30 5PQ E: moraynairn@scotlandsgardens.org
Area Organisers:	Lorraine Dingwall	10 Pilmuir Road West, Forres IV36 2HL
	David & Gwynne Hetherington	Haugh Garden, College of Roseisle IV30 5YE
	Rebecca Russell	12 Duff Avenue, Elgin, Moray IV30 1QS
	Annie Stewart	33 Albert Street, Nairn IV12 4HF
Treasurer:	Michael Barnett	Drumdelnies, Nairn IV12 5NT

GARDENS OPEN ON A SPECIFIC DATE

10 Stuart Avenue, Ardersier, Inverness	Saturday, 27 April
10 Stuart Avenue, Ardersier, Inverness	Saturday, 25 May
Gordonstoun, Duffus, nr Elgin	Sunday, 2 June
Haugh Garden, College of Roseisle	Saturday, 15 June
Haugh Garden, College of Roseisle	Saturday, 6 July
Gordon Castle Walled Garden, Fochabers, Moray	Sunday, 14 July
Haugh Garden, College of Roseisle	Saturday, 20 July
Glenrinnes Lodge, Dufftown, Keith, Banffshire	Sunday, 28 July
Haugh Garden, College of Roseisle	Saturday, 17 August

GARDENS OPEN REGULARLY

Logie House, Dunphail, Forres	1 January - 31 December
Gordon Castle Walled Garden, Fochabers, Moray	1 January - 31 December
Burgie, Between Forres and Elgin	1 April - 31 October

GARDENS OPEN BY ARRANGEMENT

10 Pilmuir Road West, Forres	1 February - 31 March
Haugh Garden, College of Roseisle	1 May - 31 August
10 Pilmuir Road West, Forres	1 June - 31 July

Moray & Nairn

10 PILMUIR ROAD WEST
Forres IV36 2HL
Mrs Lorraine Dingwall
T: 01309 674634 **E:** fixandig@aol.com

Plantswoman's small town garden with over 300 cultivars of hostas, an extensive collection of hardy geraniums together with many other unusual plants. Managed entirely without the use of artificial fertilisers or chemicals, the owner encourages hedgehogs, toads and wild birds to control slugs. In early spring there are approximately 150 named snowdrops to be seen, some of which are very rare.

Open: Open by arrangement 1 February - 31 March for Snowdrops and Winter Walks. Also open by arrangement 1 June - 31 July. Admission £3.00, children free. Well-stocked plant sales with some rare varieties available, specialising in hostas and geraniums and with snowdrops in season.

Directions: From Tesco roundabout at Forres continue along Nairn Road. Take the first left onto Ramflat Road, then go right at the bottom and first left onto Pilmuir Road West.

· *Macmillan Cancer Support*

10 STUART AVENUE
Ardersier, Inverness IV2 7SA
Mr and Mrs Kevin Reid

A cottage style garden with vibrant rich and dense plantings of perennials and shrubs that bring colour and scent across the seasons, and makes the most of the limited space. Winner of the *Inverness Courier Garden of the Year* (medium category) in 2015, featured in *The Beechgrove Garden* in 2016 and overall winner of the *Inverness Courier Garden of the Year* in 2017.

Open: Saturday 27 April and Saturday 25 May, 10am - 4pm, admission £3.00, children free.

Directions: From Inverness or Nairn take the A96, then the B9039 to Ardesier. After the *30mph* sign turn right to Nairn, then first left into Reaybank Road and left again. Limited parking in Stuart Avenue, more in adjoining streets.

· *Marie Curie*

10 Stuart Avenue, Moray & Nairn

Moray & Nairn

BURGIE

Between Forres and Elgin IV36 2QU
Hamish Lochore
T: 01343 850 231 **E:** hamish@burgie.org

A rare opportunity to see a sizeable woodland garden / arboretum in its infancy. It has a good collection of rhododendrons, sorbus, alder, birch and tilia but also includes many unusual trees from around the world. The arboretum is zoned into geographic areas and species type. It includes a Japanese Garden, bog garden, bog wood, loch and Quarry Garden. First created in 2005 and is ongoing. Most plants are grown from hand collected seed and propagated in the Georgian greenhouse.

Open: 1 April - 31 October, 8am - 5pm, admission £3.00, children free. Please use honesty box. Disabled persons should get in touch by email so the gate can be opened for buggies.

Directions: A96 between Forres and Elgin. Four miles east of Forres. Six miles west of Elgin. Sign to *Burgie Mains* along the A96 is set in wrought iron decorated with horses and cattle. South off the main road and one mile to the Woodland Garden car park.

· *Sandpiper Trust & World Horse Welfare*

GLENRINNES LODGE

Dufftown, Keith, Banffshire AB55 4BS
Mrs Kathleen Locke
T: 01340 820384
W: www.glenrinnes.com

The garden and policies surrounding Glenrinnes Lodge are typical of a Victorian Lodge. There is a semi-formal garden that lends itself to quiet reflection with stunning views up Glenrinnes. A walled kitchen garden with a large heated greenhouse supply plants, cut flowers and fruit and vegetables. Here you will also find a newly developed herbaceous border displaying vibrant colours through the use of perennial and half-hardy plantings. There are delightful walks in the meadow around the pond and into the woodland, watch out for red squirrels! Some major works have been undertaken recently and much of the garden is still a 'work in progress'. In keeping with the rest of the estate, Glenrinnes Lodge is gardened following organic principles.

Open: Sunday 28 July, 2pm - 5pm, admission £4.00, children free.

Directions: In the centre of Dufftown at the Clock Tower take the B9009 road to Tomintoul for about one mile. After passing Dufftown Golf Club on your right there is a lane to the left, which leads to two stone pillars to Glenrinnes Lodge.

· *Alzheimer's Research UK*

'Gardening may be
important in preventing
cognitive decline'
The Kings Fund, 2016

Moray & Nairn

5 GORDON CASTLE WALLED GARDEN
Fochabers, Moray IV32 7PQ
Angus and Zara Gordon Lennox
T: 01343 612317 **E:** info@gordoncastlescotland.com
W: www.gordoncastlescotland.com

Gordon Castle has one of the largest and oldest walled gardens in Britain. Eight acres in size, it is being lovingly restored to its former glory with a new design by award-winning Arne Maynard which includes vegetables, fruit, herbs and cut-flower beds alongside the amazing 259 espaliered trees on the 15-foot high walls. This wonderful kitchen garden has a 'Plant.Pick.Plate' ethos for its onsite cafe and there is a children's natural play area and shop.

Open: Sunday 14 July, 10am - 4pm. Also open daily, 10am - 4pm. Admission £5.00, children free (for Sunday 14 July) and details can be found on the garden's website for general admission.

Directions: The main entrance is situated at the western end of the village of Fochabers on the A96, approximately nine miles east of Elgin and 12 miles west of Keith.

· Gordon Lennox Fochabers Trust (Sunday 14 July) & Donation to SGS Beneficiaries (1 January - 31 December)

Gordon Castle Walled Garden

6 GORDONSTOUN
Duffus, nr Elgin IV30 5RF
Gordonstoun School
T: 01343 837837 **E:** richardss@gordonstoun.org.uk
W: www.gordonstoun.org.uk

The gardens consist of good formal herbaceous borders around lawns, a terrace and an orchard. The school grounds include Gordonstoun House, a Georgian house of 1775/6 incorporating an earlier 17th-century house built for the First Marquis of Huntly, and the school chapel, both of which will be open to visitors. There is also a unique circle of former farm buildings known as the Round Square, and a scenic lake.

Open: Sunday 2 June, 2pm - 4pm, admission £5.00, children free.

Directions: Entrance off B9012, four miles from Elgin at Duffus village.

· SGS Beneficiaries

Moray & Nairn

HAUGH GARDEN
College of Roseisle IV30 5YE
Gwynne and David Hetherington
T: 01343 835790

Our garden is now in the sixth year of being developed. From what was an unmaintained woodland we have created a spring garden criss-crossed with informal paths and with extensive drifts of snowdrops and over 40 varieties of tulips. Colour interest continues with a collection of hellebores, daffodils, narcissi and rhododendrons. A wildlife pond is situated in a corner of the woodland close to the ruins of an 18th-century farmhouse. Extensive herbaceous borders enclose the lawn, with a central rose bed and a small orchard. The immature pine and birch woodland has been thinned out allowing the bluebells to flower, and it has now been planted with a wide range of under storey shrubs to give year-round interest. There is a productive polytunnel and organic vegetable beds.

Open: Saturday 15 June, Saturday 6 July, Saturday 20 July and Saturday 17 August, 2pm - 5pm. Also open by arrangement 1 May - 31 August. Admission £4.00, children free. Car parking at Roseisle Village Hall with drop-off and disabled car parking available at the house.

Directions: From Elgin take the A96 west, then the B9013 Burghead Road to the crossroads at the centre of College of Roseisle. The garden is on the right, enter from the Duffus Road. Village Hall car parking is to the left off Kinloss Road.

· *Children's Hospice Association Scotland & Alzheimer Scotland*

LOGIE HOUSE
Dunphail, Forres IV36 2QN
Alasdair and Panny Laing
E: panny@logie.co.uk
W: www.logie.co.uk

Originally a formal garden with a large area of vegetable production, Logie House garden has been developed since 1991 with emphasis on trees, shrubs and hardy perennials, giving all-year-round interest. The meandering burn and dry stone walls support the creation of a wide variety of planting habitats from dry sunny banks to damp shady areas. Many of the unusual plants are propagated for sale in the Garden Shop at Logie Steading. Also features forest and river walks.

Open: Daily, 10am - 5pm, admission £2.00, children free.

Directions: Six miles south of Forres off A940. Follow signs to Logie Steading.

· *Donation to SGS Beneficiaries*

A well laden apple tree at Logie House

PEEBLESSHIRE & TWEEDDALE

Scotland's Gardens Scheme 2019 Guidebook is sponsored by **INVESTEC WEALTH & INVESTMENT**

1. 8 Halmyre Mains
2. Abbotsford
3. Dawyck Botanic Garden
4. Drumelzier Old Manse
5. Glen House
6. Kailzie Gardens
7. Laidlawstiel House
8. Portmore
9. Quercus Garden Plants
10. Stobo Japanese Water Garden
11. The Potting Shed
12. The Schoolhouse
13. West Linton Village Gardens

PEEBLESSHIRE & TWEEDDALE

OUR VOLUNTEER ORGANISERS

District Organiser:	Lesley McDavid	Braedon, Medwyn Road, West Linton EH46 7HA E: peeblesshire@scotlandsgardens.org
Area Organisers:	Jennifer Barr Jenny Litherland	Allerly, Gattonside, Melrose TD6 9LT Laidlawstiel House, Clovenfords, Galashiels TD1 1TJ
Treasurer:	John Bracken	Gowan Lea, Croft Road, West Linton EH46 7DZ

GARDENS OPEN ON A SPECIFIC DATE

Kailzie Gardens, Peebles	Sunday, 24 February
Laidlawstiel House, Clovenfords, Galashiels	Wednesday, 22 May
Stobo Japanese Water Garden, Home Farm, Stobo	Sunday, 2 June
West Linton Village Gardens, The Graham Institute	Sunday, 9 June
Laidlawstiel House, Clovenfords, Galashiels	Wednesday, 12 June
8 Halmyre Mains, West Linton	Sunday, 23 June
Glen House, Glen Estate, Innerleithen	Sunday, 30 June
Drumelzier Old Manse, Drumelzier, nr Broughton	Sunday, 7 July
Quercus Garden Plants, Whitmuir Farm, West Linton	Saturday, 27 July
The Schoolhouse, Skirling by Biggar	Sunday, 28 July
Quercus Garden Plants, Whitmuir Farm, West Linton	Saturday, 24 August
Kailzie Gardens, Peebles	Sunday, 8 September
Dawyck Botanic Garden, Stobo	Sunday, 6 October

GARDENS OPEN REGULARLY

Abbotsford, Melrose	1 March - 31 October
The Potting Shed, Broughton Place, Broughton, Biggar	18 June - 9 July (Tuesdays only)
Portmore, Eddleston	3 July - 28 August (Wednesdays only)
Abbotsford, Melrose	1 November - 30 November

GARDENS OPEN BY ARRANGEMENT

The Potting Shed, Broughton Place, Broughton, Biggar	1 January - 31 December
Portmore, Eddleston	1 June - 31 August
Drumelzier Old Manse, Drumelzier, nr Broughton	1 June - 31 July

Peeblesshire & Tweeddale

8 HALMYRE MAINS
West Linton EH46 7BX
Joyce and Mike Madden
T: 07774 609 547 **E:** agentromanno@gmail.com

A half-acre organic garden with newly replanted deep herbaceous borders surrounding the main lawn. Raised plots, a greenhouse, keder house and polytunnel producing fruit and vegetables. A pergola leads to a composting area and then down to the pond with viewing areas and sun house.

Open: Sunday 23 June, 2pm - 5pm, admission £4.00, children free. Homemade teas are available at the Lamancha Hub nearby.

Directions: Five miles south of Leadburn Junction on the A701 (Moffat).

· *Lamancha Hub*

ABBOTSFORD
Melrose TD6 9BQ
The Abbotsford Trust
T: 01896 752043 **E:** enquiries@scottsabbotsford.co.uk
W: www.scottsabbotsford.com

The garden was designed by Sir Walter Scott with advice from artists, architects and friends. It is a rare surviving example of a Regency Garden layout – and completely different from the English Landscape Garden style which 'Capability' Brown made his own in the previous decades. Abbotsford's garden aims to provide a harmonious transition between the luxury and comfort of the interiors of the house with wonders of nature in the wider estate through a series of secluded, richly detailed and sheltered 'rooms'. In its day it would have showcased the latest plants discovered from around the globe, both in its borders and 'stove houses', and was tended by William Bogie, a Frenchman trained by James MacDonald one of the most celebrated gardeners of the day.

Open: 1 March - 31 March, 10am - 4pm. Also open 1 April - 31 October, 10am - 5pm. And open 1 November - 30 November, 10am - 4pm. Admission details can be found on the garden's website. Abbotsford is open throughout the year and is delighted to be involved with Gardens and Health week.

Directions: Off the A6091, near Melrose. Bus X62 and 72 from Edinburgh and Peebles. Train from Waverley to Tweedbank. Minibus or one-mile walk from train station.

· *Donation to SGS Beneficiaries*

DAWYCK BOTANIC GARDEN
Stobo EH45 9JU
A Regional Garden of the Royal Botanic Garden Edinburgh
T: 01721 760 254
W: www.rbge.org.uk/dawyck

Stunning collection of rare trees and shrubs. With over 300 years of tree planting, Dawyck is a world-famous arboretum with mature specimens of Chinese conifers, Japanese maples, Brewer's spruce, the unique Dawyck beech and sequoiadendrons from North America which are over 150 feet tall. Bold herbaceous plantings run along the burn. Range of trails and walks. Fabulous autumn colours.
National Plant Collection: *Larix* and *Tsuga*
Champion Trees: Numerous.

Open: Sunday 6 October, 10am - 5pm, admission details can be found on the garden's website.

Peeblesshire & Tweeddale

Directions: Eight miles southwest of Peebles on B712.

· *Donation to SGS Beneficiaries*

DRUMELZIER OLD MANSE
Drumelzier, nr Broughton ML12 6JD
Mr and Mrs Julian Birchall
T: 01899 830319 **E:** birchall@oldmanse.org.uk

A traditional Manse garden in the attractive Upper Tweed Valley. Colourful herbaceous border within a walled garden. Unusual selection of plants throughout the garden including many varieties of geraniums and rare *Meconopsis baileyi* 'Hensol Violet'. There is a rock border and kitchen garden. A wide variety of shrubs have been planted in the last 15 years in the lower garden leading down to the path along burn with shade-loving plants and hostas. A beautiful setting and surrounding walks.

Open: Sunday 7 July, 2pm - 5pm. Also open by arrangement 1 June - 31 July. Admission £4.00, children free.

Directions: On the B712, ten miles south west of Peebles, two miles east of Broughton.

· *Stobo and Drumelzier Church of Scotland: Drumelzier Church & The John Buchan Story: Peebles*

Herbaceous borders at Abbotsford, © Angus Bremner

Peeblesshire & Tweeddale

GLEN HOUSE
Glen Estate, Innerleithen EH44 6PX
The Tennant family
T: 01896 830210 **E:** info@glenhouse.com
W: www.glenhouse.com

Surrounding the outstanding Scots Baronial mansion designed by David Bryce in the mid-19th century, Glen House gardens are laid out on shallow terraces overhanging the glen itself, which offers one of the loveliest designed landscapes in the Borders. The garden expands from the formal courtyard through a yew colonnade, and contains a fine range of trees, long herbaceous border and pool garden with pergola, all arranged within the curve of slopes sheltering the house.

Open: Sunday 30 June, 11am - 4pm, admission £5.00, children free. Visitors are welcome to bring along a picnic.

Directions: Follow B709 out of Innerleithen for approximately two and a half miles. Right turn at signpost for *Glen Estate*.

· *Borders General Hospital, Margaret Kerr Unit: fund 21: palliative care*

KAILZIE GARDENS
Peebles EH45 9HT
Lady Buchan-Hepburn
T: 01721 720007 **E:** angela.buchanhepburn@btinternet.com
W: www.kailziegardens.com

Semi-formal walled garden with shrubs and herbaceous borders, rose garden and excellent display of plants in large Victorian greenhouses. Woodland and burnside walks among spring bulbs, snowdrops, bluebells, rhododendrons and azaleas. The garden is set among fine old trees. Watch osprey with live CCTV recordings of ospreys nesting in the recently extended nature centre. Kailzie has been featured on *Landward* and *The Beechgrove Garden*.
Champion Trees: Larch planted 1725.

Open: Sunday 24 February, 10am - 4pm for the Snowdrops and Winter Walks. Also open Sunday 8 September, 10am - 4pm. Admission £4.00, children free (Sunday 24 February) and £5.00, children free (Sunday 8 September). See website for other opening times.

Directions: Two and a half miles east of Peebles on B7062.

· *Erskine Hospital*

LAIDLAWSTIEL HOUSE
Clovenfords, Galashiels TD1 1TJ
Mr and Mrs P Litherland

Walled garden containing herbaceous border, fruit, and vegetables in raised beds. There are colourful rhododendrons and azaleas as well as splendid views down to the River Tweed.

Open: Wednesday 22 May and Wednesday 12 June, 1pm - 5pm. Admission £4.00, children free.

Directions: A72 between Clovenfords and Walkerburn, turn up the hill signposted for *Thornielee*. The house is on the right at the top of the hill.

· *CLIC Sargent: Ciaran's House, Edinburgh*

Peeblesshire & Tweeddale

An open gate at Laidlawstiel House, photo by Kathy Henry

PORTMORE

8

Eddleston EH45 8QU
Mr and Mrs David Reid
T: 07825 294388
W: www.portmoregardens.co.uk

Lovingly created by the current owners over the past 30 years, the gardens, surrounding the David Bryce-designed mansion house contain mature trees and offer fine views of the surrounding countryside. Large walled garden with box-edged herbaceous borders is planted in stunning colour harmonies, potager, rose garden, pleached lime walk and ornamental fruit cages. The Victorian glasshouses contain fruit trees, roses, geraniums, pelargoniums and a wide variety of tender plants. There is also an Italianate Grotto and water garden with shrubs and meconopsis. The woodland walks are lined with rhododendrons, azaleas and shrub roses. Starred in *Good Gardens Guide* and featured in Kenneth Cox's book *Scotland for Gardeners* and on *The Beechgrove Garden*.

Open: 3 July - 28 August (Wednesdays only), 1pm - 5pm. Also open by arrangement 1 June - 31 August. Admission £6.00, children free. Self service refreshments for Wednesday openings. Homemade cream teas for groups over 15 people by prior arrangement.

Directions: Off A703 one mile north of Eddleston. Bus 62.

· *RNIB Charity: Peebles Community Talking Book*

Peeblesshire & Tweeddale

QUERCUS GARDEN PLANTS
Whitmuir Farm, West Linton EH46 7BB
Rona Dodds
T: 01968 660708 **E:** rona@quercusgardenplants.co.uk
W: www.quercusgardenplants.co.uk

We are a small independent nursery growing and selling a wide range of happy, healthy plants propagated from our nursery gardens. At just under two acres, these gardens were started in 2015 to show visitors and customers what can be grown in our conditions here on a north-west-facing hill at 850 feet above sea level. Explore our herb garden, scented garden, wildlife garden and all the other inspirational smaller borders. Many of the plants seen in the gardens are available to buy in the nursery.

Open: Saturday 27 July and Saturday 24 August, 7pm - 9pm. Admission £7.00, children free. Rona, the owner, will give a guided tour and refreshments will be provided at these two events. See garden website for nursery opening times.

Directions: On the A701, four miles south of the Leadburn junction or two miles north of West Linton.

· *Breast Cancer Care*

STOBO JAPANESE WATER GARDEN
Home Farm, Stobo EH45 8NX
Hugh and Georgina Seymour
T: 01721 760245 **E:** stobo.home.farm@gmail.com

Secluded woodland garden. While water is probably the main feature of the garden now, the layout echoes facets of a more conventional Japanese Garden - stepping stones, humpback bridges, the 40-foot waterfall, azaleas and rhododendrons, acers and other specialist trees and shrubs, many of far eastern origins. Several Japanese lanterns and a tea house still remain from when the garden was created in the early years of the 20th century. Recently featured in the November issue of *Scottish Field* magazine. 2018 storms have altered some aspects of the garden and lightened the canopy.

Open: Sunday 2 June, 1pm - 4pm, admission £5.00, children free.

Directions: Off the B712. Follow signs for *Stobo Castle* then yellow *SGS* signs on the drive.

· *Stobo Hall Committee*

THE POTTING SHED
Broughton Place, Broughton, Biggar ML12 6HJ
Jane and Graham Buchanan-Dunlop
T: 01899 830574 **E:** buchanandunlop@btinternet.com

A one-acre garden, begun from scratch in 2008, on an exposed hillside at 900 feet. It contains herbaceous plants, climbers, shrubs and trees, all selected for wind resistance and ability to cope with the poor, stony soil. There are (usually) fine views to the Southern Uplands.

Open: 18 June - 9 July (Tuesdays only), 11am - 5pm. Also open by arrangement. Admission £4.00, children free.

Directions: Signposted from the main A701 Edinburgh - Moffat Road, immediately north of Broughton village.

· *Macmillan Cancer Support: Borders General Hospital*

Peeblesshire & Tweeddale

THE SCHOOLHOUSE
Skirling by Biggar ML12 6HD
Mike and Annie Thompson
T: 01899 860396 **E:** info@schoolhouseflowers.co.uk
W: www.schoolhouseflowers.co.uk
....

A developing and informal village garden which is also home to a cut flower business. In addition to the cutting beds there are herbaceous borders, a vegetable patch, young orchard and a recently created wildlife pond.

Open: Sunday 28 July, 2pm - 5pm, admission £4.00, children free. Homemade teas are available at the village hall nearby.

Directions: Take the A701 or A702 and follow road signs to *Skirling*. The garden is directly opposite the village green.

· *Skirling Village Hall*

WEST LINTON VILLAGE GARDENS
The Graham Institute, Lower Green, West Linton EH46 7EW
West Linton Village Gardeners
T: 01968 660669
....

A group of gardens on the west side of the village near the golf course and including Srongarbh (last opened in 2015). Surrounding the Arts and Crafts House, this large garden dating from the 1930's includes many features. There are many rhododendrons and azaleas, which will look their best in early June. Old and fragrant rose varieties surround a formal terrace and original pool and Japanese acers surround a naturalistic pond. Other gardens include a living green roof, woodland paths and colourful herbaceous borders.

Open: Sunday 9 June, 1pm - 5pm, admission £5.00, children free. Tickets, teas and plants are sold at the Graham Institute from where a courtesy bus may be taken as there is very limited parking at the gardens.

Directions: About 15 miles south west of Edinburgh, take the A701 or A702 and follow signs. Bus 101 or 102 to Gordon Arms Hotel.

· *Ben Walton Trust & Borders General Hospital, Margaret Kerr Unit*

The Potting Shed, photo by Kathy Henry

PERTH & KINROSS

Scotland's Gardens Scheme 2019 Guidebook is sponsored by **INVESTEC WEALTH & INVESTMENT**

1. 7 Drum Gate
2. Abernethy Open Gardens
3. Allotment Association of Crieff
4. Arduvorlich
5. Blair Castle Gardens
6. Bolfracks
7. Bonhard House
8. Braco Castle
9. Bradystone House
10. Bridge of Earn Gardens
11. Carig Dhubh
12. Cloan
13. Delvine
14. Dowhill
15. Drummond Castle Gardens
16. Eastbank Cottage
17. Explorers Garden
18. Fingask Castle
19. Glendoick
20. Gleneagles House
21. Glenericht House Arboretum
22. Glenlyon House
23. Hollytree Lodge
24. Kilgraston School
25. Megginch Castle
26. Mill of Forneth
27. Mount Tabor House
28. Parkhead House
29. Pitcurran House
30. Rossie Gardens
31. SGS Plant Sale at
    Bradystone House
32. The Bield at Blackruthven
33. The Garden at Craigowan
34. The Steading at Clunie
35. The Steading at Muckhart
36. Tombuie and Little Tombuie
37. Wester House of Ross

PERTH & KINROSS

OUR VOLUNTEER ORGANISERS

District Organisers:	Margaret Gimblett	Fehmarn, Clayton Road, Bridge of Earn PH2 9AH E: perthkinross@scotlandsgardens.org
Area Organisers:	Henrietta Harland	Easter Carmichael Cottage, Forgandenny Road, Bridge of Earn PH2 9EZ
	Elizabeth Mitchell	Woodlee, 28 St Mary's Drive, Perth PH2 7BY
	Lizzie Montgomery	Burleigh House, Milnathort, Kinross KY13 9SR
	Judy Norwell	Dura Den, 20 Pitcullen Terrace, Perth PH2 7EQ
	Richenda Pearson	Spinneyburn, Rumbling Bridge KY13 0PY
	Clarinda Snowball	The Limes, Dallerie, Crieff PH7 4JH
	Fiona Stewart	7 Craigend Cottages, Craigend PH2 8PX
	Heather Wood	Mill of Forneth, Forneth, Blairgowrie PH10 6SP
Treasurer:	Michael Tinson	Parkhead House, Parkhead Gardens, Burghmuir Road, Perth PH1 1JF

GARDENS OPEN ON A SPECIFIC DATE

Cloan, by Auchterarder	Sunday, 17 February
Kilgraston School, Bridge of Earn	Sunday, 24 February
Rossie Gardens, Forgandenny	Sunday, 3 March
Megginch Castle, Errol	Sunday, 21 April
The Steading at Clunie, Newmill of Kinloch, Clunie, Blairgowrie	Sunday, 28 April
Cloan, by Auchterarder	Sunday, 5 May
Fingask Castle, Rait	Sunday, 5 May
Gleneagles House, Auchterader	Monday, 6 May
Gleneagles House, Auchterader	Monday, 13 May
SGS Plant Sale at Bradystone House, Murthly	Sunday, 19 May
Rossie Gardens, Forgandenny	Saturday, 25 May
The Steading at Muckhart, Yetts O'Muckhart, Dollar	Sunday, 26 May
Delvine, Murthly	Sunday, 26 May
Gleneagles House, Auchterader	Monday, 27 May
Explorers Garden, Pitlochry	Sunday, 2 June
Bonhard House, Perth	Sunday, 2 June
Gleneagles House, Auchterader	Monday, 3 June
Cloan, by Auchterarder	Sunday, 9 June
Mill of Forneth, Forneth, Blairgowrie	Sunday, 9 June
Abernethy Open Gardens, Abernethy	Saturday, 15 June
The Bield at Blackruthven, Blackruthven House, Tibbermore	Saturday, 15 June
Blair Castle Gardens, Blair Atholl	Saturday, 29 June
Allotment Association of Crieff, Turretbank Road Crieff	Saturday, 6 July
Bridge of Earn Gardens, The Institute, Station Road	Sunday, 28 July
Mount Tabor House, Mount Tabor Road, Perth	Sunday, 4 August
Drummond Castle Gardens, Crieff	Sunday, 4 August
Wester House of Ross, Comrie	Saturday/Sunday, 10/11 August
Cloan, by Auchterarder	Wednesday, 14 August

PERTH & KINROSS

GARDENS OPEN REGULARLY

Glenericht House Arboretum, Blairgowrie	24 January - 31 December
Braco Castle, Braco	27 January - 31 October
Bolfracks, Aberfeldy	1 April - 31 October
Glendoick, Glencarse, Perthshire	1 April - 31 May
The Garden at Craigowan, Ballinluig	15 April - 31 August
Ardvorlich, Lochearnhead	1 May - 2 June
Carig Dhubh, Bonskeid, Pitlochry	1 May - 30 August
Bradystone House, Murthly	30 May - 8 August (Thursdays only)

GARDENS OPEN BY ARRANGEMENT

Fingask Castle, Rait	28 January - 7 March (Mondays & Thursdays)
Mill of Forneth, Forneth, Blairgowrie	1 April - 31 July
Eastbank Cottage, Perth Road, Abernethy	1 April - 30 June
Hollytree Lodge, Muckhart, Dollar	1 April - 31 October
Glenlyon House, Fortingall	1 April - 30 September
Tombuie and Little Tombuie, Killiechassie, Aberfeldy	1 May - 31 July
Parkhead House, Parkhead Gardens, Burghmuir Road, Perth	1 May - 30 September
Pitcurran House, Abernethy	1 May - 30 September
7 Drum Gate, Abernethy, Perthshire	30 May - 30 June
Dowhill, Cleish	4 June - 25 June (Tuesdays only)

Perth & Kinross

7 DRUM GATE

Abernethy, Perthshire PH2 9SA
Helen Morrison
E: helen72.hm@gmail.com

What started out in 2004 as just under an acre of bare earth has now turned into an attractive garden split into extensive herbaceous borders, large lawn areas and a young woodland with metasequoias, tulip tree, rhododendrons and wonderful views across the Tay Valley and upwards to the Ochils. The garden continues to develop and mature with earlier planting of topiary and hedging now being able to be sculptured and fruit trees and shrubs bearing produce. Visitors can meander through the garden, pausing in the children's Hideaway Cottage to listen and observe the many species of birds attracted to the garden. Work is ongoing but this is a rare example of what can be achieved from a blank canvas given vision, determination and plenty of time and patience.

Open: Open by arrangement 30 May - 30 June, admission by donation.

Directions: Seven miles south of Perth. Leave the M90 at Junction 9 and follow signs for *Abernethy, Newburgh* and *Cupar* on the A912 for approximately five miles. Garden Owner will give detailed directions on request.

· *Search and Rescue Dog Association Scotland (SCIO)*

ABERNETHY OPEN GARDENS

Abernethy PH2 9JJ
The Gardeners of Abernethy
E: keir.allen@gmail.com

An na Beatha 27-29 Main Street PH29JH (Heather and Reid Martin): The garden is on the main street within the conservation village and is a classic example of the village long garden that is common to the area. An orchard, vegetable patch and polytunnels are complemented by a wide range of perennials.
Carey House PH2 9LN (Caroline Boyle): An artist's garden with impressive planting, sculptures dotted throughout, ponds, summerhouse and much more. This large garden has been created from bare fields in the last ten years and continues to improve with age.
Eastbank Cottage Perth Road PH2 9LR (Mike and Elsa Thompson): Traditional Scottish cottage, a third of an acre garden, walled and bounded by a small burn to the east. Erythroniums, varieties of wood anemones, trillium, a fine display of clematis, rhododendrons and azaleas. This garden is also open by arrangement 1 April - 30 June.
Gattaway PH2 9LQ (Mr Chris Farmer): A work in progress but the progress has been spectacular. A pair of walled gardens, one with hens, the other with soft fruit and pigs, a series of lawns with border are all being developed into a beautiful garden with views down onto the village.
Mornington Cottage School Wynd PH2 9JJ (Keir Allen): A large vegetable garden, bordered by espalier apple trees and a range of soft fruits. The garden is linked to the old garden of the house with an orchard, a croquet lawn and borders of shrubs and flowers.
Nurse Peattie's Garden Main Street PH2 (Abernethy in Bloom): This garden is the hub of the work that *Abernethy in Bloom* carry out around the whole village. It is a colourful and tranquil escape which has been restored to its former glory in the last four years.

Open: Saturday 15 June, 10am - 5pm, admission £5.00, children free. The main ticket hub is at Mornington Cottage, School Wynd PH2 9JJ (just up the wynd from the village museum) and they can also be obtained from individual gardens.

Directions: Abernethy is seven miles south of Perth. Leave M90 and follow signs for Abernethy. Parking will be clearly signed on the day and will be in the potato factory (Brantons) and the school car park. Hourly buses run from Perth and Glenrothes.

· *Abernethy in Bloom*

Perth & Kinross

3

ALLOTMENT ASSOCIATION OF CRIEFF
Turretbank Road Crieff PH7 4AR
The Allotmenteers
E: crieffplots@gmail.com

The allotments sit high above the River Turret with panoramic views of Glen Turret and towards St Fillans, one of the most scenic allotment locations in Scotland. Previously the ground was used for grazing and lacked vehicular access, so allotmenteers created this little bit of paradise by hand. Guests can enjoy the 30 allotments with a huge variety of vegetables, fruit and flowers. Despite no mains water or electricity and facing high winds and cold winter temperatures, the allotments produce asparagus, grapes and specialist raspberries along with the more usual vegetables and fruit.

Open: Saturday 6 July, 10am - 4pm, admission £4.00, children free.

Directions: Leaving Crieff on the A85, turn right towards The Famous Grouse Distillery then immediately left up a track. From the small parking area is a signposted path. It is uphill and not wheelchair accessible. Parking on Turretbank Road also possible.

· *Charity to be confirmed*

4

ARDVORLICH
Lochearnhead FK19 8QE
Mr and Mrs Sandy Stewart
T: 01567 830218

Beautiful hill garden featuring over 170 different species of rhododendrons and many hybrids, grown in a glorious setting of oaks and birches on either side of the Ardvorlich Burn. The paths are quite steep and rough in places and boots are advisable, especially when wet.

Open: 1 May - 2 June, 9am - Dusk, admission £4.00, children free.

Directions: On South Loch Earn Road three miles from Lochearnhead, five miles from St Fillans.

· *The Gurkha Welfare Trust*

5

BLAIR CASTLE GARDENS
Blair Atholl PH18 5TL
Blair Charitable Trust
T: 01796 481207 **E:** office@blair-castle.co.uk
W: www.blair-castle.co.uk

Blair Castle stands as the focal point in a designed landscape of some 2,500 acres within a large and traditional estate. Hercules Garden is a walled enclosure of about nine acres recently restored to its original 18th-century form with landscaped ponds, a Chinese bridge, plantings, vegetables and an orchard of more than 100 fruit trees. The glory of this garden in summer is the herbaceous border, which runs along the 275 yard south-facing wall. A delightful sculpture trail incorporates contemporary and 18th-century sculpture as well as eight new works, letter-carving on stone from the Memorial Arts Charity's Art and Memory Collection. Diana's Grove is a magnificent stand of tall trees including grand fir, Douglas fir, larch and wellingtonia in just two acres.

Open: Saturday 29 June, 9:30am - 4:30pm, for admission details see the Blair Castle website.

Directions: Off A9, follow signs to *Blair Castle*, *Blair Atholl*.

· *Donation to SGS Beneficiaries*

PERTH & KINROSS

GARDENS OPEN ON A SPECIFIC DATE

Cloan, by Auchterarder	Sunday, 17 February
Kilgraston School, Bridge of Earn	Sunday, 24 February
Rossie Gardens, Forgandenny	Sunday, 3 March
Megginch Castle, Errol	Sunday, 21 April
The Steading at Clunie, Newmill of Kinloch, Clunie, Blairgowrie	Sunday, 28 April
Cloan, by Auchterarder	Sunday, 5 May
Fingask Castle, Rait	Sunday, 5 May
Gleneagles House, Auchterader	Monday, 6 May
Gleneagles House, Auchterader	Monday, 13 May
SGS Plant Sale at Bradystone House, Murthly	Sunday, 19 May
Rossie Gardens, Forgandenny	Saturday, 25 May
The Steading at Muckhart, Yetts O'Muckhart, Dollar	Sunday, 26 May
Delvine, Murthly	Sunday, 26 May
Gleneagles House, Auchterader	Monday, 27 May
Explorers Garden, Pitlochry	Sunday, 2 June
Bonhard House, Perth	Sunday, 2 June
Gleneagles House, Auchterader	Monday, 3 June
Cloan, by Auchterarder	Sunday, 9 June
Mill of Forneth, Forneth, Blairgowrie	Sunday, 9 June
Abernethy Open Gardens, Abernethy	Saturday, 15 June
The Bield at Blackruthven, Blackruthven House, Tibbermore	Saturday, 15 June
Blair Castle Gardens, Blair Atholl	Saturday, 29 June
Allotment Association of Crieff, Turretbank Road Crieff	Saturday, 6 July
Bridge of Earn Gardens, The Institute, Station Road	Sunday, 28 July
Mount Tabor House, Mount Tabor Road, Perth	Sunday, 4 August
Drummond Castle Gardens, Crieff	Sunday, 4 August
Wester House of Ross, Comrie	Saturday/Sunday, 10/11 August
Cloan, by Auchterarder	Wednesday, 14 August

PERTH & KINROSS

GARDENS OPEN REGULARLY

Glenericht House Arboretum, Blairgowrie	24 January - 31 December
Braco Castle, Braco	27 January - 31 October
Bolfracks, Aberfeldy	1 April - 31 October
Glendoick, Glencarse, Perthshire	1 April - 31 May
The Garden at Craigowan, Ballinluig	15 April - 31 August
Ardvorlich, Lochearnhead	1 May - 2 June
Carig Dhubh, Bonskeid, Pitlochry	1 May - 30 August
Bradystone House, Murthly	30 May - 8 August (Thursdays only)

GARDENS OPEN BY ARRANGEMENT

Fingask Castle, Rait	28 January - 7 March (Mondays & Thursdays)
Mill of Forneth, Forneth, Blairgowrie	1 April - 31 July
Eastbank Cottage, Perth Road, Abernethy	1 April - 30 June
Hollytree Lodge, Muckhart, Dollar	1 April - 31 October
Glenlyon House, Fortingall	1 April - 30 September
Tombuie and Little Tombuie, Killiechassie, Aberfeldy	1 May - 31 July
Parkhead House, Parkhead Gardens, Burghmuir Road, Perth	1 May - 30 September
Pitcurran House, Abernethy	1 May - 30 September
7 Drum Gate, Abernethy, Perthshire	30 May - 30 June
Dowhill, Cleish	4 June - 25 June (Tuesdays only)

Perth & Kinross

1 7 DRUM GATE

Abernethy, Perthshire PH2 9SA
Helen Morrison
E: helen72.hm@gmail.com

What started out in 2004 as just under an acre of bare earth has now turned into an attractive garden split into extensive herbaceous borders, large lawn areas and a young woodland with metasequoias, tulip tree, rhododendrons and wonderful views across the Tay Valley and upwards to the Ochils. The garden continues to develop and mature with earlier planting of topiary and hedging now being able to be sculptured and fruit trees and shrubs bearing produce. Visitors can meander through the garden, pausing in the children's Hideaway Cottage to listen and observe the many species of birds attracted to the garden. Work is ongoing but this is a rare example of what can be achieved from a blank canvas given vision, determination and plenty of time and patience.

Open: Open by arrangement 30 May - 30 June, admission by donation.

Directions: Seven miles south of Perth. Leave the M90 at Junction 9 and follow signs for *Abernethy, Newburgh* and *Cupar* on the A912 for approximately five miles. Garden Owner will give detailed directions on request.

· *Search and Rescue Dog Association Scotland (SCIO)*

2 ABERNETHY OPEN GARDENS

Abernethy PH2 9JJ
The Gardeners of Abernethy
E: keir.allen@gmail.com

An na Beatha 27-29 Main Street PH29JH (Heather and Reid Martin): The garden is on the main street within the conservation village and is a classic example of the village long garden that is common to the area. An orchard, vegetable patch and polytunnels are complemented by a wide range of perennials.
Carey House PH2 9LN (Caroline Boyle): An artist's garden with impressive planting, sculptures dotted throughout, ponds, summerhouse and much more. This large garden has been created from bare fields in the last ten years and continues to improve with age.
Eastbank Cottage Perth Road PH2 9LR (Mike and Elsa Thompson): Traditional Scottish cottage, a third of an acre garden, walled and bounded by a small burn to the east. Erythroniums, varieties of wood anemones, trillium, a fine display of clematis, rhododendrons and azaleas. This garden is also open by arrangement 1 April - 30 June.
Gattaway PH2 9LQ (Mr Chris Farmer): A work in progress but the progress has been spectacular. A pair of walled gardens, one with hens, the other with soft fruit and pigs, a series of lawns with border are all being developed into a beautiful garden with views down onto the village.
Mornington Cottage School Wynd PH2 9JJ (Keir Allen): A large vegetable garden, bordered by espalier apple trees and a range of soft fruits. The garden is linked to the old garden of the house with an orchard, a croquet lawn and borders of shrubs and flowers.
Nurse Peattie's Garden Main Street PH2 (Abernethy in Bloom): This garden is the hub of the work that *Abernethy in Bloom* carry out around the whole village. It is a colourful and tranquil escape which has been restored to its former glory in the last four years.

Open: Saturday 15 June, 10am - 5pm, admission £5.00, children free. The main ticket hub is at Mornington Cottage, School Wynd PH2 9JJ (just up the wynd from the village museum) and they can also be obtained from individual gardens.

Directions: Abernethy is seven miles south of Perth. Leave M90 and follow signs for Abernethy. Parking will be clearly signed on the day and will be in the potato factory (Brantons) and the school car park. Hourly buses run from Perth and Glenrothes.

· *Abernethy in Bloom*

Perth & Kinross

3

ALLOTMENT ASSOCIATION OF CRIEFF
Turretbank Road Crieff PH7 4AR
The Allotmenteers
E: crieffplots@gmail.com

The allotments sit high above the River Turret with panoramic views of Glen Turret and towards St Fillans, one of the most scenic allotment locations in Scotland. Previously the ground was used for grazing and lacked vehicular access, so allotmenteers created this little bit of paradise by hand. Guests can enjoy the 30 allotments with a huge variety of vegetables, fruit and flowers. Despite no mains water or electricity and facing high winds and cold winter temperatures, the allotments produce asparagus, grapes and specialist raspberries along with the more usual vegetables and fruit.

Open: Saturday 6 July, 10am - 4pm, admission £4.00, children free.

Directions: Leaving Crieff on the A85, turn right towards The Famous Grouse Distillery then immediately left up a track. From the small parking area is a signposted path. It is uphill and not wheelchair accessible. Parking on Turretbank Road also possible.

· *Charity to be confirmed*

4

ARDVORLICH
Lochearnhead FK19 8QE
Mr and Mrs Sandy Stewart
T: 01567 830218

Beautiful hill garden featuring over 170 different species of rhododendrons and many hybrids, grown in a glorious setting of oaks and birches on either side of the Ardvorlich Burn. The paths are quite steep and rough in places and boots are advisable, especially when wet.

Open: 1 May - 2 June, 9am - Dusk, admission £4.00, children free.

Directions: On South Loch Earn Road three miles from Lochearnhead, five miles from St Fillans.

· *The Gurkha Welfare Trust*

5

BLAIR CASTLE GARDENS
Blair Atholl PH18 5TL
Blair Charitable Trust
T: 01796 481207 **E:** office@blair-castle.co.uk
W: www.blair-castle.co.uk

Blair Castle stands as the focal point in a designed landscape of some 2,500 acres within a large and traditional estate. Hercules Garden is a walled enclosure of about nine acres recently restored to its original 18th-century form with landscaped ponds, a Chinese bridge, plantings, vegetables and an orchard of more than 100 fruit trees. The glory of this garden in summer is the herbaceous border, which runs along the 275 yard south-facing wall. A delightful sculpture trail incorporates contemporary and 18th-century sculpture as well as eight new works, letter-carving on stone from the Memorial Arts Charity's Art and Memory Collection. Diana's Grove is a magnificent stand of tall trees including grand fir, Douglas fir, larch and wellingtonia in just two acres.

Open: Saturday 29 June, 9:30am - 4:30pm, for admission details see the Blair Castle website.

Directions: Off A9, follow signs to *Blair Castle*, *Blair Atholl*.

· *Donation to SGS Beneficiaries*

Perth & Kinross

6

BOLFRACKS
Aberfeldy PH15 2EX
The Douglas Hutchison Trust
T: 01887 820344 **E:** athel@bolfracks.com

Special three acre garden with wonderful views overlooking the Tay Valley. Burn garden with rhododendrons, azaleas, primulas and meconopsis in a woodland garden setting. Walled garden with shrubs, herbaceous borders and rose 'rooms' with old-fashioned roses. There is also a beautiful rose and clematis walk. Peony beds are underplanted with tulips and Japanese anemone. The garden has a great selection of bulbs in spring and good autumn colour.

Open: 1 April - 31 October, 10am - 6pm, admission £5.00, children free.

Directions: Two miles west of Aberfeldy on A827. White gates and lodge are on the left. Look out for the brown tourist signs.

· *SGS Beneficiaries*

7

BONHARD HOUSE
Perth PH2 7PQ
Stephen and Charlotte Hay
T: 01738 552471

A traditional 19th-century garden of five acres approached through an avenue of magnificent oaks. Mature trees, six classified by the National Tree Register as 'remarkable', including a handsome monkey puzzle, sequoias, Douglas fir and a wide variety of hollies. Grassy paths wind around ponds, rockeries, flowering shrubs and smaller trees, providing some splendid perspectives. Rhododendron and azalea beds and a productive kitchen garden. There is a Pinetum on a knoll behind the house containing 25 species.

Open: Sunday 2 June, 10am - 4pm, admission £4.00, children free.

Directions: On A94 just under a mile north of Perth take right turn, signed *Murrayshall Hotel*. After approxiamately one mile take entrance right marked *Bonhard House* at a sharp left turn. From Balbeggie turn left, signposted for *Bonhard*, one mile north of Scone. Turn right in a half a mile, pass any sign for *Bonhard Nursery,* and enter drive at sharp right turn.

· *Freedom from Fistula Foundation*

'Gardens are perfect for
younger visitors to explore
and open their minds'

Perth & Kinross

8

BRACO CASTLE
Braco FK15 9LA
Mr and Mrs M van Ballegooijen
T: 01786 880437

A 19th-century landscaped garden with a plethora of wonderful and interesting trees, shrubs, bulbs and plants. An old garden for all seasons that has been extensively expanded over the last 26 years. The partly walled garden is approached on a rhododendron-and-tree-lined path featuring an ornamental pond. Spectacular spring bulbs, exuberant shrub and herbaceous borders, and many ornamental trees are all enhanced by the spectacular views across the park to the Ochils. From snowdrops through to vibrant autumn colour this garden is a gem. Look out for the embothrium in June, hoheria in August, eucryphia in September and an interesting collection of rhododendrons and azaleas with long flowering season.

Open: 27 January - 31 October, 10am - 5pm, including for Snowdrops and Winter Walks, admission £4.00, children free.

Directions: Take a one-and-a-half-mile drive from the gates at the north end of Braco Village, just west of the bridge on the A822. Parking at the castle is welcome.

· *The Woodland Trust Scotland*

9

BRADYSTONE HOUSE
Murthly PH1 4EW
Mrs James Lumsden
T: 01738 710308 **E:** pclumsden@me.com

This cottage garden was converted from a derelict farm steading to create a unique courtyard garden that bursts with colour throughout the season. It has been imaginatively planted by Patricia and her gardener Scott and has recently undergone some exciting changes. There is a woodland walk, with interesting trees underplanted with shrubs that leads to a duck pond where ducks and hens roam freely. There is also a small productive kitchen garden. A real gem of a garden; visitors who are fortunate enough to meet the owner and Scott will be impressed by their enthusiasm and knowledge.

Open: 30 May - 8 August (Thursdays only), 11am - 4pm, admission £5.00, children free.

Directions: From south/north follow A9 to Bankfoot, then sign to *Murthly*. At crossroads in Murthly take private road to Bradystone.

· *Scotland's Charity Air Ambulance*

Vibrant planting at Bradystone House, photo by Mike Nicoll

Perth & Kinross

10 BRIDGE OF EARN GARDENS
The Institute, Station Road, Bridge of Earn, Perthshire PH2 9EA
The Gardeners of Bridge of Earn

Bridge of Earn village gardens include a new-award winning Community Garden, and a variety of individual gardens. Key features to look out for include herbaceous borders, a small alpine rockery, mature trees in particular a huge copper beech tree, cordon fruit trees namely apple, pear and plum, vegetable-growing areas, wildlife areas including a beaver run and bug hotel, agricultural machinery and a collection of old implements celebrating Bridge of Earn's agricultural heritage. There are a couple of greenhouses and polytunnels, a magnificent lawn to rival Gleneagles golf course, pagodas and a pergola supporting roses and clematis. Some unusual shrubs and shade loving plants along with perennials and colourful annuals in pots and borders can be seen. The open gardens are:

2 Kilgraston Cottages PH2 9HG (William Robertson)
2 The Orchard PH2 9DX (Stanley and Kareen Robertson)
Brickhall Community Garden Edinburgh Road, PH2 (Avril Fulton)
Craigievairn Heughfield Road, PH2 9BG (George Watson)
Heughfield House Walled Garden Heughfield Road, Bridge of Earn PH2 9BH (Ian Cuthbert Imrie)
Inver Heughfield Road, PH2 9BH (Jack and Norma)
Kirkwall Manse Road, PH2 9DY (Angela Beale)
Tigh-na-Coille Rhynd Road, PH2 8PZ (Charlie and Carolyn Hamilton)

Open: Sunday 28 July, 2pm - 5pm, admission £5.00, children free.

Directions: From the north and south, take the exit on the M90 for *Bridge of Earn* and follow the road into the village, which is about 500 yards. Follow the *SGS* signs to the *Institute* in Station Road which is just off the Main Street in the centre of the village. There will be signs for *Tickets* and *Car Parks* (at the Institute and the Primary School).

· *Keep Scotland Beautiful: Brig in Bloom*

11 CARIG DHUBH
Bonskeid, Pitlochry PH16 5NP
Jane and Niall Graham-Campbell
T: 01796 473469 **E:** niallgc@btinternet.com

'I don't know how Niall and Jane manage to grow their splendid meconopsis on the sand and rock of their garden but they do, most successfully'. In this stunning situation, when not admiring the views, you will find wonderful primulas, cardiocrinum, meconopsis all interspersed between beautiful shrubs and other herbaceous plants. Look up and in July you will see roses flowering forty feet up in the tree. This is a gem of a garden and you will be welcomed by Niall and Jane Graham-Campbell with all their expert knowledge.

Open: 1 May - 30 August, 10:30am - 4:30pm, admission £5.00, children free.

Directions: Take the old A9 between Pitlochry and Killiecrankie, turn west on the Tummel Bridge Road B8019, Carig Dhubh is three-quarters of a mile on north side of the road.

· *Earl Haig Fund Poppy Scotland*

Perth & Kinross

12 **CLOAN**
by Auchterarder PH3 1PP
Neil Mitchison
T: 01764 664907 **E:** niall@fastmail.co.uk

Two acres of wild garden, with a wide variety of rhododendrons and azaleas, and an impressive collection of trees, including metasequoia, cryptomeria, *Acer cappadocicum*, *Sequoia sempervirens*, *Quercus robur* 'Filicifolia', liriodendron, several Japanese maples, magnificent beech and Scots pines trees, and extensive yew topiary; also an acre of walled garden with embothriums, *Acer griseum*, liquidamber, several sorbus varieties, parrotia and a large herbaceous border. Fine views of Strathearn from the front of the house.

Open: Sunday 17 February, 10am - 3pm for Snowdrops and Winter Walks. Also open Sunday 5 May, Sunday 9 June and Wednesday 14 August, 11am - 5pm. Admission £4.00, children free. Limited parking.

Directions: From A823, just south of A9, follow small road heading north east, signposted *Duchally*. Continue for approximately two and a half miles, turn right at sign *Coulshill*. Continue just under half a mile. Entrance through stone pillars on right.

· Camphill Scotland: Tiphereth (Sunday 17 February) & Camphill Scotland: Tipereth (Sunday 5 May, Wednesday 14 August & Sunday 9 June)

Herbaceous borders in the garden at Cloan

13 **DELVINE**
Murthly PH1 4LD
Mr and Mrs David Gemmell
T: 01738 710485 **E:** gemmell.david@googlemail.com

The gardens at Delvine are situated around the famous Roman legionary fortress of Inchtuthil. The old gardens of the original Delvine House now merge with a most unusual venture. Below the great banks of Inchtuthil surrounded by water, a very different landscape emerges. You will find great drifts of miscanthus grasses, the wonderful and rare bamboos of *Chusquea gigantea* and chimonobambusa, unusual birches and some very special trees. For the adventurous, this garden is recommended.

Open: Sunday 26 May, 2pm - 6pm, admission £5.00, children free. Boots or waterproof shoes are a must if it is wet. For those needing help, a utility vehicle is available with a driver.

Directions: On A984, seven miles east of Dunkeld, four miles south west of Blairgowrie.

· ABF The Soldiers' Charity

Perth & Kinross

DOWHILL
Cleish KY4 0HZ
Mrs Colin Maitland Dougall
T: 01577 850207 **E:** pippamd@icloud.com

....

A peaceful garden that has matured over the last 25 years, with magnificent trees and woodland walks, ponds, poppies and swathes of primulas.

Open: Open by arrangement 4 June - 25 June (Tuesdays only), admission £5.00, children free.

Directions: Three quarters of a mile off the M90, exit five, towards Crook of Devon on the B9097 in the trees.

· **MND Scotland**

DRUMMOND CASTLE GARDENS
Crieff PH7 4HZ
Grimsthorpe & Drummond Castle Trust Ltd
W: www.drummondcastlegardens.co.uk

....

Activities and events for a great family day out. The gardens of Drummond Castle were originally laid out in 1630 by John Drummond, second Earl of Perth. In 1830 the parterre was changed to an Italian style. One of the most interesting features is the multi-faceted sundial designed by John Mylne, Master Mason to Charles I. The formal garden is said to be one of the finest in Europe and is the largest of its type in Scotland.

Open: Sunday 4 August, 1pm - 5pm, admission details can be found on the garden's website.

Directions: Entrance two miles south of Crieff on Muthill road (A822).

· **BLESMA**

EASTBANK COTTAGE
Perth Road, Abernethy PH2 9LR
Mike and Elsa Thompson
T: 01738 850539 **E:** mikestuartthompson@hotmail.com

....

Traditional Scottish cottage, a third-of-an-acre garden, walled and bounded by a small burn to the east. Erythroniums, varieties of wood anemones, trillium, a fine display of clematis, rhododendrons and azaleas. Altogether a little haven in the country.

Open: Open by arrangement 1 April - 30 June, admission by donation. Also open on Saturday 15 June as part of Abernethy Open Gardens.

Directions: When coming from Perth, drive past the Abernethy *30 mph* sign. A layby is on the left. The gate has the property name on it. Bus 36 stops very close.

· **SGS Beneficiaries**

Perth & Kinross

17
EXPLORERS GARDEN
Pitlochry PH16 5DR
Pitlochry Festival Theatre
W: www.explorersgarden.com

This six-acre woodland garden celebrates the Scottish plant hunters who risked their lives in search of new plants. The Explorers Garden is divided into geographic areas, each containing examples of the plants collected from that corner of the globe. Set in beautiful Highland Perthshire countryside, the garden is known for its meconopsis collection, stunning vistas and interesting sculptures and structures. Each year a photographic exhibition is held in the David Douglas Pavilion.
National Plant Collection: *Meconopsis*

Open: Sunday 2 June, 10am - 4:30pm, admission details can be found on the garden's website.

Directions: Take the A9 to Pitlochry town, then follow signs to *Pitlochry Festival Theatre*.

· *Acting for Others*

18
FINGASK CASTLE
Rait PH2 7SA
Mr and Mrs Andrew Murray Threipland
T: 01821 670777 ext 2 **E:** andrew@fingaskcastle.com
W: www.fingaskcastle.com

The garden with a sense of humour: *Alice in Wonderland* topiary staggers across the lawn, bumping into stone globes, marble balls and statues from three centuries. Historical and literary figures are scattered among pleasure gardens first laid out in the 18th century. Both Bonnie Prince Charlie and his father are said to have approached the castle from the longer yew parade, the Kings Walk. There is a marked 15-minute walk down the steep dell to a medieval wishing well (St Peter's), over a Chinese bridge crossing the Fingask Burn via the Iron Age Fort to Fingask Loch and Sir Stuart's House, back along another path to the orchard car park (wellies recommended). There are large drifts of snowdrops, daffodils and flowering shrubs depending on the season.
Champion Trees: *Pinus wallichiana* (Japanese maple)

Open: Open by arrangement 28 January - 7 March (Mondays & Thursdays) for Snowdrops and Winter Walks. Also open Sunday 5 May, 1:30pm - 4:30pm. Admission £3.00, children free (28 January - 7 March) and £4.00, children free (Sunday 5 May). Homemade teas only on 5 May.

Directions: Half-way between Perth and Dundee. From the A90 follow signs to Rait until small crossroad, turn right and follow signs to *Fingask*.

· *Fingask Follies & All Saints Church, Glencarse*

19
GLENDOICK
Glencarse, Perthshire PH2 7NS
Mr Kenneth Cox
T: 01738 860260 **E:** manager@glendoick.com
W: www.glendoick.com

Glendoick is the ideal spring day out with a visit to both the gardens and garden centre in April and May. The garden was included in the *Independent on Sunday* survey of Europe's top 50 gardens and has a unique collection of plants from Cox's plant-hunting expeditions in China and the Himalaya. Glendoick's five acres includes spectacular rhododendrons, magnolias and meconopsis, grown in the woodland garden with its burn and waterfalls, the walled garden and the gardens surrounding the house. Many Glendoick plants have been bred by the Cox family, and new unnamed hybrids are in the walled garden. The award-winning Glendoick Garden Centre has one of

Perth & Kinross

Scotland's best selections of plants including their world-famous rhododendrons and azaleas. National Plant Collection: *Rhododendron* sect. *Pogonanthum*, subsect. *Uniflora*, subsect. *Campylogyna* & subsect. *Glauca* and Cox hybrids.

Open: 1 April - 31 May, 10am - 4pm, admission £5.00, children free.

Directions: Follow brown signs to *Glendoick Garden Centre* off A90 Perth - Dundee road. Drive up driveway and park on gravel, gardens are a short walk up a slope. Bus X8 is hourly except on Sunday. Stops by garden centre, a half mile from garden.

· *Donation to SGS Beneficiaries*

GLENEAGLES HOUSE
Auchterader PH3 1PJ
Petronella Haldane
T: 01764 682388 **E:** petronella@gleneagles.org

Home of the Haldanes since the 13th century. This is a newly created wild garden which has been evolving for the last 20 years. There's a walk round the pond and along the burn past the 15th-century chapel to the ruins of a laird's tower.

Open: Monday 6 May, Monday 13 May, Monday 27 May & Monday 3 June, 2pm - 5pm, admission £5.00, children free.

Directions: A832 Crieff/Dunfermiline road just south of the A9.

· *St Kessog's Episcopal Church - Auchterarder*

GLENERICHT HOUSE ARBORETUM
Blairgowrie PH10 7JD
Mrs Mary McCosh
T: 01250 872092 **E:** m.mccosh123@gmail.com

Spectacular collection of Victorian-planted trees and shrubs which are centred around a Grade 'A' listed suspension bridge (1846). Ninety-two tree varieties, mostly conifers including a top Douglas fir which is 171 feet and still growing, also a collection of younger trees. In May you will be able to view the wonderful daffodils and the rhododendrons in flower.

Open: 24 January - 31 December, dawn - dusk, admission £4.00, children free. Honesty box in car parking area close to the river bridge.

Directions: Off the A93, the Lodge House is five miles north of Blairgowrie on the right-hand side A93 when coming from Blairgowrie. Follow the avenue to the bridge.

· *Sands*

Perth & Kinross

22 GLENLYON HOUSE
Fortingall PH15 2LN
Mr and Mrs Iain Wotherspoon
T: 07974 350533 **E:** thewotherspoons@ednet.co.uk

....

Interesting garden framed by hedges, with colourful herbaceous borders and fruit trees underplanted with perennials and annuals. There is a kitchen and cutting garden as well as a wildlife pond.

Open: Open by arrangement 1 April - 30 September, admission £5.00, children free.

Directions: Take the A827 to Aberfeldy, then B846 to Coshieville then turn off for Glen Lyon.

· *Fortingall Parish Church*

The gardens at Glenlyon House, photo by David Hay

23 HOLLYTREE LODGE
Muckhart, Dollar FK14 7JW
Liz and Peter Wyatt
T: 0797 337 4687 **E:** elizwyatt @aol.com

....

A tranquil one-acre garden, divided by internal hedges into 'rooms' as featured in *Country Homes & Interiors* January 2018. Highlights include a small Japanese garden, mini orchard, naturalised spring bulbs and wildflowers, rill and wildlife pond, mixed herbaceous borders, a variety of unusual trees, shrubs and a good collection of rhododendrons and azaleas, snow gum, *Metasequoia glyptostroboides*, Persian ironwood and acers, many producing spectacular autumn colours. Our aim is to garden with nature, complementing our beekeeping interests.

Open: Open by arrangement 1 April - 31 October, admission £4.00, children free.

Directions: Approximately 100 yards from the A91 (between Dollar and Milnathort) down the small lane directly opposite the entrance to the Inn at Muckhart.

· *Coronation Hall, Muckhart*

Perth & Kinross

24 KILGRASTON SCHOOL
Bridge of Earn PH2 9BQ
Suzanne Littlejohn
T: 01738 815517 **E:** marketing@kilgraston.com
W: www.kilgraston.com
....

Enjoy the carpet of snowdrops, admire the ancient yews, towering wellingtonias, and the resident red squirrels, whilst exploring the pathways and woodlands within the extensive grounds of this 19th-century house. Formerly home to the Grant family, it has been a girls' boarding school since 1930. Statues and sculptures, some by renowned architect Hew Lorimer, dot the landscape. There is a ruined chapel to visit in the grounds, a good children's play area and an excellent display of artwork within the school.

Open: Sunday 24 February, 1:30pm - 4pm for Snowdrops and Winter Walks, admission £4.00, children free.

Directions: Bridge of Earn is three miles south of Perth on the A912. *Kilgraston School* is well signposted from the main road. Maps are available at the school website.

· *Newlife - The Charity for Disabled Children*

25 MEGGINCH CASTLE
Errol PH2 7SW
Mr Giles Herdman and The Hon Mrs Drummond-Herdman of Megginch
T: 01821 642222 **E:** catherine@megginch.com
W: megginchcastle.com
....

Megginch Castle has been the much loved home of the Drummonds of Megginch since July 1664. Come and join with us in our traditional Easter Day celebrations: we need help from all ages to hunt for copious chocolate eggs hidden by the Easter Bunny. He will have hidden them among the swathes of heritage daffodils, in amongst the formal gardens, down the Beech Avenue (aided by his friend the Lollipop Tree Fairy), in the 18th-century cobbled courtyard, in the walled garden and extensive orchard and in amongst the two National Apple Collections! When you have had a good search round, head back for hot mugs of tea, home made cakes and sandwiches under the ancient yew trees.
National Plant Collection: Scottish cider apples, Scottish Heritage apples and pears.
Champion Trees: *Acer Palmatum* (Bhutan pine).

Open: Sunday 21 April, 2pm - 5pm, admission £4.00, children free.

Directions: Ten miles from Perth and Dundee directly off the A90, Perth-bound carriageway, 600 yards after the Errol/ Rait flyover, on the left hand side, 300 yards after *Beware Pedestrians Crossing* sign.

· *SGS Beneficiaries*

Perth & Kinross

26 **MILL OF FORNETH**
Forneth, Blairgowrie PH10 6SP
Mr and Mrs Graham Wood
E: gaw@gwpc.demon.co.uk

Built on the site of a watermill on the Lunan Burn, originally laid out in the 1970s by James Aitken, the Scottish landscape designer and naturalist. The sheltered four-acre garden has a range of mature trees, including a Himalayan blue cedar, large rhododendrons, azaleas and a wide range of shrubs. The former mill lade feeds rocky waterfalls and a lily pond. Planting includes established perennials with seasonal colours, many bulbs, primulas and heathers, plus a vegetable garden on the site of an old tennis court.

Open: Sunday 9 June, 2pm - 5pm. Also open by arrangement 1 April - 31 July. Admission £4.50, children free.

Directions: Take the A923 Dunkeld to Blairgowrie road. Six miles east of Dunkeld turn south onto a minor road signposted *Snaigow* and *Clunie*. Mill of Forneth is the first gate on the left-hand side.

· *Charity information to come*

The lily pond at the Mill of Forneth

27 **MOUNT TABOR HOUSE**
Mount Tabor Road, Perth PH2 7DE
Mr and Mrs John McEwan

Mature terraced town garden originally laid out in the late 19th century, but constantly evolving. A sheltered and peaceful garden surrounded by mature trees and hedges with well-filled herbaceous borders. There is a cascade of ponds filled with carp and other wildlife and lots of places to sit in the sun and relax.

Open: Sunday 4 August, 12pm - 4:30pm, admission £3.50, children free.

Directions: From Dundee Road in Perth at Isle of Skye Hotel, turn right into Manse Road, over the mini-roundabout and into Mount Tabor Road.

· *The Katie McKerracher Trust*

Perth & Kinross

PARKHEAD HOUSE
Parkhead Gardens, Burghmuir Road, Perth PH1 1RB
Mr and Mrs M S Tinson
T: 01738 625983 **M:**07748 186 815 **E:** maddy.tinson@gmail.com
W: www.parkheadgardens.com

Parkhead is an old farmhouse sited within an acre of beautiful gardens. Mature trees include an outstanding 300-year-old Spanish chestnut. This hidden gem is a garden for all seasons. Gentle terracing and meandering paths lead you past a large variety of unusual and interesting plants and shrubs. If you seek colour and inspiration come and see this garden.
National Plant Collection: *Lilium* (Mylnefield lilies).

Open: Open by arrangement 1 May - 30 September, admission £5.00, children free.

Directions: Parkhead Gardens is on a small lane off the west end of Burghmuir Road in Perth. More detailed directions on request.

· *Plant Heritage*

PITCURRAN HOUSE
Abernethy PH2 9LH
The Hon Ranald and Mrs Noel-Paton
T: 01738 850933 **E:** patricianp@pitcurran.com

This end-of-village garden was created 15 years ago. It includes an interesting combination of trees, rare shrubs and herbaceous plants including azaleas, rhododendrons, tree peonies, trillums and veratrum. Also a rose pergola, eucryphias and a large west-facing hydrangea border for the later summer. Above the pond there is a good collection of pink- and white barked birches and an embryonic arboretum-

Open: Open by arrangement 1 May - 30 September, admission £5.00, children free.

Directions: South east of Perth. From M90 (exit nine) take A912 towards Glenfarg, go left at roundabout onto A913 to Abernethy. Pitcurran House is at the far eastern end of the village. Buses run through Abernethy from Perth and surrounding districts.

· *Juvenile Diabetes Research Foundation Limited*

'Hundreds of
gardens open
with us annually'

Perth & Kinross

30 ROSSIE GARDENS
Forgandenny PH2 9EH
Mr and Mrs David B Nichol
T: 01738 812265 **E:** judynichol@rossiehouse.co.uk
W: www.rossiegardens.com

This romantic garden has been establishing itself since 1657. It is a magical mystery tour of endless paths meandering under magnificent trees, unusual shrubs with a plethora of woodland bulbs and plants at your feet. Lift the branches of a *Hamamelis mollis* to find the startled heron take off from the pond and look up to the massive trunk of the *Abies alba* 100 feet up. From snowdrops to hellebores then trillium and bluebells, flowering shrubs and roses, the interest of the garden continues until the wonderful autumn colours. The sculptures are by David Annand and Nigel Ross. Look out for the ten-foot teapot and the yew table ready for the Mad Hatter's tea party! The garden is at its best in May.

Open: Sunday 3 March, 11am - 3pm. Also open Saturday 25 May, 2pm - 5pm. Admission £5.00, children free. Soup and rolls on Sunday 3 March, cream teas on Saturday 25 May.

Directions: Forgandenny is on the B935 between Bridge of Earn and Dunning.

· *Lyme Disease Action*

31 SGS PLANT SALE AT BRADYSTONE HOUSE
Murthly PH1 4EW
Mrs James Lumsden
T: 01738 710308 **E:** pclumsden@me.com

Plant sale of herbaceous plants, shrubs, including plants not normally found in garden centres.

Open: Sunday 19 May, 11am - 6pm, admission by donation.

Directions: From south/north follow A9 to Bankfoot, then sign to *Murthly*. At crossroads in Murthly take private road to Bradystone.

· *Blairgowrie Riding For The Disabled (SCIO) & Guide Dogs*

Perth & Kinross

32

THE BIELD AT BLACKRUTHVEN
Blackruthven House, Tibbermore PH1 1PY
The Bield Christian Co Ltd
T: 01738 583238 **E:** info@bieldatblackruthven.org.uk

The Bield is set in extensive grounds with well-maintained lawns, clipped hedges, flower meadow and specimen trees. Visitors can stroll around the grounds and explore the labyrinth cut into the grass of the old orchard. The main traditional walled garden has extensive herbaceous borders, manicured lawns and an organic vegetable plot. The walled garden has trained fruit trees, a fruit cage, a glasshouse and a healing garden. Garden visitors may also wish to visit Southron Smallholding - a ten-minute walk through the grounds to extensive vegetable plots, polytunnels and various animals. Not staffed on open day.

Open: Saturday 15 June, 2pm - 5pm, admission £5.00, children free.

Directions: From Dundee or Edinburgh, follow signs for *Glasgow, Stirling* and *Crianlarich* which lead onto the Perth bypass. Head west on the A85 signed to *Crieff/Crianlarich* to West Huntingtower. Turn left at the crossroads to *Madderty/Tibbermore*. Entrance is left after a half mile passing the gate lodge on your right. Parking signed to right at the steading.

· *The Bield At Blackruthven: Southron*

Water feature at Bradystone House, photo by Mike Nicoll

Perth & Kinross

33

THE GARDEN AT CRAIGOWAN
Ballinluig PH9 0NE
Ian and Christine Jones
T: 01796 482244 **E:** i.q.jones@btinternet.com

'I am just bowled over! I have never ever seen so many and such a variety of species rhododendrons growing in a private garden in this country!' - the reaction of an eminent gardener from Ireland. Craigowan is a hidden gem overlooking the Tay and Tummel valleys at an elevation of 600 feet. The garden of five acres has woodland, lawns and beautiful herbaceous and planted areas. The plant collection is mainly rhododendrons, magnolias, lilies and traditional companion plants as well as a wonderful show of meconopsis, and giant Himalayan lilies in June.

Open: 15 April - 31 August, 9am - dusk, admission £5.00, children free.

Directions: From north or south A9 to Ballinluig junction. Follow sign for *Tulliemet* and *Dalcapon*. Pass the filling station and Red Brolly Cafe. Turn right following the *Tulliemet/ Dalcapo* sign. This is a steep narrow road so take care. About a half mile up the road take a left turning with fields on either side and Craigowan is the first house on the left about a half mile along. Park on paviours adjoining house.

· *LUPUS UK*

34

THE STEADING AT CLUNIE
Newmill of Kinloch, Clunie, Blairgowrie PH10 6SG
Jean and Dave Trudgill
T: 01250 884263

The Steading at Newmill is situated on the Lunan Burn midway between lochs Clunie and Marlee. There is a small cottage garden with a fish pond that leads on to the wildflower meadow that, hopefully, will be carpeted with cowslips. A bridge over the tail-race of the old mill is the start of the woodland walk around two ponds and for about 600 yards along the Lunan Burn with displays of wood anemones, lady's smock and primoses. The area is a haven for wildlife with beavers burrowing into the banks of the mill race.

Open: Sunday 28 April, 2pm - 5pm, admission £4.50, children free.

Directions: Three miles west of Blairgowrie on the A923. About 600 yards after the Kinloch Hotel in the direction of Dunkeld take the track on the left, just after a mobile phone mast and a breeze-block wall. There is parking for ten vehicles on a paved area, and ample parking in a neighbour's field, provided the ground is not soft.

· *Save the Children UK*

Perth & Kinross

THE STEADING AT MUCKHART
Yetts O'Muckhart, Dollar FK14 7JT
Fiona Chapman
T: 01259 781559 **E:** davidfiona.chapman@gmail.com

Now 25 years old, this south-facing, rural garden situated at the foot of the Ochil hills continues to develop and rejuvenate. Curvaceous paths meander through a variety of terraced beds and ponds planted with a wide range of seasonal plants and species trees to give all-year colour and interest.

Open: Sunday 26 May, 2pm - 5pm, admission £5.00, children free. Opened as part of Muckhart village gardens within the last six years.

Directions: Situated at the Yetts of Muckhart junction on the A823/A91 Dunfermline/Crieff Road.

· *Support in Mind Scotland*

TOMBUIE AND LITTLE TOMBUIE
Killiechassie, Aberfeldy PH15 2JS
Mrs Sally Crystal
T: 01887 829344 **E:** sallycrystal1@gmail.com

Two adjoining gardens on a slope with fabulous views over the Tay valley by Aberfeldy, surrounded by native birch and oak plantations and an oriental arboretum. Tombuie garden was designed by Jean Crystal in the 1950s. Six drystone terraces of Mediterranean shrubs fan out below the house. Features include pink carpet thyme, shrub roses, nepeta, a dark *Acer palmatum* and bright rhododendron and hydrangea plants. Little Tombuie garden comprises two terraces, designed by Donald and Sally Crystal in 2010. A native hedgerow and wildflower bank provide a backdrop to specimen trees with seasonal colour. A rose pergola leads to raised beds and greenhouse. The lawn is a wildflower meadow, with rocks evoking fallen boulders once found here.

Open: Open by arrangement 1 May - 31 July, admission by donation.

Directions: From the A9 take the A827 to Aberfeldy. At traffic lights turn right onto the B846 and cross the river. Take the first right to Strathtay. Tombuie is about two miles along, opposite a small graveyard on the right and beside a large copper beech tree.

· *Alzheimer Scotland*

WESTER HOUSE OF ROSS
Comrie PH6 2JS
Mrs Sue Young

Wester House of Ross is a three-acre garden which has been developed over the last 18 years, including since it last opened two years ago. There will be a large plant stall, some in flower and others for September/October such as asters, phlox, agapanthus and rudbeckias. There is plenty for children to do in the woodlands and rolling down the steep grassy hill!

Open: Saturday/Sunday, 10/11 August, 1:30pm - 5pm, admission £4.00, children free.

Directions: On the A85 drive westwards through Comrie, past the White Church and at the end of the village take a left turn over a small bridge, signposted *Ross*. Then take the first right, signposted *Dalchonzie*. After a quart of a mile, turn left at the three large dustbins and follow the signs to parking and the garden.

· *Blythswood Care*

RENFREWSHIRE

Scotland's Gardens Scheme 2019 Guidebook is sponsored by INVESTEC WEALTH & INVESTMENT

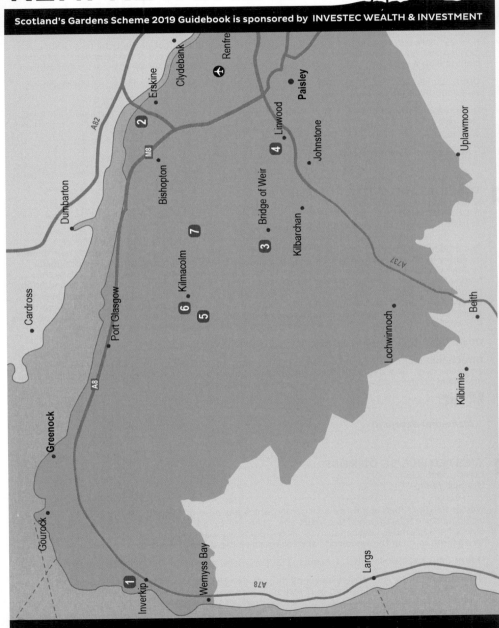

1. Ardgowan
2. Bravehound –
   Erskine Hospital
3. Carruth
4. Craig Hepburn Memorial
   Garden
5. Highwood
6. SGS Kilmacolm Plant Sale
7. Wraes

Renfrewshire

OUR VOLUNTEER ORGANISERS

District Organisers:	Rosemary Leslie	High Mathernock Farm, Auchentiber Road, Kilmacolm PA13 4SP T: 01505 874032
	Alexandra MacMillan	Langside Farm, Kilmacolm PA13 4SA T: 01475 540423 E: renfrewshire@scotlandsgardens.org
Area Organisers:	Helen Hunter	2 Bay Street, Fairlie, North Ayrshire KA29 0AL
	Barbara McLean	49 Middlepenny Road, Langbank PA14 6XE
Treasurer:	Jean Gillan	Bogriggs Cottage, Carlung, West Kilbride, North Ayrshire KA23 9PS

GARDENS OPEN ON A SPECIFIC DATE

SGS Kilmacolm Plant Sale, outside Kilmacolm Library, Kilmacolm	Saturday, 27 April
Highwood, off Lochwinnoch Road, Kilmacolm	Sunday, 12 May
Wraes, Corseliehill Road, nr Houston	Sunday, 19 May
Carruth, Bridge of Weir	Saturday, 25 May
Ardgowan, Inverkip	Sunday, 2 June
Bravehound - Erskine Hospital, Old Garden Centre, Bishopton	Sunday, 21 July
Craig Hepburn Memorial Garden, Stirling Drive, Linwood	Saturday, 7 September

Renfrewshire

ARDGOWAN
Inverkip PA16 0DW
Sir Ludovic Shaw Stewart
T: 01475 521656 **E:** info@ardgowan.co.uk
W: www.ardgowan.co.uk

In a lovely setting overlooking the River Clyde, James Ramsay laid out the beautifully landscaped 400-acre parkland in 1797. There is a rich and varied selection of trees from ancient, indigenous to native hardwoods. In the formal gardens, divided into different smaller areas, there is also an array of ornamental shrubs, herbaceous beds and several unique species of rhododendron. This is the first summer opening of the gardens at Ardgowan under Scotland's Garden Scheme.

Open: Sunday 2 June, 2pm - 5pm, admission £2.50, children free. The house will be open for tours, admissions charges apply. Please consult website for further details.

Directions: Inverkip one and a half miles. Glasgow/Largs buses to and from Inverkip village. Please use the main entrance at the roundabout to come in and leave by the Marina entrance, to avoid congestion.

· *Ardgowan Hospice*

Stunning view of Ardgowan and the River Clyde

Renfrewshire

2

BRAVEHOUND – ERSKINE HOSPITAL
Old Garden Centre, Bishopton PA7 5PU
Glen Art Volunteers
E: bravehound@glenart.co.uk
W: bravehhound.co.uk

A quirky enclosed tarmac garden, run by the charity Glen Art, features an assortment of outdoor raised planters, covered growing areas, shady/quiet garden and other features embracing the upcycling ethos. Glen Art helps those from a military background return to civilian life through a variety of creative ventures, and this garden can testify to the therapeutic benefits of gardens and dogs. Being the 'Bravehound' site, this new project looks to provide companion dogs to veterans to support their transition to civilian life. There may be doggy displays in an enclosed part of the garden.

Open: Sunday 21 July, 1pm - 4pm, admission £3.50, children free.

Directions: From the M8, take the exit for Erskine Bridge and turn off to Bishopton. From the North, go over Erskine Bridge, take the turning to Bishopton. Located on the south side of the Erskine Bridge, enter the Erskine Home Estate and follow signs for *Bravehound*.

· *BRAVEHOUND*

Bravehound–Erskine Hosptial

3

CARRUTH
Bridge of Weir PA11 3SG
Mr and Mrs Charles Maclean

Over 20 acres of long-established rhododendrons, woodland with good bluebells, young arboretum and lawn gardens in a lovely landscaped setting.

Open: Saturday 25 May, 2pm - 5pm, admission £4.00, children free.

Directions: Access from B786 Kilmacolm/Lochwinnoch road. Turn right and after about 100 yards, the garden entrance is on the right. About three and a half miles from Kilmacolm and five and a half miles from Lochwinnoch on the B786.

· *Marie Curie: Renfrewshire*

Renfrewshire

CRAIG HEPBURN MEMORIAL GARDEN
Stirling Drive, Linwood PA3 3NB
Linwood High School
T: 01505 336146 **E:** craighepburnmemorialgarden@yahoo.co.uk
W: Facebook (Craig Hepburn Memorial Garden)

The Craig Hepburn Memorial Garden and Outdoor Learning Centre is located in Linwood High School. Our original garden with an outdoor classroom has been expanded to include community raised beds, an orchard, greenhouse and presentation area. We work with all years in the school reconnecting them to the natural world whether it is through growing in our organic garden, encouraging biodiversity or learning ab,out sustainability.

Open: Saturday 7 September, 2pm - 5pm, admission £3.50, children free. Face painting, bouncy castle, 'how-to' classes and planting seeds.

Directions: Exit the M8 at St James Interchange and take the A737. Take the exit for Linwood onto the A761, follow to Clippens Road and then Stirling Drive. Accessible by McGill buses.

· *Accord Hospice*

HIGHWOOD
off Lochwinnoch Road, Kilmacolm PA13 4TF
Dr Jill Morgan

A beautiful woodland walk around 50 acres of native bluebells in a delightful setting bordering the Green Water river with tumbling waterfalls. A haven of tranquility only three miles from the centre of Kilmalcolm.

Open: Sunday 12 May, 2pm - 5pm, admission £3.00, children free. Stout waterproof footwear is recommended as the footpath is uneven and can be muddy in inclement weather. Dogs are welcome on a lead. Fantastic opportunities for lovers of wild flowers and photography.

Directions: Take the B786 Lochwinnoch road out of Kilmacolm and continue for approximately two miles. From Lochwinnoch take the B786 Kilmacolm road for approximately six miles. Then follow the yellow *SGS* signs.

· *Orkidstudio*

SGS KILMACOLM PLANT SALE
outside Kilmacolm Library, Kilmacolm PA13 4LE
Scotland's Garden Scheme Renfrewshire Committee

Spring plant sale in the middle of Kilmacolm.

Open: Saturday 27 April, 10am - 12pm, admission by donation.

Directions: The plant sale will be held at the Cross outside the Library and Cargill centre. Accessible by McGill Buses.

· *SGS Beneficiaries*

Renfrewshire

WRAES

7

Corseliehill Road, nr Houston PA6 7HU
Tim and Jo Mack

A new seven acre garden developed since 2012, with far reaching rural views. Only surviving historic 1860 wood planted by Lady Anne Spiers of Houston House for the Wraes. Formal garden with raised herbaceous borders, with 100 plus rhododendron species and hybrids. Pond, burnside walk, peaceful woodland walk with seating areas to allow visitors to take in the surrounding views. Large productive garden. Croquet lawn.

Open: Sunday 19 May, 2pm - 5pm, admission £4.00, children free. Walking boots or wellies recommended.

Directions: From Houston follow Barochan Road towards Langbank B789 for about a mile, turn left down Corseliehill Road. From Kilmacolm leave the village on Houston Road, past golf course, turn left down Corseliehill Road for about a mile. Follow the yellow *SGS* signs.

· *Breast Cancer Care*

Tulips and scenic views from Wraes

ROXBURGHSHIRE

Scotland's Gardens Scheme 2019 Guidebook is sponsored by INVESTEC WEALTH & INVESTMENT

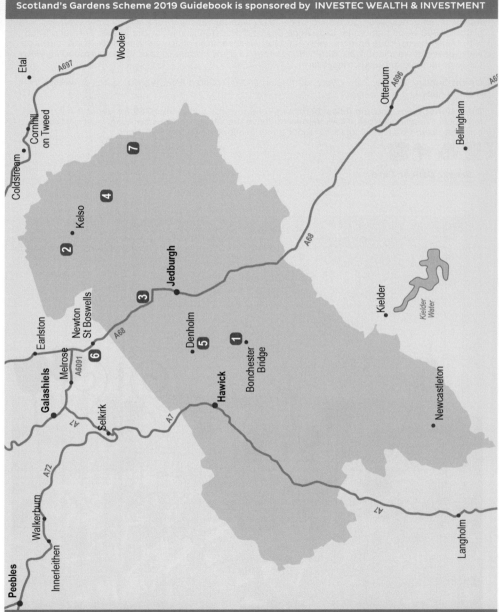

1. Easter Weens
2. Floors Castle
3. Monteviot
4. Thirlestane
5. West Leas
6. Whiterigg
7. Yetholm Village Gardens

Renfrewshire

7 WRAES
Corseliehill Road, nr Houston PA6 7HU
Tim and Jo Mack

A new seven acre garden developed since 2012, with far reaching rural views. Only surviving historic 1860 wood planted by Lady Anne Spiers of Houston House for the Wraes. Formal garden with raised herbaceous borders, with 100 plus rhododendron species and hybrids. Pond, burnside walk, peaceful woodland walk with seating areas to allow visitors to take in the surrounding views. Large productive garden. Croquet lawn.

Open: Sunday 19 May, 2pm - 5pm, admission £4.00, children free. Walking boots or wellies recommended.

Directions: From Houston follow Barochan Road towards Langbank B789 for about a mile, turn left down Corseliehill Road. From Kilmacolm leave the village on Houston Road, past golf course, turn left down Corseliehill Road for about a mile. Follow the yellow *SGS* signs.

· *Breast Cancer Care*

Tulips and scenic views from Wraes

ROXBURGHSHIRE

Scotland's Gardens Scheme 2019 Guidebook is sponsored by **INVESTEC WEALTH & INVESTMENT**

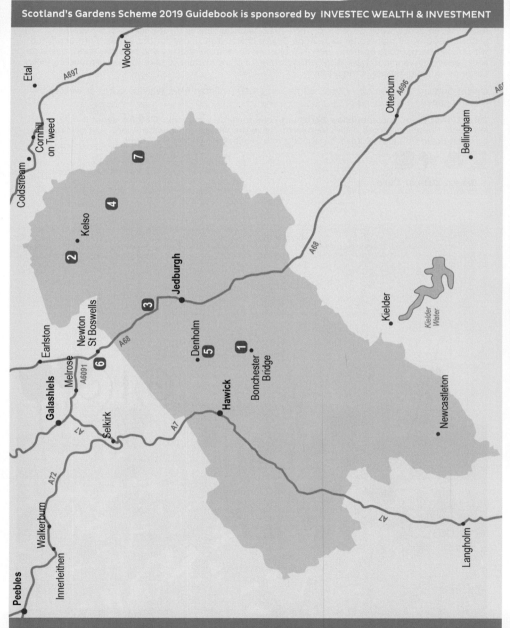

1. Easter Weens
2. Floors Castle
3. Monteviot
4. Thirlestane
5. West Leas
6. Whiterigg
7. Yetholm Village Gardens

ROXBURGHSHIRE

GARDENS OPEN ON A SPECIFIC DATE

West Leas, Bonchester Bridge   Sunday, 2 June
Easter Weens, Bonchester Bridge, Hawick   Saturday, 6 July
Yetholm Village Gardens, Town Yetholm   Sunday, 7 July
Whiterigg, nr Melrose   Sunday, 28 July
West Leas, Bonchester Bridge   Sunday, 4 August

GARDENS OPEN REGULARLY

Floors Castle, Kelso   1 January - 31 December
Monteviot, Jedburgh   1 April - 31 October

GARDENS OPEN BY ARRANGEMENT

West Leas, Bonchester Bridge   1 January - 31 December
Thirlestane, Kelso   31 March - 31 October

'Love your garden?
Why not share it with
others and open in 2020?'

Roxburghshire

EASTER WEENS
Bonchester Bridge, Hawick TD9 8JQ
Roger and Alison Curtis

Formal garden set within former stable courtyard and informal grounds designed by Percy Cane in 1958. Terraced rhododendron bank, vegetable gardens and woodland walks. Terraced parterre planted in 2005. Recently acquired revolving summer house with adjacent developing borders. Cutting garden in the process of being developed.

Open: Saturday 6 July, 2pm - 5:30pm, admission £5.00, children £1.00.

Directions: The property is on the B6357 on the Jedburgh side of Bonchester Bridge, just north of Bonchester Care Home. Parking is available in the farm yard.

· *Borders Childrens Charity*

Fine display of tulips at Easter Weens

FLOORS CASTLE
Kelso TD5 7SF
The Duke of Roxburghe
T: 01573 223333
W: www.floorscastle.com

The gardens are situated within the grounds of Floors Castle. Meander through to the formal Millennium Parterre and soak up the spectacular visions of colour, texture and the most delicious scents around the four herbaceous borders in one of the finest Victorian kitchen gardens in Scotland. New perennial gardens, fruit cage, Tapestry Garden and glasshouse access. Terrace Cafe, Castle Kitchen Deli shop and play area. Explore the grounds, which offer woodland and riverside walks from Easter to October.

Open: Daily, 11am - 5pm, admission details can be found on the garden's website. See website for details on the snowdrop, Easter and daffodil weekends and winter and summer opening hours. Please note that last admission is 30 minutes before closing time.

Directions: Floors Castle can be reached by following the A6089 from Edinburgh; the B6397 from Earlston; or the A698 from Coldstream. Go through Kelso, up Roxburgh Street to the Golden Gates.

· *Donation to SGS Beneficiaries*

Roxburghshire

3

MONTEVIOT
Jedburgh TD8 6UQ
Marquis and Marchioness of Lothian
T: 01835 830380
W: www.monteviot.com

A series of differing gardens including a herb garden, rose garden, water garden linked by bridges, and river garden with herbaceous and shrub borders of foliage plants. The Garden of Persistent Imagination has been recently created and planted with rose and clematis avenues leading to a Moonstone Gate.

Open: 1 April - 31 October, 12pm - 5pm, admission details can be found on the garden's website. Last entry to the garden is 4pm.

Directions: Turn off A68, three miles north of Jedburgh on to B6400. After one mile turn right.

· *Donation to SGS Beneficiaries*

4

THIRLESTANE
Kelso TD5 8PD
Catherine Ross and John Wylie
T: 01573 420487

Thirlestane is a large, informal garden, with some rough ground and long grass. It previously opened as one of the Yetholm gardens, but since then a nine-acre wood has been planted. This young woodland has a wide mix of trees, including some specimen trees. A spiral mount gives views of the Cheviot hills. There are two ponds and a burn. An orchard has about 50 varieties of apples and other fruit trees. Beech hedges enclose prairie planting in a formal setting. There is an enclosed flower garden, raised beds for vegetables and colour-themed planting.

Open: Open by arrangement 31 March - 31 October, admission £4.00, children free.

Directions: Thirlestane is near Yetholm, not to be confused with Thirlestane, Lauder. Do not follow SatNav, it will try to take you to Lochside. From Kelso, take the B6352 towards Yetholm for about six miles. Continue past a cottage on the edge of the road. Thirlestane is next on the left, opposite the road to Lochside. From Yetholm, take the road to Kelso for about two miles. After a very sharp corner, Thirlestane is on the right.

· *Macmillan Cancer Support*

Impressive herbaceous borders at Floors Castle, photo by Pete Seaward

Roxburghshire

WEST LEAS
Bonchester Bridge TD9 8TD
Mr and Mrs Robert Laidlaw
T: 01450 860711 **E:** ann@johnlaidlawandson.co.uk

The visitor to West Leas can share in the exciting and dramatic project on a grand scale still in the making. At its core is a passion for plants allied to a love and understanding of the land in which they are set. Collections of perennials and shrubs, many in temporary holding quarters, lighten up the landscape to magical effect. New lily pond and woodland planting are ongoing for 2019.

Open: Sunday 2 June and Sunday 4 August, 2pm - 5pm. And open by arrangement on request. Admission £4.00, children free. Teas for the specific date openings will be served in Bedrule Hall.

Directions: Signposted off the Jedburgh/Bonchester Bridge Road.

· *Macmillan Cancer Support: Borders Appeal*

Primulas at the water edge in the garden at West Leas, photo by Bernie Gajos

WHITERIGG
nr Melrose TD6 9HE
Robert Miller-Bakewell

A combination of formal and woodland gardens plus walled orchard/vegetable gardens. Substantially created since 2006. A ha-ha optimises the southerly views to Cheviots and Carter Bar.

Open: Sunday 28 July, 2pm - 5pm, admission £5.00, children free.

Directions: One mile west of the A68 on the south side of the Eildon Hills.

· *The Injured Jockeys Fund*

Roxburghshire

YETHOLM VILLAGE GARDENS
Town Yetholm TD5 8RL
The Gardeners of Yetholm village

The villages of Town and Kirk Yetholm are situated at the north end of the Pennine Way and lie close to the Bowmont Water in the dramatic setting of the foothills of the Cheviots. A variety of gardens with their own unique features, variety of styles and reflecting distinctive horticultural interests will be open. The Yew Tree Allotments running along the High Street, will open again, providing an ever-popular feature with their unique water collection and distribution system. The short walking distance between the majority of the gardens provides magnificent views of the surrounding landscape to include Staerough and The Curr, which straddle both the Bowmont and Halterburn valleys where evidence of ancient settlement remains. Attractions include the ever-popular music, local wood-turning products at Almond Cottage, home baking and produce stall. An excellent plant stall supported by Woodside Walled Garden Centre is also planned for the afternoon. Additional events include 'The Newest of Books' fair plus a Small Craft Stall feature.

Open: Sunday 7 July, 1pm - 5:30pm, admission £5.00, children free. Tickets are available in the local village hall.

Directions: Equidistant between Edinburgh and Newcastle. South of Kelso in the Scottish Borders take the B6352 to Yetholm village. Ample parking is available along the High Street.

· *Border Group Of Riding For The Disabled (SCIO)*

'60% of a garden's gross proceeds can be donated to garden owner's choice of charity'

STIRLINGSHIRE

Scotland's Gardens Scheme 2019 Guidebook is sponsored by **INVESTEC WEALTH & INVESTMENT**

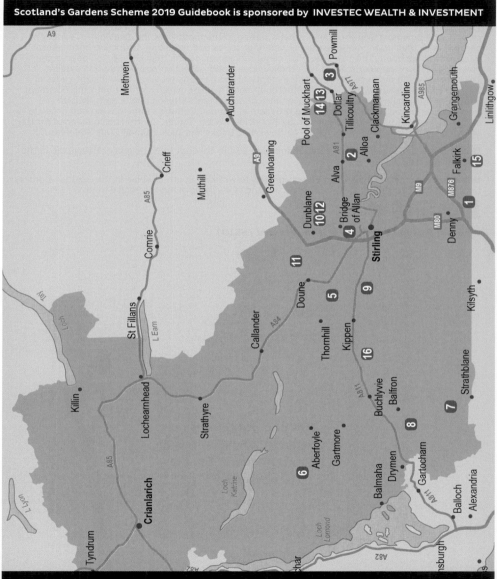

1. **43 Thornton Avenue**
2. **60 Greenhead**
3. **Arndean**
4. **Bridge of Allan Gardens**
5. **Coldoch**
6. **Dun Dubh**
7. **Duntreath Castle**
8. **Gardener's Cottage Walled Garden**
9. **Gargunnock House Garden**
10. **Hutcheson Farm**
11. **Kilbryde Castle**
12. **Kippenrait with St Blanes House**
13. **Rowberrow**
14. **The Japanese Garden at Cowden**
15. **The Tors**
16. **Thorntree**

STIRLINGSHIRE

OUR VOLUNTEER ORGANISERS

District Organiser:	Mandy Readman	Hutcheson Farm, Auchinlay Road, Dunblane FK15 9JS
		E: stirlingshire@scotlandsgardens.org
Area Organisers:	Clare Giles	Carselea Farm, Sommers Lane FK9 4UP
	Maurie Jessett	The Walled Garden, Lanrick, Doune FK16 6HJ
	Miranda Jones	122 High Street, Dunblane FK15 0ER
	Morna Knottenbelt	Gardener's Cottage Walled Garden, Killearn G63 9QB
	Rosemary Leckie	Auchengarroch, 16 Chalton Road FK9 4DX
	Ian Lumsden	The Myretoun, Menstrie FK11 7EB
	Iain Morrison	Clifford House, Balkerach Street, Doune FK16 6DE
	Ann Shaw	Plaka, 5 Pendreich Road, Bridge of Allan FK9 4LY
Treasurer:	David Ashton	Moon Cottage, Greenyards, Dunblane FK15 9NX

GARDENS OPEN ON A SPECIFIC DATE

Kilbryde Castle, Dunblane	Sunday, 5 May
Hutcheson Farm, Auchinlay Road, Dunblane	Sunday, 12 May
Gargunnock House Garden, Gargunnock	Sunday, 19 May
Bridge of Allan Gardens , Bridge of Allan	Sunday, 26 May
Coldoch, Blairdrummond, Stirling	Sunday, 2 June
The Japanese Garden at Cowden, Dollar, Clackmannanshire	Wednesday, 5 June
Kippenrait with St Blanes House, Sheriffmuir, Dunblane	Sunday, 9 June
Thorntree, Arnprior	Sunday, 23 June
43 Thornton Avenue, Bonnybridge	Sunday, 21 July
The Tors, 2 Slamannan Road, Falkirk	Sunday, 28 July
60 Greenhead, Alva, Clackmannanshire	Sunday, 4 August

GARDENS OPEN REGULARLY

Gargunnock House Garden, Gargunnock	9 February - 27 September (weekdays only)

GARDENS OPEN BY ARRANGEMENT

Duntreath Castle, Blanefield	1 February - 30 November
Rowberrow, 18 Castle Road, Dollar	1 February - 31 December
Kilbryde Castle, Dunblane	24 February - 30 September
Thorntree, Arnprior	1 April - 15 October
Dun Dubh, Kinlochard Road, Aberfoyle	19 April - 16 June & 1 September - 25 October
The Tors, 2 Slamannan Road, Falkirk	1 May - 30 September
Arndean, by Dollar	14 May - 10 June
Gardener's Cottage Walled Garden, Ballochruin Road, Killearn	15 June - 15 October

Stirlingshire

1

43 THORNTON AVENUE
Bonnybridge FK4 1AR
Tom Williamson and David Gallacher

Astonishing hidden garden on a corner site, almost in the shadow of the Antonine Wall. With over 450 different plants, mostly named, and nearly half in pots and containers. The display is outstanding and should readily inspire others to try gardening whatever the size of their plot.

Open: Sunday 21 July, 12pm - 4pm, admission £3.00, children free. Please park with consideration for other houses in the area. There may be plants for sale.

Directions: Signed from the A803. Bus from Glasgow.

· *Support Adoption for Pets*

2

60 GREENHEAD
Alva, Clackmannanshire FK12 5HH
Lynn Cameron

A delightful hidden garden in Alva behind the primary school. Divided into 'rooms' with themes, two being Mediterranean and Oriental, there is extensive planting and clever use of pots throughout. Recycled materials are much in evidence, and there is a wide variety of shrubs, perennials and annuals as well as vegetables and fruit. There is a pond and a small wildlife area. An inspiration for those trying to garden in a small spaces.

Open: Sunday 4 August, 2pm - 5pm, admission £3.00, children free. Please park with consideration for other houses in the area.

Directions: Signed from A91.

· *CAP: Stirling/Clacks Debt Centre*

The hidden garden at 60 Greenhead

Stirlingshire

3

ARNDEAN
by Dollar FK14 7NH
Johnny and Katie Stewart
T: 01259 743525 **E:** johnny@arndean.co.uk

Opening for more than 40 years, this is a beautiful mature garden extending to 15 acres including the woodland walk. There is a formal herbaceous part, a small vegetable garden and an orchard. In addition, there are flowering shrubs, abundant and striking rhododendrons and azaleas as well as many fine specimen trees. There is a tree house for children.

Open: Open by arrangement 14 May - 10 June, admission £5.00, children free.

Directions: Arndean is well signposted off the A977.

· *Marie Curie*

4

BRIDGE OF ALLAN GARDENS
Bridge of Allan FK9 4LY
The Gardeners of Bridge of Allan
E: r.leckie44@btinternet.com

Once again this year's Open Gardens will be a mixture of a few larger gardens and some smaller ones. A Victorian garden has a small Japanese Garden with a dry stream opening onto a dry pond with a turtle island in the middle. Various Japanese plants surround. One of the larger gardens is divided into different 'rooms', with various plantings, and a variety of sculptures and water features. Many of Bridge of Allan gardens are good spring ones so you should see varieties of azaleas, rhododendrons, magnolias, camellias and spring blossoms.

Open: Sunday 26 May, 1pm - 5pm, admission £5.00, children free. Teas from 1:30pm at St Saviours Church Hall, Keir Street, Bridge of Allan. Tickets and maps from all gardens. See SGS website for further details about the gardens nearer the time.

Directions: Signposted from village.

· *St Saviours Episcopal Church: Bridge Of Allan & Strathcarron Hospice*

5

COLDOCH
Blairdrummond, Stirling FK9 4XD
David & Kim Stewart and Tim Black
T: 01786 841217

The garden at Coldoch is sheltered by belts of mature woodland on three sides and looks south over the Carse of Stirling. The parterre courtyard garden and border have replaced the old farm buildings and lead on to a kitchen garden created by using the three old walls of an earlier rose garden. The less formal areas include a stream, a pond, paddocks and woodland. The drives are lined with old oaks and sycamores mixed with new trees from Eastern Europe, Central Asia and some fine mature cherry trees.

Open: Sunday 2 June, 2pm - 5pm, admission £5.00, children free.

Directions: Signed from the A84. Take the A873 for Aberfoyle, after just under one mile turn left on to Coldoch Road, B8031 and continue for approximately half a mile. Wrought iron gates on the left mark the entrance.

· *St Modocs Episcopal Church*

Stirlingshire

DUN DUBH
Kinlochard Road, Aberfoyle FK8 3TJ
Callum Pirnie, Head Gardener
T: 01877 382698 **E:** callumpirnie@gmail.com

A late Victorian garden of six acres undergoing restoration and development. It is set on a series of terraces and slopes, which run down to the shores of Loch Ard, with superb views west to Ben Lomond framed by stands of mature conifers. There is an enclosed, colour-themed formal garden laid out on three terraces and a new Victorian-style glasshouse overlooking a terraced kitchen and fruit garden. The formal paved terrace at the front of the house overlooks a newly developed rock garden and crag while the lower walk running from the boat house to the main lawn gives views across the loch. A developing woodland garden leads on to a formal late summer herbaceous border and terraced heather garden, all of which provide wonderful autumn colour.

Open: Open by arrangement 19 April - 16 June and 1 September - 25 October, admission £4.00, children free. Groups welcome.

Directions: Full directions will be given when contacting the garden.

· *Help for Heroes*

DUNTREATH CASTLE
Blanefield G63 9AJ
Sir Archibald and Lady Edmonstone
T: 01360 770215 **E:** juliet@edmonstone.com
W: www.duntreathcastle.co.uk

Extensive gardens with mature and new plantings. Ornamental landscaped lake and bog garden. Sweeping lawns below formal fountain and rose parterre with herbaceous border leading up to an attractive waterfall garden with shrubs and spring plantings. There is a good variety of herbaceous planting round the formal lawn which are overlooked by three terraces of ornamental shrubs. There is a woodland walk and a 15th-century keep and chapel.

Open: Open by arrangement 1 February - 30 November and including Snowdrops and Winter Walks, admission £4.00, children free.

Directions: A81 north of Glasgow between Blanefield and Killearn.

· *SGS Beneficiaries*

Stirlingshire

8

GARDENER'S COTTAGE WALLED GARDEN
Ballochruin Road, Killearn G63 9QB
Derek and Morna Knottenbelt
T: 01360 551682 **E:** mornaknottenbelt@hotmail.com

The walled garden, acquired in 2013 by the present owners, has been planted with extensive herbaceous borders, box hedging, roses and many unusual plants. There is a White Garden, a long shrub border with primulas and gentians and a former fernery with a collection of salvias and peach and pear trees. June is a good time to visit when the roses are in bloom and borders with lupins, peonies and other perennials are in flower. By late summer, the borders have argyranthemums as well as dahlias, Michaelmas daisies, rudbeckias and blue aconitums. There are fine views of the Campsie Hills and the garden is surrounded by the conifers of the Designed Landscape of Carbeth.

Open: Open by arrangement 15 June - 15 October, admission £5.00, children free.

Directions: Follow Satnav to G63 0LF, which is Carbeth Home Farm. We are next entrance below the farm. Turn left on to gravel road and follow yellow *SGS* signs.

· **The British Horse Society**

Blue skies at the Gardener's Cottage Walled Garden

Stirlingshire

GARGUNNOCK HOUSE GARDEN
Gargunnock FK8 3AZ
The Gargunnock Trustees
T: 01786 860392 **E:** gargunnockgardens@btinternet.com

Large mature garden five miles from Stirling, with a walled garden, well established house garden, woodland walks with species and hybrid rhododendrons, massed plantings of azaleas and wonderful specimen trees. Snowdrops in February/March are followed by over 40 varieties of daffodils and the glorious displays of azaleas and rhododendrons in May. In autumn, stunning colours develop on the many wonderful trees along the drive to the house. The three acre walled garden contains perennial borders, cut-flower beds, greenhouses, fruit orchard and newly planted arboretum of specimen trees.

Open: Sunday 19 May, 2pm - 5pm. Admission £5.00, children free. Also open 9 February - 17 March, 11am - 3:30pm for Snowdrops and Winter Walks. And open 18 March - 27 September (not Saturdays & Sundays), 11am - 3:30pm. Admission £4.00, children free. Teas and plant sale only on Sunday 19 May.

Directions: Five miles west of Stirling on A811, follow the yellow *SGS* signs. Car parking at entrance by lodge. Honesty box in car park.

· *Gargunnock Community Trust Ltd & Scotland's Charity Air Ambulance*

HUTCHESON FARM
Auchinlay Road, Dunblane FK15 9JS
Johnnie and Mandy Readman

On the site of a demolished farm steading of about an acre, a young garden is slowly evolving. Initial plantings of trees and hedges are beginning to give shelter to rhododendrons and azaleas, many grown from cuttings by the owners, and other shrubs, perennials and bulbs. A small walled vegetable garden, a rockery and a pond provide variety, with views of Sheriffmuir as backdrop.

Open: Sunday 12 May, 2pm - 5pm, admission £4.00, children free.

Directions: From A820 turn down Kilbryde Crescent and into Auchinlay Road, about two miles, Satnav stops short. From Kinbuck follow the yellow *SGS* signs. Parking in adjacent field.

· *Society Of Friends Of Dunblane Cathedral*

'I like gardening — it's a
place where I find myself
when I need to lose myself.'
Alice Sebold

Stirlingshire

11

KILBRYDE CASTLE
Dunblane FK15 9NF
Sir James and Lady Campbell
T: 01786 824897 **E:** kilbryde1@aol.com
W: www.kilbrydecastle.com

The Kilbryde Castle gardens cover some 12 acres and are situated above the Ardoch Burn and below the castle. The gardens are split into three parts: formal, woodland and wild. Natural planting (azaleas, rhododendrons, camellias and magnolias) is found in the woodland garden. There are glorious spring bulbs, and autumn colour provided by clematis and acers. Some new plantings for additional late summer/autumn colour was added in 2017. Featured in *Scotland on Sunday* in September 2016.

Open: Open Sunday 5 May, 2pm - 5pm. Also open by arrangement 24 February - 15 March for Snowdrops and Winter Walks. And open by arrangement 16 March - 30 September. Admission £5.00, children free.

Directions: Three miles from Dunblane and Doune, off the A820 between Dunblane and Doune. On Scotland's Gardens Scheme open days the garden is signposted from A820.

· *Leighton Library Trust*

12

KIPPENRAIT, SHERIFFMUIR WITH ST BLANES HOUSE, DUNBLANE
Sheriffmuir, Dunblane FK15 0LP
Richard Stirling-Aird and Guy & Maud Crawford

Kippenrait Sheriffmuir, Dunblane FK15 0LP (Richard Stirling-Aird): Created over the last 14 years from a field, this garden has incredible views over the Carse of Stirling, east to Dumyat and the mountains in the west. A delightful space of two and a half acres, spring bulbs, rhododendrons, azaleas and other spring-flowering shrubs, primulas and specimen trees. There is a small orchard and a water feature.

St Blanes House High Street, Dunblane FK15 0ER (Guy & Maud Crawford): Opened as part of Dunblane Gardens in 2010. Well-established two-acre garden with a wide variety of trees, rhododendrons, azaleas and other shrubs and herbaceous perennials. There is a short walk through a wooded area.

Open: Sunday 9 June, 2pm - 5pm, admission £5.00, children free.

Directions: Please note these gardens are about one and half miles apart.For Kippenrait turn up the Glen Road from Fourways roundabout in Dunblane. After three-quarters of a mile, turn left signposted *Sheriffmuir*, and after about a quarter mile turn right onto drive. St Blanes House is almost directly opposite Dunblane Library.

· *Turn2us & Forth Driving Group RDA SCIO*

Stirlingshire

13 ROWBERROW
18 Castle Road, Dollar FK14 7BE
Bill and Rosemary Jarvis
T: 01259 742584 **E:** rjarvis1000@hotmail.com

On the way up to Castle Campbell overlooking Dollar Glen, this colourful garden has several mixed shrub and herbaceous borders, a wildlife pond, two rockeries, alpine troughs, fruit and vegetable gardens, and a mini-orchard. The owner is a plantaholic and likes to collect unusual specimens. Rowberrow was featured on *The Beechgrove Garden* in summer 2011.

Open: Open by arrangement 1 February - 31 December, admission £4.00, children free.

Directions: Pass along the burn side in Dollar, turn right at T junction, follow signs for *Castle Campbell* and *Dollar Glen*. Park at the bottom of Castle Road or in the Quarry car park just up from the house.

· *Hillfoot Harmony Barbershop Singers*

14 THE JAPANESE GARDEN AT COWDEN
Dollar, Clackmannanshire FK14 7PJ
Cowden Castle SCIO
E: info@cowdengarden.com
W: www.cowdengarden.com

Created in 1908, The Japanese Garden at Cowden is listed as an important example of its type in Western Europe. Nestled beneath the Ochil Hills the seven-acre garden wraps around a large pond. Enjoy the meandering walk by the water, taking in the changing scenes created by sculpted landforms, carefully placed stones, clipped shrubs and original stone lanterns. Restoration of this historic garden is ongoing, so this is an opportunity to see the project in its early stages.

Open: Wednesday 5 June, 5pm - 8pm, admission £6.00, children free. A wonderful opportunity to see round this amazing site, outside normal garden opening times. To help us with catering and parking please buy advance tickets from the garden's website.

Directions: The entrance to the garden is from the Upper Hillfoots Road, about half a mile west from the junction with the A91. There is limited public transport, bus 23 Stirling - St. Andrews stops at Cowden Farm Road End, at the end of the Upper Hillfoot Road, just before the Pools of Muckhart. There is a half-mile walk (no pavement) to the entrance.

· *Cowden Castle SCIO & St. James the Great Scottish Episcopal Church, Dollar*

15 THE TORS
2 Slamannan Road, Falkirk FK1 5LG
Dr and Mrs D M Ramsay
T: 01324 620877 **E:** dmramsay28@yahoo.co.uk
W: www.torsgarden.co.uk

An award-winning Victorian garden of just over one-acre with a secret woodland garden to the side and an orchard leading off to a wild area at the rear of the house. Many unusual maple trees, hydrangeas and rhododendrons are the main interest of this garden and two fine avenues of Chinese paperbark maples are especially noteworthy. Featured on *The Beechgrove Garden* for autumn colour in September 2010, but the best time to see this garden is at the end of July or the beginning of August. The *Scotland on Sunday* featured the house and garden in an article with many lovely photographs in September 2015.

Open: Sunday 28 July, 2pm - 5:30pm. Also open by arrangement 1 May - 30 September. Admission £4.00, children free.

Stirlingshire

Directions: The B803 to the south of Falkirk leads to Glenbrae Road. Turn right at the traffic lights into Slamannan Road and The Tors is a Victorian building immediately on the left. The house is within 200 yards of Falkirk High Station.

· *Strathcarron Hospice*

THORNTREE
Arnprior FK8 3EY
Mark and Carol Seymour
T: 01786 870710 **E:** info@thorntreebarn.co.uk
W: www.thorntreebarn.co.uk

The amazing views from Ben Lomond to Ben Ledi and on to Stirling sold Thorntree to Carol and Mark 25 years ago. The garden evolved while trying to keep a 'cottage' feel. Carol sold old silver, which had not been used in years, to build the dry stone wall. An apple arch was given to Mark to encourage him into the garden. The lawns are mown like a bowling green (or to a millimetre) by Mark. The courtyard includes flower beds. The saltire bed was designed in 2002 when Carol stopped growing dried flowers in a 20x20 metre square. The slightly sunken bed, all that they inherited on arrival, now holds meconopsis. Carol is now making a wooded area filled with primroses and Martagon lilies. Do come and see!

Open: Sunday 23 June, 2pm - 5pm. Also open by arrangement 1 April - 15 October. Admission £4.00, children free. There may be coffee/teas and a biscuit on 23 June, if the weather is fine.

Directions: Go on A811, in to Arnprior, then take Fintry Road; Thorntree is second on the right.

· *Forth Driving Group RDA SCIO*

The colour filled borders at Thorntree

WIGTOWNSHIRE

Scotland's Gardens Scheme 2019 Guidebook is sponsored by INVESTEC WEALTH & INVESTMENT

St John's Town
of Dalry

New Galloway

Clatteringshaws
Loch

Gatehouse
of Fleet

Creetown

Wigtown Bay

Garlieston

Isle of Whithorn

Burrow Head

Whithorn

4 Newton Stewart

6

Kirkcowan

Wigtown

9

3

A75

Port William

Barrhill

Glenluce

Luce Bay

Mull of Galloway

5

Dunragit

Sandhead

Ardwell

Drummore

8

Cairnryan

Loch
Ryan

2

1

7

A77

Ballantrae

Stranraer

Kirkcolm

Portpatrick

1. Balker Farmhouse
2. Castle Kennedy and Gardens
3. Craichlaw

4. Fernlea Garden
5. Glenwhan Gardens
6. Liggat Cheek Cottage

7. Logan Botanic Garden
8. Seabank
9. Woodfall Gardens

WIGTOWNSHIRE

OUR VOLUNTEER ORGANISERS

District Organiser:	Ann Watson	Doonholm, Cairnryan Road, Stranraer DG9 8AT E: wigtownshire@scotlandsgardens.org
Area Organisers:	Eileen Davie	Whitehills House, Minnigaff DG8 6SL
	Mary Gladstone	Craichlaw, Kirkcowan, Newton Stewart DG8 0DQ
	Shona Greenhorn	Burbainie, Westwood Avenue, Stranraer DG9 8BT
	Enid Innes	Crinan, Creetown, Newton Stewart DG8 7EP
	Annmaree Mitchell	Cottage 2, Little Float, Sandhead DG9 9LD
	Vicky Roberts	Logan House Gardens, Port Logan DG9 9ND
Treasurer:	George Fleming	Stablesend, Culreoch, Stranraer DG9 8LZ

GARDENS OPEN ON A SPECIFIC DATE

Logan Botanic Garden, Port Logan, by Stranraer	Sunday, 19 May
Balker Farmhouse, Stranraer	Sunday, 2 June
Castle Kennedy and Gardens, Stranraer	Sunday, 9 June
Woodfall Gardens, Glasserton	Sunday, 16 June
Seabank, Drummore	Sunday, 21 July

GARDENS OPEN REGULARLY

Glenwhan Gardens, Dunragit, by Stranraer	1 January - 31 December

GARDENS OPEN BY ARRANGEMENT

Craichlaw, Kirkcowan, Newton Stewart	1 January - 31 December
Liggat Cheek Cottage, Baltersan, Newton Stewart	1 April - 30 September
Fernlea Garden, Corvisel Road, Newton Stewart	1 April - 30 September

'Our volunteers
organise open days
and promote gardens,
could this be you?'

Wigtownshire

1 BALKER FARMHOUSE
Stranraer DG9 8RS
The Earl and Countess of Stair
T: 01581 400225/01776 702024

Balker Farmhouse was restored in 2002 and the garden, formerly a ploughed field, was started in 2003-4 by Davina, Dowager Countess of Stair and Anne-Marie Mitchell. It is now full of wonderful shrubs and plants for all seasons, and is opened in memory of Davina, who died in 2017.

Open: Sunday 2 June, 2pm - 5pm, admission £4.00, children free.

Directions: One and a half miles off the A75, three miles from Stranraer. Go through the farmyard to the blue gate.

· *Inch Parish Church*

2 CASTLE KENNEDY AND GARDENS
Stranraer DG9 8SL
The Earl and Countess of Stair
T: 01581 400225
W: www.castlekennedygardens.com

Romantically situated, these famous 75 acres of landscaped gardens are located on an isthmus surrounded by two large natural lochs. At one end the ruined Castle Kennedy overlooks a beautiful herbaceous walled garden with Lochinch Castle at the other end. With over 300 years of planting there is an impressive collection of rare trees, rhododendrons, exotic shrubs and many spectacular Champion Trees. The stunning snowdrop walks, daffodils, spring flowers, rhododendron and magnolia displays, and herbaceous borders make this a 'must visit' garden throughout the year. Champion Trees: 6 British, 11 Scottish and 25 for Dumfries and Galloway.

Open: Sunday 9 June, 10am - 5pm, admission details can be found on the garden's website.

Directions: On the A75, five miles east of Stranraer. The nearest train station is in Stranraer. On a local bus route.

· *Home-Start Wigtownshire*

Wigtownshire

Topiary at Craichlaw

3

CRAICHLAW
Kirkcowan, Newton Stewart DG8 0DQ
Mr and Mrs Andrew Gladstone
T: 01671 830208 **E:** craichlaw@aol.com

Formal garden with herbaceous borders around the house. Set in extensive grounds with lawns, lochs and woodland. A path around the main loch leads to a water garden returning past a recently planted arboretum in the old walled garden. The best times to visit the garden are early February for snowdrops, May to mid-June for the water garden and rhododendrons, and mid-June to August for herbaceous borders.

Open: Open by arrangement throughout the year, including February through mid-March for Snowdrops and Winter Walks, admission £4.00, children free.

Directions: Take the B733 for Kirkcowan off the A75 at the Halfway House eight miles west of Newton Stewart. Craichlaw House is the first turning on the right.

· Donation to SGS Beneficiaries

Wigtownshire

FERNLEA GARDEN
Corvisel Road, Newton Stewart DG8 6LW
Mrs Jenny Gustafson
T: 07909 951 885 **E:** jennygustafson2@hotmail.com

A secluded town garden of a third of an acre. It was created 12 years ago to complement a new house. There are many rare and unusual trees and shrubs. Two herbaceous borders, one with hot colours and the other pastels. A Chinese-inspired corner, small pond, fruit trees including a Galloway pippin apple and soft fruit. The upper part of the garden is hidden behind a tall beech hedge, where there is a summer house and adjacent woodland planting.

Open: Open by arrangement 1 April - 30 September, admission £4.50, children free. Homemade teas can be provided by prior arrangement.

Directions: Turn right at the roundabout on the A75 if coming from Dumfries direction. Go left at the cattle market (opposite Crown Hotel), first through road on the right.

· *Host*

GLENWHAN GARDENS
Dunragit, by Stranraer DG9 8PH
Tess Knott
T: 07787 990702
W: www.glenwhangardens.co.uk

Described as one of the most beautiful gardens in Scotland, Glenwhan Gardens is situated at 300 feet, and overlooks Luce Bay and the Mull of Galloway, with clear views to the Isle of Man. Thirty-six years ago there was wild moorland, but now, following considerable dedication and vision, you can see glorious collections of plants from around the world. There is colour in all seasons and the winding paths, well-placed seats, and varied sculptures, set around small lakes, add to the tranquil atmosphere. There is a 17 acre moorland wildflower walk, the chance to see red squirrels and a well-marked Tree Trail.

Open: Daily 10am - 5pm, admission details can be found on the garden's website.

Directions: Seven miles east of Stranraer, one mile off the A75 at Dunragit (follow brown *VisitScotland* and yellow *SGS* arrows).

· *WWF-UK*

LIGGAT CHEEK COTTAGE
Baltersan, Newton Stewart DG8 6AX
Philip and Jennifer Bradley
T: 01671 402639 **E:** bradley@liggat.plus.com

The garden is approximately half an acre and includes a small woodland and shade area with ferns, hostas, trilliums, erythroniums and many other shade-loving plants. The rest of the garden is divided into informal 'rooms' with large borders containing herbaceous perennials, shrubs, conifers, grasses, etc. There is one south-facing bed devoted to less hardy plants including agaves, yuccas, cordylines, aeoniums and tetrapanax.

Open: Open by arrangement 1 April - 30 September, admission £4.00, children free. Teas and plants may be available by prior request.

Wigtownshire

Directions: From Newton Stewart roundabout (A75) towards Wigtown (A714) *Scotland's National Book Town*. Approximately two miles from the roundabout on the right, above Baltersan Farm on the left.

· *Euan Macdonald Centre for Motor Neurone Disease Research*

Hydrangeas at Glenwahn Gardens

LOGAN BOTANIC GARDEN
Port Logan, by Stranraer DG9 9ND
A Regional Garden of the Royal Botanic Garden Edinburgh
T: 01776 860231 **E:** logan@rbge.org.uk
W: www.rbge.org.uk/logan

....

At the south western tip of Scotland lies Logan, which is unrivalled as the country's most exotic garden. With a mild climate washed by the Gulf Stream, a remarkable collection of bizarre and beautiful plants, especially from the southern hemisphere, flourish out of doors. Enjoy the colourful walled garden with its magnificent tree ferns, palms and borders along with the contrasting woodland garden with its unworldly gunnera bog. Visit the Logan Conservatory, which houses a special collection of tender South African species.
National Plant Collection: *Gunnera, Leptospermum, Griselinia, Clianthus* and *Sutherlandia*.
Champion Trees: *Polylepis* and *Eucalyptus*.

Open: Sunday 19 May, 10am - 5pm, admission details and other opening dates can be found on the garden's website.

Directions: Ten miles south of Stranraer on the A716 then 2½ miles from Ardwell village.

· *Board Of Trustees Of The Royal Botanic Garden Edinburgh*

Wigtownshire

8

SEABANK
Drummore DG9 9QE
Bill and Helen Miller
T: 07823 772 257 **E:** seabankgarden@gmail.com

Seabank overlooks Luce Bay and is situated at the entrance to Drummore. The garden is approximately half an acre comprising of a series of 'rooms' created by a variety of hedging including camellia, fuchsia, escallonia, veronica and cupressus. The rooms include herbaceous and annual plantings, a Sunshine Garden, Japanese-style area, greenhouses, wildflowers, and a small woodland garden. There are also some unusual trees including *Metrosideros umbellata* and grevillea.

Open: Sunday 21 July, 11am - 4pm, admission £4.00, children free. Self-service tea/coffee and biscuits. Unsuitable for wheelchair users.

Directions: From Stranraer take the A716 towards Mull of Galloway; after about 15 miles, as you enter the village of Drummore, Seabank is the first house on the right.

· *Guide Dogs*

9

WOODFALL GARDENS
Glasserton DG8 8LY
Ross and Liz Muir
E: woodfallgardens@btinternet.com
W: www.woodfall-gardens.co.uk

This lovely three-acre 18th-century triple walled garden has been thoughtfully restored to provide year-round interest. Many mature trees and shrubs include some less common species; herbaceous borders and shrub roses surround the foundations of original greenhouses; grass borders; a parterre; extensive beds of fruit and vegetables; a herb garden and a small woodland walk. This unusual garden is well worth a visit.

Open: Sunday 16 June, 10:30am - 4:30pm, admission £5.00, children free. Admission includes self-service tea, coffee and scones. Garden also open by arrangement.

Directions: Two miles south west of Whithorn at junction of A746 and A747 (directly behind Glasserton Church).

· *Glasserton and the Isle Of Whithorn Church of Scotland & Macmillan Cancer Support*

'Gardening is a great distraction
and wonderful therapy'
Peeblesshire Gardener

Visit four Botanic Gardens to see one of the richest plant collections on Earth.

Royal Botanic Garden Edinburgh

Arboretum Place and Inverleith Row, Edinburgh EH3 5LR
Tel 0131 248 2909 | www.rbge.org.uk
Open every day from 10 am (except 1 January and 25 December) | Garden is free | Entry charges apply to Glasshouses

Royal Botanic Garden Edinburgh at **Logan**

Port Logan, Stranraer, Dumfries and Galloway DG9 9ND
Tel 01776 860231 | www.rbge.org.uk/logan
Open daily 1 March to 15 November
Admission charge applies

Royal Botanic Garden Edinburgh at **Benmore**

Dunoon, Argyll PA23 8QU
Tel 01369 706261 | www.rbge.org.uk/benmore
Open daily 1 March to 31 October
Admission charge applies

Royal Botanic Garden Edinburgh at **Dawyck**

Stobo, Scottish Borders EH45 9JU
Tel 01721 760254 | www.rbge.org.uk/dawyck
Open daily 1 February to 30 November
Admission charge applies

The Royal Botanic Garden Edinburgh is a Charity registered in Scotland (number SC007983) and is a Non Departmental Public Body (NDPB) sponsored and supported through Grant-in-Aid by the Scottish Government's Environment and Forestry Directorate (ENFOR).

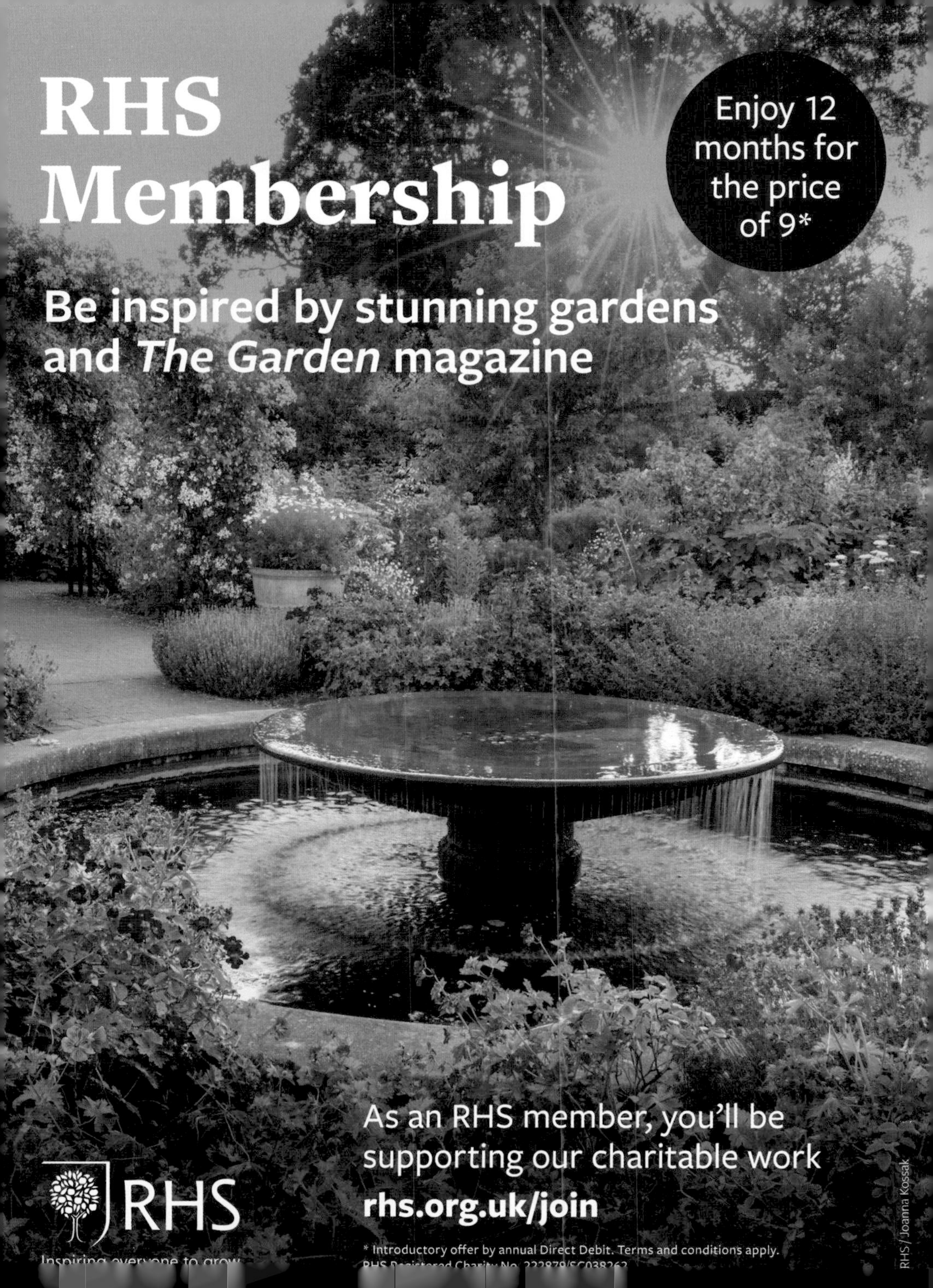

RHS Membership

Enjoy 12 months for the price of 9*

Be inspired by stunning gardens and *The Garden* magazine

As an RHS member, you'll be supporting our charitable work

rhs.org.uk/join

RHS

Inspiring everyone to grow

RHS / Joanna Kossak

* Introductory offer by annual Direct Debit. Terms and conditions apply. RHS Registered Charity No. 222879/SC038262

James Byatt BSc (Hons) MLD

Garden & Estate Cartography

---

www.jamesbyatt.com
07796 591197
enquiries@jamesbyatt.com

Lochview Cottage Scarffbanks
Pitgaveny, Elgin
Moray IV30 5PQ

THE MILL GARDEN CENTRE

Bloomin' good plants

- Japanese Maples
- Conifers
- Shrubs
- Bedding
- Herbaceous
- Grafted Pines
- Roses
- Trees
- Pots
- Compost

The Mill Garden Centre is an independent, family owned and run business where you can be assured the emphasis is firmly on the plants.

When visiting us you can be sure that you are buying plants from people who have been growing for generations and are qualified horticulturalists.

Our main strength is our constantly evolving range of unusual plants held in stock throughout the year and backed up by our own wide selection of plants grown on our adjacent nursery.

Whether you are a beginner, serious gardener, plant collector or would just like an alternative to the 'lifestyle chains', you are sure to find something to suit.

The Mill Garden Centre

Barbauchlaw Mill, Mill Road

Armadale, West Lothian, EH48 3AP

BENNYBEG
PLANT
CENTRE

Plant Paradise

Muthill Road, Crieff, Perthshire, PH7 4HN
T: 01764 656345
W: www.bennybeg.co.uk

JAMESFIELD
GARDEN
CENTRE

For all your Garden needs

Abernethy, Perthshire, KY14 6EW
T: 01738 851176
W: www.jamesfieldgardencentre.co.uk

NEW HOPETOUN GARDENS

...so much more than just a garden centre

The perfect place for a relaxed visit at any time of year. Set in six acres of woodland with 20 small themed gardens to explore and probably the biggest range of garden plants for sale in Scotland. The Scottish Home of Miniature and Fairy Gardening.

The Orangery tearoom will revive you and the gift shop will tempt you with the most exciting range of presents for everyone.

Art in the garden runs during July and August and features original works of art by artists working in Scotland installed in the gardens.

(Entry is always free to our gardens.)

OPEN EVERY DAY 10.00AM – 5.30PM
New Hopetoun Gardens, by Winchburgh
West Lothian EH52 6QZ   01506 834433
www.newhopetoungardens.co.uk

f **New Hopetoun Gardens - Edinburgh**

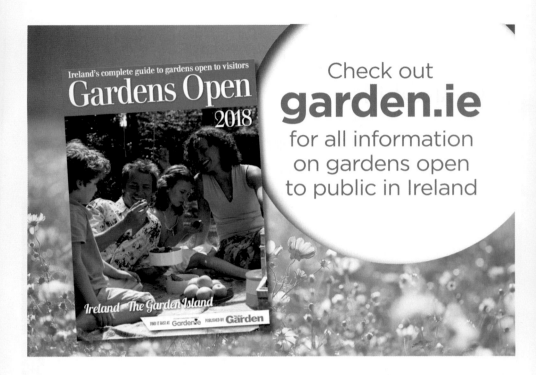

"The Most Outstanding Continuous Care Retirement Community in the UK."

UK OVER 50's HOUSING AWARDS

An integral part of our Retirement Village is Inchmarlo House Care Home which is highly rated by the Care Inspectorate. Inchmarlo's Care policy gives confidence to our Home Owners and their families as our nursing, care and security staff are on site 24 hours a day and assistance can be there in minutes.

We also reserve a room in Inchmarlo House for Home Owners who require respite care for short periods. If longer stays are required Home Owners have priority admission.

Since 1986 our policy of providing personalised care has enabled many home owners to continue to live in their own homes longer than might be the case elsewhere. The quality of our service is such that two generations of the same family have chosen to come to live in Inchmarlo.

To find out more call 01330 826242 or email dawn.ronaldson@inchmarlo-retirement.co.uk

Then come and see why Inchmarlo is the ideal spot to put down some roots.

INCHMARLO

RETIREMENT VILLAGE

Where Gracious Living Comes naturally

GARDENS OPEN ON A SPECIFIC DATE

Saturday 9 February
Dumfriesshire   Barjarg Tower, Auldgirth

Sunday 10 February
Dumfriesshire   Barjarg Tower, Auldgirth

Sunday 17 February
Dumfriesshire   Craig, Langholm
Perth & Kinross   NEW Cloan, by Auchterarder

Saturday 23 February
Angus & Dundee   Langley Park Gardens, Montrose
East Lothian   Shepherd House, Inveresk, Musselburgh

Sunday 24 February
Angus & Dundee   Langley Park Gardens, Montrose
Ayrshire & Arran   Blair House, Blair Estate, Dalry, Ayrshire
East Lothian   Shepherd House, Inveresk, Musselburgh
Kirkcudbrightshire   Danevale Park, Crossmichael
Peeblesshire & Tweeddale   Kailzie Gardens, Peebles
Perth & Kinross   Kilgraston School, Bridge of Earn

MARCH

Saturday 2 March
Angus & Dundee   Langley Park Gardens, Montrose

Sunday 3 March
Angus & Dundee   Langley Park Gardens, Montrose
Kincardine & Deeside   Ecclesgreig Castle, St Cyrus
Perth & Kinross   Rossie Gardens, Forgandenny

Saturday 9 March
Lanarkshire   Cleghorn, Stable House, Cleghorn Farm, Lanark

Sunday 17 March
Angus & Dundee   Lawton House, Inverkeilor, by Arbroath

APRIL

Sunday 7 April
East Lothian   Winton Castle, Pencaitland

Sunday 14 April
Aberdeenshire   Auchmacoy, Ellon
Dunbartonshire   Kilarden, Rosneath
Fife   NEW Fife Spring Trail, Various locations across Fife
Kirkcudbrightshire   3 Millhall, Shore Road, Kirkcudbright

Tuesday 16 April
Fife   NEW Fife Spring Trail, Various locations across Fife

Wednesday 17 April
Fife   NEW Fife Spring Trail, Various locations across Fife

Thursday 18 April
Fife   NEW Fife Spring Trail, Various locations across Fife
Inverness, Ross, Cromarty & Skye   Dundonnell House, Little Loch Broom, Wester Ross

Friday 19 April
Fife   NEW Fife Spring Trail, Various locations across Fife

Saturday 20 April
Argyll & Lochaber   Maolachy's Garden, Lochavich, by Taynuilt

Sunday 21 April
East Lothian   Humbie Dean, Humbie
Perth & Kinross   Megginch Castle, Errol

Tuesday 23 April
Fife   NEW Fife Spring Trail, Various locations across Fife

Wednesday 24 April
Fife   NEW Fife Spring Trail, Various locations across Fife

Thursday 25 April
Fife   NEW Fife Spring Trail, Various locations across Fife

Friday 26 April
Fife   NEW Fife Spring Trail, Various locations across Fife

Saturday 27 April
Argyll & Lochaber   Knock Newhouse, Lochgair
Edinburgh, Midlothian & West Lothian   41 Hermitage Gardens, Edinburgh
Fife   The Tower, 1 Northview Terrace, Wormit
Moray & Nairn   10 Stuart Avenue, Ardersier, Inverness
Renfrewshire   SGS Kilmacolm Plant Sale, outside Kilmacolm Library, Kilmacolm

Sunday 28 April
Aberdeenshire   Westhall Castle, Oyne, Inverurie
Argyll & Lochaber   Benmore Botanic Garden, Benmore, Dunoon
Argyll & Lochaber   Knock Newhouse, Lochgair
Dumfriesshire   NEW Dumfries Station Garden, Dumfries Railway Station, Lovers
Walk, Dumfries
Dunbartonshire   Glenarn Plant Sale, Glenarn Road, Rhu
East Lothian   Humbie Dean, Humbie
Edinburgh, Midlothian & West Lothian   41 Hermitage Gardens, Edinburgh
Perth & Kinross   The Steading at Clunie, Newmill of Kinloch, Clunie, Blairgowrie

Monday 29 April
Fife   NEW Fife Spring Trail, Various locations across Fife

Tuesday 30 April
Fife   NEW Fife Spring Trail, Various locations across Fife

MAY
....

Wednesday 1 May
Fife   NEW Fife Spring Trail, Various locations across Fife

Thursday 2 May
Fife   NEW Fife Spring Trail, Various locations across Fife

Friday 3 May
Fife   NEW Fife Spring Trail, Various locations across Fife

Saturday 4 May
Argyll & Lochaber   Kames Bay, Kilmelford
Edinburgh, Midlothian & West Lothian   Dr Neil's Garden, Duddingston Village
Glasgow & District   NEW Merrylee Spring Plant Sale, Merrylee Plots, Quadrant Road,
Newlands, Glasgow

The Quoy of Houton, Caithness, Sutherland, Orkney and Shetland

Sunday 5 May

Angus & Dundee	Brechin Castle, Brechin
Argyll & Lochaber	Kames Bay, Kilmelford
Dumfriesshire	Crawick Multiverse, Crawick, Sanquhar
Dumfriesshire	Portrack, The Garden of Cosmic Speculation, Holywood
Edinburgh, Midlothian & West Lothian	Dr Neil's Garden, Duddingston Village
Edinburgh, Midlothian & West Lothian	Moray Place and Bank Gardens, Edinburgh
Fife	Earlshall Castle, Leuchars
Perth & Kinross	NEW Cloan, by Auchterarder
Perth & Kinross	Fingask Castle, Rait
Stirlingshire	Kilbryde Castle, Dunblane

Monday 6 May

Perth & Kinross	NEW Gleneagles House, Auchterader

Thursday 9 May

Angus & Dundee	Inchmill Cottage, Glenprosen, nr Kirriemuir

Sunday 12 May

Angus & Dundee	Dalfruin, Kirktonhill Road, Kirriemuir
Argyll & Lochaber	Knock Newhouse, Lochgair
Dumfriesshire	Dunesslin, Dunscore
East Lothian	Tyninghame House and The Walled Garden, Dunbar
Edinburgh, Midlothian & West Lothian	Hunter's Tryst, 95 Oxgangs Road, Edinburgh
Edinburgh, Midlothian & West Lothian	Redcroft, 23 Murrayfield Road, Edinburgh
Fife	46 South Street, St Andrews
Glasgow & District	NEW Gartnaval Secret Garden, Gartnavel Royal Hospital, 1055 Great
Western Road, Glasgow	

Renfrewshire	Highwood, off Lochwinnoch Road, Kilmacolm
Stirlingshire	NEW Hutcheson Farm, Auchinlay Road, Dunblane

Monday 13 May

Perth & Kinross	NEW Gleneagles House, Auchterader

Saturday 18 May

Ayrshire & Arran	Coylbank, nr Coylton, Ayrshire

Sunday 19 May

Argyll & Lochaber	Braevallich Farm, by Dalmally
Ayrshire & Arran	Craigengillan Estate and Scottish Dark Sky Observatory, Dalmelling-
ton	
Dumfriesshire	NEW Ellisland Farm, The Poet's Wild Garden, Auldgirth, Dum-
friesshire	
Dumfriesshire	Dalswinton House, Dalswinton
Dunbartonshire	Ross Priory, Gartocharn
East Lothian	Humbie Dean, Humbie
Edinburgh, Midlothian & West Lothian	101 Greenbank Crescent, Edinburgh
Fife	Balcarres, Colinsburgh
Inverness, Ross, Cromarty & Skye	Old Allangrange, Munlochy
Kincardine & Deeside	Inchmarlo Retirement Village Garden, Inchmarlo, Banchory
Perth & Kinross	NEW Plant Sale at Bradystone House, Murthly
Renfrewshire	NEW Wraes, Corseliehill Road, nr Houston
Stirlingshire	Gargunnock House Garden, Gargunnock
Wigtownshire	Logan Botanic Garden, Port Logan, by Stranraer

Wednesday 22 May

Peeblesshire & Tweeddale	Laidlawstiel House, Clovenfords, Galashiels

Thursday 23 May

Angus & Dundee	Inchmill Cottage, Glenprosen, nr Kirriemuir

Saturday 25 May

Angus & Dundee	Gallery Garden, Gallery, by Montrose
Argyll & Lochaber	NEW Ardno and Strachur House, Cairndow
Argyll & Lochaber	Maolachy's Garden, Lochavich, by Taynuilt
Ayrshire & Arran	Craufurdland Estate, nr Fenwick, Kilmarnock
Edinburgh, Midlothian & West Lothian	Rivaldsgreen House, 48 Friars Brae, Linlithgow
Moray & Nairn	10 Stuart Avenue, Ardersier, Inverness
Perth & Kinross	Rossie Gardens, Forgandenny
Renfrewshire	Carruth, Bridge of Weir

Sunday 26 May

Angus & Dundee	Gallery Garden, Gallery, by Montrose
Argyll & Lochaber	NEW Ardno and Strachur House, Cairndow
Argyll & Lochaber	Ardverikie with Aberarder, Kinlochlaggan
Argyll & Lochaber	Maolachy's Garden, Lochavich, by Taynuilt
Ayrshire & Arran	Barnweil Garden, Craigie, nr Kilmarnock
Dumfriesshire	Dabton, Thornhill
Dumfriesshire	Holehouse, Near Penpont, Thornhill
Dumfriesshire	Westerhall, Bentpath, Langholm
East Lothian	Humbie Dean, Humbie
Fife	Kirklands, Saline
Fife	South Flisk, Blebo Craigs, Cupar
Fife	St Fort Woodland Garden, St Fort Farm, Newport-on-Tay
Kirkcudbrightshire	Corsock House, Corsock, Castle Douglas
Perth & Kinross	NEW The Steading at Muckhart, Yetts O'Muckhart, Dollar
Perth & Kinross	Delvine, Murthly
Stirlingshire	Bridge of Allan Gardens, Bridge of Allan

Monday 27 May

Perth & Kinross	NEW Gleneagles House, Auchterader

Thursday 30 May

Inverness, Ross, Cromarty & Skye   Dundonnell House, Little Loch Broom, Wester Ross

Friday 31 May
Inverness, Ross, Cromarty & Skye   Gorthleck House Garden, Stratherrick

JUNE

Saturday 1 June
Angus & Dundee   3 Balfour Cottages, Menmuir
Ayrshire & Arran   Clover Park, Langdyke, Waterside, Kilmarnock
Caithness, Sutherland, Orkney & Shetland   Amat, Ardgay
Glasgow & District   Whittingehame Drive Gardens, Glasgow
Inverness, Ross, Cromarty & Skye   Gorthleck House Garden, Stratherrick

Sunday 2 June
Angus & Dundee   NEW Brechin Gardens in Spring, Locations across Brechin
Caithness, Sutherland, Orkney & Shetland   Amat, Ardgay
Dumfriesshire   NEW Stanemuir, Parkgate, Dumfriesshire
Dumfriesshire   Dalswinton Mill, Dalswinton, Dumfries
Dumfriesshire   Whiteside, Dunscore
Fife   Earlshall Castle, Leuchars
Glasgow & District   Kilsyth Gardens, Allanfauld Road, Kilsyth
Inverness, Ross, Cromarty & Skye   Gorthleck House Garden, Stratherrick
Kincardine & Deeside   Woodend House Garden, Banchory
Kirkcudbrightshire   Seabank, The Merse, Rockcliffe
Moray & Nairn   Gordonstoun, Duffus, nr Elgin
Peeblesshire & Tweeddale   Stobo Japanese Water Garden, Home Farm, Stobo
Perth & Kinross   Bonhard House, Perth
Perth & Kinross   Explorers Garden, Pitlochry
Renfrewshire   Ardgowan, Inverkip
Roxburghshire   West Leas, Bonchester Bridge
Stirlingshire   Coldoch, Blairdrummond, Stirling
Wigtownshire   Balker Farmhouse, Stranraer

Monday 3 June
Fife   NEW Fife Summer Trail, Various locations across Fife
Perth & Kinross   NEW Gleneagles House, Auchterader

Tuesday 4 June
Fife   NEW Fife Summer Trail, Various locations across Fife

Wednesday 5 June
Fife   NEW Fife Summer Trail, Various locations across Fife
Inverness, Ross, Cromarty & Skye   House of Gruinard, Laide, by Achnasheen
Stirlingshire   The Japanese Garden at Cowden, Dollar, Clackmannanshire

Thursday 6 June
Angus & Dundee   Inchmill Cottage, Glenprosen, nr Kirriemuir
Fife   NEW Fife Summer Trail, Various locations across Fife

Friday 7 June
Aberdeenshire   Airdlin Croft, Ythanbank, Ellon

Saturday 8 June
Aberdeenshire   Airdlin Croft, Ythanbank, Ellon
Aberdeenshire   Leith Hall Plant Sale, Huntly
Ayrshire & Arran   Holmes Farm, Drybridge, by Irvine
East Lothian   Shepherd House, Inveresk, Musselburgh
Edinburgh, Midlothian & West Lothian   NEW 89 Ravenscroft Street, Edinburgh

Sunday 9 June
Aberdeenshire   Airdlin Croft, Ythanbank, Ellon
Argyll & Lochaber   Braevallich Farm, by Dalmally
Argyll & Lochaber   Knock Newhouse, Lochgair
Ayrshire & Arran   Holmes Farm, Drybridge, by Irvine

Dumfriesshire	Drumpark, Irongray
Dunbartonshire	Geilston Garden, Main Road, Cardross
East Lothian	NEW Fairnielaw, Athelstaneford, North Berwick
East Lothian	Shepherd House, Inveresk, Musselburgh
Edinburgh, Midlothian & West Lothian	Dean Gardens, Edinburgh
Edinburgh, Midlothian & West Lothian leith Row, Edinburgh	The Glasshouses at the Royal Botanic Garden Edinburgh, 20A Inver-
Inverness, Ross, Cromarty & Skye	Field House, Belladrum, Beauly
Kincardine & Deeside	Kincardine Castle, Kincardine O'Neil
Kirkcudbrightshire	The Limes, Kirkcudbright
Peeblesshire & Tweeddale West Linton	West Linton Village Gardens, The Graham Institute, Lower Green,
Perth & Kinross	NEW Cloan, by Auchterarder
Perth & Kinross	Mill of Forneth, Forneth, Blairgowrie
Stirlingshire	Kippenrait with St Blanes House, Sheriffmuir, Dunblane
Wigtownshire	Castle Kennedy and Gardens, Stranraer

Monday 10 June

Fife	NEW Fife Summer Trail, Various locations across Fife

Tuesday 11 June

Edinburgh, Midlothian & West Lothian	NEW 89 Ravenscroft Street, Edinburgh
Fife	NEW Fife Summer Trail, Various locations across Fife

Wednesday 12 June

Fife	NEW Fife Summer Trail, Various locations across Fife
Inverness, Ross, Cromarty & Skye	Brackla Wood, Culbokie, Dingwall
Peeblesshire & Tweeddale	Laidlawstiel House, Clovenfords, Galashiels

Thursday 13 June

Fife	NEW Fife Summer Trail, Various locations across Fife

Saturday 15 June

Angus & Dundee	Kilry Village Gardens, Kilry, Glen Isla
Moray & Nairn	Haugh Garden, College of Roseisle
Perth & Kinross	Abernethy Open Gardens, Abernethy
Perth & Kinross	The Bield at Blackruthven, Blackruthven House, Tibbermore

Sunday 16 June

Aberdeenshire	Birken Cottage, Burnhervie, Inverurie
Angus & Dundee	Kilry Village Gardens, Kilry, Glen Isla
Dumfriesshire	Cowhill Tower, Holywood
Edinburgh, Midlothian & West Lothian	Beech Lodge, 10 Church Hill, Edinburgh
Kirkcudbrightshire	Barmagachan House, Borgue, Kirkcudbright
Lanarkshire	Dippoolbank Cottage, Carnwath
Wigtownshire	Woodfall Gardens, Glasserton

Thursday 20 June

Angus & Dundee	Inchmill Cottage, Glenprosen, nr Kirriemuir

Saturday 22 June

East Lothian	NEW Gullane House, Sandy Loan, Gullane
Edinburgh, Midlothian & West Lothian	NEW 89 Ravenscroft Street, Edinburgh
Glasgow & District Glasgow	NEW Berridale Allotments and Gardens, Delvin Road, Cathcart,
Inverness, Ross, Cromarty & Skye	Torcroft, Balnain, Glenurquhart

Sunday 23 June

Argyll & Lochaber	Drimfern, Inveraray, Argyll
Ayrshire & Arran	NEW The Carriage House, Blair Estate, Dalry
Berwickshire	Marlfield and Ruthven Gardens, Coldstream
Dumfriesshire	Kirkcaldy House, Kirkcaldy, Burnsands, Thornhill
Dunbartonshire	Glebeside House, Spy's Lane, Rhu
East Lothian	NEW Gullane House, Sandy Loan, Gullane
Edinburgh, Midlothian & West Lothian	NEW 19 Gardiner Road, Edinburgh

Fife	Hidden Gardens of Newburgh, Newburgh
Fife	Pittenweem: Gardens in the Burgh, Pittenweem
Inverness, Ross, Cromarty & Skye	Torcroft, Balnain, Glenurquhart
Kincardine & Deeside	Finzean House, Finzean, Banchory
Kirkcudbrightshire	Threave Garden, Castle Douglas
Peeblesshire & Tweeddale	8 Halmyre Mains, West Linton
Stirlingshire	Thorntree, Arnprior

Tuesday 25 June

Edinburgh, Midlothian & West Lothian	NEW 89 Ravenscroft Street, Edinburgh

Saturday 29 June

Argyll & Lochaber	Dal an Eas, Kilmore, Oban
Argyll & Lochaber	Maolachy's Garden, Lochavich, by Taynuilt
Edinburgh, Midlothian & West Lothian	Open Gardens of the Lower New Town, 24 Fettes Row, Edinburgh
Glasgow & District	Kew Terrace Gardens: Back to Front, Kew Terrace Lane, Glasgow
Perth & Kinross	Blair Castle Gardens, Blair Atholl

Sunday 30 June

Aberdeenshire	Bruckhills Croft, Rothienorman, Inverurie
Angus & Dundee	Newtonmill House, by Brechin
Argyll & Lochaber	Dal an Eas, Kilmore, Oban
Argyll & Lochaber	Maolachy's Garden, Lochavich, by Taynuilt
Berwickshire	Netherbyres, Eyemouth
Dumfriesshire	NEW Dumfries Station Garden, Dumfries Railway Station, Lovers Walk, Dumfries
Dumfriesshire	NEW Townhead of Glencairn, Kirkland, by Moniaive
East Lothian	Tyninghame House and The Walled Garden, Dunbar
Edinburgh, Midlothian & West Lothian	NEW 5 Greenbank Crescent, Edinburgh
Fife	Backhouse at Rossie Estate, by Collessie
Fife	Boarhills Village Gardens, St Andrews
Inverness, Ross, Cromarty & Skye	House of Aigas and Field Centre, by Beauly
Kincardine & Deeside	Findrack, Torphins
Kirkcudbrightshire	Southwick House, Southwick
Peeblesshire & Tweeddale	Glen House, Glen Estate, Innerleithen

JULY

Tuesday 2 July

Ayrshire & Arran	Dougarie, Isle of Arran

Wednesday 3 July

Caithness, Sutherland, Orkney & Shetland	The Castle and Gardens of Mey, Mey

Thursday 4 July

Angus & Dundee	Inchmill Cottage, Glenprosen, nr Kirriemuir

Saturday 6 July

Moray & Nairn	Haugh Garden, College of Roseisle
Perth & Kinross	NEW Allotment Association of Crieff, Turretbank Road Crieff
Roxburghshire	Easter Weens, Bonchester Bridge, Hawick

Sunday 7 July

Ayrshire & Arran	NEW Waterslap Gardens, 15 & 19 Waterslap, Fenwick
Berwickshire	Lennel Bank, Coldstream
East Lothian	Humbie Dean, Humbie
Glasgow & District	NEW Milton Community Gardens, Liddesdale Square, Milton, Glasgow
Kincardine & Deeside	Douneside House, Tarland
Kirkcudbrightshire	NEW Kings Grange House, Castle Douglas
Peeblesshire & Tweeddale	Drumelzier Old Manse, Drumelzier, nr Broughton
Roxburghshire	Yetholm Village Gardens, Town Yetholm

Wednesday 10 July

Aberdeenshire	NEW Glenkindie House Plant Sale, Glenkindie, Alford

Aberdeenshire	Cruickshank Botanic Gardens, 23 St Machar Drive, Aberdeen

Saturday 13 July

Angus & Dundee	Arbroath Collection of Gardens, Locations across Arbroath
Angus & Dundee	Gallery Garden, Gallery, by Montrose
Ayrshire & Arran	Whitewin House, Golf Course Road, Girvan
Caithness, Sutherland, Orkney & Shetland	Three Gardens near Dornoch, Dornock

Sunday 14 July

Aberdeenshire	Drumrossie Mansion House, Insch
Aberdeenshire	Middle Cairncake, Cuminestown, Turriff
Angus & Dundee	Gallery Garden, Gallery, by Montrose
Ayrshire & Arran	NEW Gardens of Kilmaurs, Kilmaurs
Ayrshire & Arran	Whitewin House, Golf Course Road, Girvan
Dumfriesshire	Whiteside, Dunscore
Glasgow & District	NEW Gartnaval Secret Garden, Gartnavel Royal Hospital, 1055 Great Western Road, Glasgow
Moray & Nairn	Gordon Castle Walled Garden, Fochabers, Moray

Wednesday 17 July

Caithness, Sutherland, Orkney & Shetland	The Castle and Gardens of Mey, Mey

Thursday 18 July

Angus & Dundee	Inchmill Cottage, Glenprosen, nr Kirriemuir

Saturday 20 July

Argyll & Lochaber	Caol Ruadh, Colintraive
Ayrshire & Arran	Whitewin House, Golf Course Road, Girvan
Fife	NEW Crail: Small Gardens in the Burgh, 2 Castle Street, Crail
Fife	NEW Dalgety Bay Gardens, Dalgety Bay
Moray & Nairn	Haugh Garden, College of Roseisle

Sunday 21 July

Angus & Dundee	NEW Brechin Gardens in Summer, Locations across Brechin
Argyll & Lochaber	Caol Ruadh, Colintraive
Ayrshire & Arran	Clover Park, Langdyke, Waterside, Kilmarnock
Ayrshire & Arran	Whitewin House, Golf Course Road, Girvan
Berwickshire	Coldstream Open Gardens, Coldstream Community Centre, High Street, Coldstream
Fife	NEW Crail: Small Gardens in the Burgh, 2 Castle Street, Crail
Fife	NEW Dalgety Bay Gardens, Dalgety Bay
Glasgow & District	Strathbungo Garden, March Street, Glasgow
Inverness, Ross, Cromarty & Skye	2 Durnamuck, Little Loch Broom, Wester Ross
Inverness, Ross, Cromarty & Skye	Kiltarlity Gardens, Kiltarlity
Kirkcudbrightshire	Crofts, Kirkpatrick Durham, Castle Douglas
Lanarkshire	Wellbutts, Elsrickle, by Biggar
Renfrewshire	Bravehound - Erskine Hospital, Old Garden Centre, Bishopton
Stirlingshire	NEW 43 Thornton Avenue, Bonnybridge
Wigtownshire	NEW Seabank, Drummore

Saturday 27 July

Aberdeenshire	Parkvilla, 47 Schoolhill, Ellon
Argyll & Lochaber	Maolachy's Garden, Lochavich, by Taynuilt
Ayrshire & Arran	Whitewin House, Golf Course Road, Girvan
Edinburgh, Midlothian & West Lothian	45 Northfield Crescent, Longridge, Bathgate
Peeblesshire & Tweeddale	NEW Quercus Garden Plants, Whitmuir Farm, West Linton

Sunday 28 July

Aberdeenshire	Middle Cairncake, Cuminestown, Turriff
Aberdeenshire	Parkvilla, 47 Schoolhill, Ellon
Argyll & Lochaber	Maolachy's Garden, Lochavich, by Taynuilt
Ayrshire & Arran	NEW Auldbyres Farm Garden, Coylton
Ayrshire & Arran	Whitewin House, Golf Course Road, Girvan
East Lothian	Broadwoodside, Gifford
Edinburgh, Midlothian & West Lothian	45 Northfield Crescent, Longridge, Bathgate

Nonavaar, Caithness, Sutherland, Orkney and Shetland. Photo by Andrea Jones

Edinburgh, Midlothian & West Lothian	Craigentinny Telferton Allotments, Telferton Road, off Portobello Road, Edinburgh
Glasgow & District	NEW Kilmardinny Gardens, Glasgow
Inverness, Ross, Cromarty & Skye	House of Aigas and Field Centre, by Beauly
Lanarkshire	Viewpark Allotments, Bairds Avenue, Viewpark
Moray & Nairn	Glenrinnes Lodge, Dufftown, Keith, Banffshire
Peeblesshire & Tweeddale	NEW The Schoolhouse, Skirling by Biggar
Perth & Kinross	NEW Bridge of Earn Gardens, The Institute, Station Road, Bridge of Earn, Perthshire
Roxburghshire	NEW Whiterigg, nr Melrose
Stirlingshire	The Tors, 2 Slamannan Road, Falkirk

AUGUST

Saturday 3 August
Ayrshire & Arran	Whitewin House, Golf Course Road, Girvan
Edinburgh, Midlothian & West Lothian	39 Nantwich Drive, Edinburgh
Fife	The Tower, 1 Northview Terrace, Wormit
Fife	Willowhill, Forgan, Newport-on-Tay

Sunday 4 August
Ayrshire & Arran	Whitewin House, Golf Course Road, Girvan
Caithness, Sutherland, Orkney & Shetland	Langwell, Berriedale

Dumfriesshire	Dalswinton Mill, Dalswinton, Dumfries
Kincardine & Deeside	Glenbervie House, Drumlithie, Stonehaven
Lanarkshire	The Walled Garden, Shieldhill, Quothquan, Biggar
Perth & Kinross	Drummond Castle Gardens, Crieff
Perth & Kinross	Mount Tabor House, Mount Tabor Road, Perth
Roxburghshire	West Leas, Bonchester Bridge
Stirlingshire	NEW 60 Greenhead, Alva, Clackmannanshire

Thursday 8 August

Angus & Dundee	Inchmill Cottage, Glenprosen, nr Kirriemuir

Saturday 10 August

Ayrshire & Arran	Netherthird Community Garden, Craigens Road, Netherthird, Cum-
nock	
Ayrshire & Arran	Whitewin House, Golf Course Road, Girvan
Caithness, Sutherland, Orkney & Shetland	The Castle and Gardens of Mey, Mey
Fife	Willowhill, Forgan, Newport-on-Tay
Perth & Kinross	Wester House of Ross, Comrie

Sunday 11 August

Aberdeenshire	Pitmedden Garden, Ellon
Ayrshire & Arran	Whitewin House, Golf Course Road, Girvan
Caithness, Sutherland, Orkney & Shetland	The Quoy of Houton, Orphir, ORKNEY
Perth & Kinross	Wester House of Ross, Comrie

Wednesday 14 August

Perth & Kinross	NEW Cloan, by Auchterarder

Saturday 17 August

Fife	Willowhill, Forgan, Newport-on-Tay
Moray & Nairn	Haugh Garden, College of Roseisle

Sunday 18 August

Ayrshire & Arran	NEW Barrmill Community Garden, Barrmill Park and Gardens
Caithness, Sutherland, Orkney & Shetland	The Garden at the Auld Post Office B&B, Spittal-by-Mybster
Glasgow & District	NEW Woodbourne House, Seven Sisters, Lenzie, Glasgow
Inverness, Ross, Cromarty & Skye	Kilcoy Castle, Redcastle, by Muir of Ord
Lanarkshire	Culter Allers, Coulter, Biggar

Thursday 22 August

Angus & Dundee	Inchmill Cottage, Glenprosen, nr Kirriemuir
Inverness, Ross, Cromarty & Skye	Dundonnell House, Little Loch Broom, Wester Ross

Saturday 24 August

Argyll & Lochaber	Maolachy's Garden, Lochavich, by Taynuilt
Fife	Willowhill, Forgan, Newport-on-Tay
Peeblesshire & Tweeddale	NEW Quercus Garden Plants, Whitmuir Farm, West Linton

Sunday 25 August

Argyll & Lochaber	Maolachy's Garden, Lochavich, by Taynuilt
Glasgow & District	The Good Life Gardens, Cambuslang, Glasgow
Inverness, Ross, Cromarty & Skye	2 Durnamuck, Little Loch Broom, Wester Ross

Saturday 31 August

Fife	Willowhill, Forgan, Newport-on-Tay

SEPTEMBER

Sunday 1 September

Glasgow & District	Horatio's Gardens, National Spinal Injuries Unit, Queen Elizabeth University Hospital, 1345 Govan Road, Glasgow
Inverness, Ross, Cromarty & Skye	Old Allangrange, Munlochy
Kirkcudbrightshire	3 Millhall, Shore Road, Kirkcudbright

Thursday 5 September

Angus & Dundee   Inchmill Cottage, Glenprosen, nr Kirriemuir

Friday 6 September
Edinburgh, Midlothian & West Lothian   Silverburn Village, Hopelands Road

Saturday 7 September
Angus & Dundee   Angus Plant Sale, Logie Walled Garden
Renfrewshire   Craig Hepburn Memorial Garden, Stirling Drive, Linwood

Sunday 8 September
Dumfriesshire   NEW Dumfries Station Garden, Dumfries Railway Station, Lovers
Walk, Dumfries
Dunbartonshire   James Street Community Garden Plant Sale, Helensburgh
Peeblesshire & Tweeddale   Kailzie Gardens, Peebles

Thursday 19 September
Angus & Dundee   Inchmill Cottage, Glenprosen, nr Kirriemuir

Saturday 28 September
Argyll & Lochaber   Maolachy's Garden, Lochavich, by Taynuilt

Sunday 29 September
Argyll & Lochaber   Maolachy's Garden, Lochavich, by Taynuilt
East Lothian   NEW Fairnielaw, Athelstaneford, North Berwick
Fife   Hill of Tarvit Plant Sale and Autumn Fair, Hill of Tarvit, Cupar

OCTOBER

Sunday 6 October
Peeblesshire & Tweeddale   Dawyck Botanic Garden, Stobo

Saturday 12 October
Angus & Dundee   12 Glamis Drive, Dundee

Sunday 13 October
Angus & Dundee   12 Glamis Drive, Dundee

Saturday 26 October
Angus & Dundee   Hospitalfield Gardens, Hospitalfield House, Westway, Arbroath

INDEX OF GARDENS

ORDER YOUR GUIDEBOOK FOR 2020

The first Scotland's Gardens Scheme Guidebook was created in 1931, and it has become the 'go to' guide for garden visitors in Scotland ever since. So, don't go without your copy in 2020!

Order now and your copy will be posted to you on publication. Fill in the form below and send to: Scotland's Gardens Scheme, 23 Castle Street, Edinburgh EH2 3DN

' The daffodil-coloured tome of horticultural promise'

Joanna, Edinburgh Garden Diary

'Supporting your community through local charities'

✂

Scotland's
GARDENS
Scheme
OPEN FOR CHARITY

Please send me _____ copy / copies of our Guidebook for 2020, price £5.00 plus £2.00 UK p&p, as soon as it is available.

I enclose a cheque / postal order made payable to Scotland's Gardens Scheme.

Name _____

Address _____

_____

Postcode _____

Scotland's Gardens Scheme, 23 Castle Street, Edinburgh EH2 3DN
Copies of our Guidebook may also be purchased on our website: **www.scotlandsgardens.org**

WELCOMING YOU IN 2020

OUR DISTRICTS BY GEOGRAPHICAL AREA